KB100516

적중 100

영어 기출 문제집

중 3

지학 | 민찬규

Best Collection

구성과 특징

교과서의 주요 학습 내용을 중심으로 학습 영역별 특성에 맞춰 단계별로 다양한 학습 기회를 제공하여
단원별 학습능력 평가는 물론 중간 및 기말고사 시험 등에 완벽하게 대비할 수 있도록 내용을 구성

Words & Expressions

Step1 Key Words 단원별 핵심 단어 설명 및 풀이
Key Expression 단원별 핵심 숙어 및 관용어 설명
Word Power 반대 또는 비슷한 뜻 단어 배우기
English Dictionary 영어로 배우는 영어 단어

Step2 실력평가 단원별 수시평가 대비 주관식, 객관식 문제풀이

Step3 서술형 대비 학업성취도 및 수행능력평가 대비 서술형 문제풀이

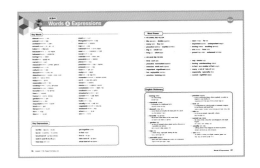

Conversation

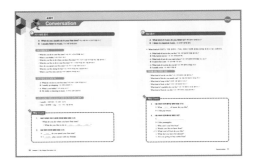

Step1 핵심 의사소통 소통에 필요한 주요 표현 방법 요약
핵심 Check 기본적인 표현 방법 및 활용능력 확인

Step2 대화문 익히기 교과서 대화문 심층 분석 및 확인

Step3 교과서 확인학습 빈칸 채우기를 통한 문장 완성 능력 확인

Step4 기본평가 시험대비 기초 학습 능력 평가

Step5 실력평가 단원별 수시평가 대비 주관식, 객관식 문제풀이

Step6 서술형 대비 학업성취도 및 수행능력평가 대비 서술형 문제풀이

Grammar

Step1 주요 문법 단원별 주요 문법 사항과 예문을 알기 쉽게 설명
핵심 Check 기본 문법사항에 대한 이해 여부 확인

Step2 기본평가 시험대비 기초 학습 능력 평가

Step3 실력평가 단원별 수시평가 대비 주관식, 객관식 문제풀이

Step4 서술형 대비 학업성취도 및 수행능력평가 대비 서술형 문제풀이

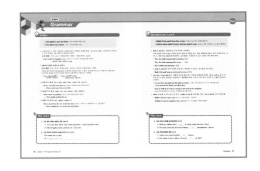

Reading

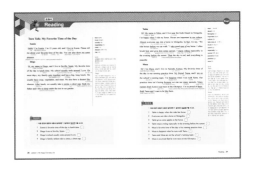

Step1 구문 분석 단원별로 제시된 문장에 대한 구문별 분석과 내용 설명
확인문제 문장에 대한 기본적인 이해와 인지능력 확인

Step2 확인학습A 빈칸 채우기를 통한 문장 완성 능력 확인

Step3 확인학습B 제시된 우리말을 영어로 완성하여 작문 능력 키우기

Step4 실력평가 단원별 수시평가 대비 주관식, 객관식 문제풀이

Step5 서술형 대비 학업성취도 및 수행능력평가 대비 서술형 문제풀이
교과서 구석구석 교과서에 나오는 기타 문장까지 완벽 학습

Composition

|영역별 핵심문제|

단어 및 어휘, 대화문, 문법, 독해 등 각 영역별 기출문제의 출제 유형을 분석하여 실전에 대비하고 연습할 수 있도록 문제를 배열

|단원별 예상문제|

기출문제를 분석한 후 새로운 시험 출제 경향을 더하여 새롭게 출제될 수 있는 문제를 포함하여 시험에 완벽하게 대비할 수 있도록 준비

|서술형 실전 및 창의사고력 문제|

학교 시험에서 점차 늘어나는 서술형 시험에 집중 대비하고 고득점을 취득하는데 만전을 기하기 위한 학습 코너

|단원별 모의고사|

영역별, 단계별 학습을 모두 마친 후 실전 연습을 위한 모의고사

교과서 파헤치기

- **단어Test1~3** 영어 단어 우리말 쓰기, 우리말을 영어 단어로 쓰기, 영영풀이에 해당하는 단어와 우리말 쓰기
- **대화문Test1~2** 대화문 빈칸 완성 및 전체 대화문 쓰기
- **본문Test1~5** 빈칸 완성, 우리말 쓰기, 문장 배열연습, 영어 작문하기 복습 등 단계별 반복 학습을 통해 교과서 지문에 대한 완벽한 습득
- **구석구석지문Test1~2** 지문 빈칸 완성 및 전문 영어로 쓰기

Contents

Lesson 3

Learning from Nature's Genius

 의사소통 기능

- 알고 있는지 묻기
  You know that Leonardo da Vinci painted the *Mona Lisa*, don't you?
- 관심 표현하기
  I'm fascinated by this noodle cooling fan.

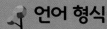 **언어 형식**

- not only A but also B
  The fastener was **not only** strong **but also** easy to use.

- 간접의문문
  Do you know **where the key is**?

Words & Expressions

Key Words

- **absorb**[æbsɔ́:rb] 동 흡수하다
- **all-purpose**[ɔ:lpə:rpəs] 형 만능의, 다용도의
- **amazing**[əméiziŋ] 형 놀라운
- **apply**[əplái] 동 적용하다
- **article**[á:rtikl] 명 기사, 논문
- **beak**[bi:k] 명 (새의) 부리
- **bite**[bait] 명 물린 상처
- **bug**[bʌg] 명 곤충, 벌레
- **burr**[bə:r] 명 가시 식물
- **cause**[kɔ:z] 동 초래하다
- **closely**[klóusli] 부 자세히
- **contact**[kántækt] 명 접촉
- **cooling fan** 냉각팬
- **creative**[kriéitiv] 형 창의적인
- **decide**[disáid] 동 결심하다
- **design**[dizáin] 동 설계하다, 고안하다
- **dive**[daiv] 동 잠수하다
- **explain**[ikspléin] 동 설명하다
- **explore**[iksplɔ́:r] 동 탐색하다
- **fascinate**[fǽsənèit] 동 매혹하다
- **fastener**[fǽsnər] 명 잠금장치, 고정 장치
- **front**[frʌnt] 명 앞쪽
- **genius**[dʒí:njəs] 명 천재
- **goat**[gout] 명 염소
- **gracefully**[gréisfəli] 부 우아하게
- **hairy**[hɛ́əri] 형 털이 많은
- **high-speed**[háispí:d] 형 고속의
- **holder**[hóuldər] 명 받침, 걸이
- **imitate**[ímətèit] 동 모방하다

- **increase**[ínkri:s] 명 증가 동 증가하다
- **inspire**[inspáiər] 동 영감을 불러일으키다
- **inspiration**[inspəréiʃən] 명 영감
- **invention**[invénʃən] 명 발명
- **last**[læst] 동 지속하다
- **length**[leŋkθ] 명 길이
- **material**[mətíərəl] 명 물질, 재료
- **necessity**[nəsésəti] 명 필요성
- **needle**[ní:dl] 명 바늘
- **notice**[nóutis] 동 주목하다
- **observe**[əbzɔ́:rv] 동 관찰하다
- **painful**[péinfəl] 형 고통스러운
- **polar bear** 북극곰
- **pressure**[préʃər] 명 압력
- **redesign**[rì:dizáin] 동 다시 디자인하다
- **reduce**[ridjú:s] 동 줄이다
- **reflect**[riflékt] 동 반사하다
- **solution**[səlú:ʃən] 명 해결책
- **space**[speis] 명 공간, 우주
- **successful**[səksésfəl] 형 성공적인
- **sudden**[sʌ́dn] 형 갑작스러운
- **surface**[sɔ́:rfis] 명 표면
- **survivor**[sərváivər] 명 생존자
- **talent**[tǽlənt] 명 타고난 재능
- **tiny**[táini] 형 작은
- **weight**[weit] 명 무게
- **wing**[wiŋ] 명 날개
- **wonder**[wʌ́ndər] 동 궁금해 하다

Key Expressions

- **as a result** 결과적으로
- **be stuck to** ~에 붙다
- **be good at** ~을 잘하다
- **be covered with** ~로 덮여 있다
- **float away** 떠다니다
- **go -ing** ~하러 가다
- **glide over** 활주하다
- **How come** ~? 어떻게 ~?, 왜 ~?
- **in search of** ~을 찾고 있는

- **keep A from -ing** A가 ~하지 못하게 하다
- **make contact with** ~와 연락하다, 접촉하다
- **make a note of** ~을 메모하다, 기록하다
- **not only A but also B** A뿐만 아니라 B도 역시
- **on one's way to** ~로 가는 길에
- **That's why** ~. 그것이 ~하는 이유이다.
- **try to** ~하기 위해 노력하다, ~하기 위해 애쓰다
- **take a look at** ~을 보다

Word Power

※ 서로 비슷한 뜻을 가진 어휘

- □ **absorb** 흡수하다 – **soak** 빨아들이다
- □ **beak** (새의) 부리 – **bill** (새의) 부리
- □ **creative** 창의적인 – **inventive** 창의적인
- □ **imitate** 모방하다 – **mimic** 모방하다

- □ **amazing** 놀라운 – **surprising** 놀라운
- □ **bug** 곤충, 벌레 – **insect** 곤충
- □ **fascinate** 매혹하다 – **charm** 매혹하다
- □ **reduce** 줄이다 – **diminish** 줄이다

※ 서로 반대의 뜻을 가진 어휘

- □ **increase** 증가 ↔ **decrease** 감소
- □ **reduce** 줄이다 ↔ **enlarge** 확대하다
- □ **tiny** 작은 ↔ **huge** 거대한

- □ **melt** 녹다 ↔ **freeze** 얼다
- □ **solution** 해결책 ↔ **problem** 문제점

※ 동사 – 명사

- □ **absorb** 흡수하다 – **absorption** 흡수
- □ **decide** 결심하다 – **decision** 결심
- □ **explore** 탐색하다 – **exploration** 탐험
- □ **imitate** 모방하다 – **imitation** 모방
- □ **observe** 관찰하다 – **observation** 관찰
- □ **reflect** 반사하다 – **reflection** 반사

- □ **apply** 적용하다 – **application** 적용
- □ **explain** 설명하다 – **explanation** 설명
- □ **fascinate** 매혹하다 – **fascination** 매혹
- □ **invent** 발명하다 – **invention** 발명
- □ **reduce** 줄이다 – **reduction** 감소

※ 명사 – 형용사

- □ **imitation** 모방 – **imitative** 모방적인
- □ **necessity** 필요성 – **necessary** 필요한
- □ **reflection** 반사 – **reflective** 빛을 반사하는

- □ **invention** 발명 – **inventive** 창의적인
- □ **pain** 고통 – **painful** 고통스러운
- □ **success** 성공 – **successful** 성공적인

English Dictionary

- □ **all**-purpose 만능의, 다용도의
  → suitable for many uses 여러 가지 용도에 적절한
- □ **beak** (새의) 부리
  → the hard usually pointed parts that over a bird's mouth
  새 입 위에 있는 딱딱하고 보통 뾰족한 부분
- □ **dive** 뛰어들다, 잠수하다
  → to move down through the air at a steep angle
  가파르게 공중에서 아래로 뛰어내리다
- □ **fastener** 잠금장치, 고정 장치
  → a device used to close a piece of clothing, a window, suitcase, etc. tightly
  옷, 창문, 가방 등을 단단히 닫기 위하여 사용되는 도구
- □ **genius** 천재
  → a very smart or talented person
  매우 똑똑하거나 재능을 가진 사람
- □ **headache** 두통

  → a pain in your head
  머리에 느끼는 통증
- □ **imitate** 모방하다
  → to make or do something the same way as something else
  무엇인가를 다른 것과 똑같이 하거나 똑같이 만들다
- □ **narrow** 좁은
  → long and not wide
  길고 넓지 않은
- □ **redesign** 다시 디자인하다
  → to change the design of something
  어떤 것의 디자인을 바꾸다
- □ **tunnel** 터널, 굴
  → a passage that goes under the ground
  지하로 지나가는 통로
- □ **wing** 날개
  → a part of an animal's body that is used for flying or gliding
  날거나 활공하기 위하여 사용되는 동물의 신체 부위

서답형

[01~02] 〈보기〉와 같은 관계가 되도록 빈칸에 알맞은 말을 쓰시오. (주어진 철자로 시작할 것)

01
┌─ 보기 ─┐
narrow : wide

(1) m_____ : freeze
(2) t_____ : huge

02
┌─ 보기 ─┐
absorb : absorption

(1) apply : _____
(2) decide : _____

중요

03 다음 중 밑줄 친 부분의 뜻풀이가 바르지 <u>않은</u> 것은?

① This candle holder can make candles <u>last</u> twice as long. (마지막)
② The <u>way</u> nature works fascinates us. (방식)
③ The <u>high-speed</u> train was first made in Japan. (고속의)
④ It often <u>woke</u> people up and caused headaches. (깨웠다)
⑤ He <u>wondered</u> how the bird entered the water so gracefully. (궁금했다)

서답형

04 다음 빈칸에 들어갈 말로 적절한 말을 쓰시오.

Even though his invention was not successful, he _____d a bird's wings to try to make a flying machine.

➡ _____

중요

05 다음 중 〈보기〉에 있는 단어를 사용하여 자연스러운 문장을 만들 수 <u>없는</u> 것은?

┌─ 보기 ─┐
apply   amazing   beak   all-purpose

① This room is used for many purposes. This is an _____ room.
② It's really interesting. That's an _____ story!
③ His theory is so old that it can't _____ to modern society.
④ I'm reading an _____ about a bug robot.
⑤ The gull held the fish in its _____.

06 다음 밑줄 친 부분과 의미가 가장 가까운 것을 고르시오.

The aim is to <u>reduce</u> traffic at peak hours.

① absorb   ② forgive
③ decide   ④ diminish
⑤ explore

07 다음 빈칸에 공통으로 들어가기에 알맞은 것은?

• Can I take a look _____ your work?
• He's good _____ making things with hands.

① from   ② at   ③ with
④ by   ⑤ during

01 다음 주어진 단어를 이용해 빈칸을 완성하시오.

> She has a very _____ mind.

➡ _____ (invent)

02 다음 짝지어진 단어의 관계가 같도록 빈칸에 알맞은 말을 쓰시오. (주어진 철자로 시작할 것)

> beak : bill = bug : i_____

[03~04] 다음 빈칸에 공통으로 들어갈 단어를 쓰시오.

03
> • They have to _____ contact with the leader.
> • I'll _____ a note of our next meeting in my diary.

04
> • I was a little sick. That's _____ I left early.
> • I'd like to know the reason _____ you're so late.

05 밑줄 친 부분과 의미가 가장 가까운 단어를 주어진 철자로 시작하여 쓰시오.

> The heavy rain will <u>keep</u> them from going out to play.

➡ s_____

06 다음 빈칸에 알맞은 단어를 〈보기〉에서 골라 쓰시오.

| 보기 |
| burns   burrs   bite   bug |

(1) When you have a mosquito _____, you shouldn't scratch it.

(2) Many people use _____ sprays to keep insects away.

(3) When a candle _____, it melts into the tube below the holder to form a new candle.

(4) On his way home, he saw that _____ were stuck to his clothes and his dog's hair.

07 다음 우리말에 맞게 빈칸에 알맞은 말을 쓰시오.

(1) 그녀는 마실 것을 찾아 부엌으로 들어갔다.
➡ She went into the kitchen in _____ of a drink.

(2) 신발에 껌이 달라붙어 있었다.
➡ A piece of chewing gum was _____ to my shoe.

(3) 그 기름이 유출된 결과 많은 바닷새들이 죽었다.
➡ Many seabirds died as a _____ of the oil spill.

(4) 그녀는 이지적일뿐만 아니라 또한 음악성도 대단했다.
➡ She was not _____ intelligent but also very musical.

Conversation

1 알고 있는지 묻기

You know that Leonardo da Vinci painted the *Mona Lisa*, don't you?
레오나르도 다빈치가 모나리자를 그린 것을 알지, 그렇지 않니?

■ 어떤 사실을 상대방이 알고 있는지 물어보는 말은 know를 사용하여 "Do you know about ~?"(~을 아십니까?) 또는 "You know about ~, don't you?", "Did you know that ~?"이라고 물어볼 수도 있다. "You know ~, don't you?"는 "너는 ~을 알고 있지?"라는 뜻으로 상대방이 이미 알고 있을 법한 소재의 이야기를 꺼낼 때 사용한다.

■ know를 사용하여 직접적으로 물어보는 것보다는 완화된 느낌으로 hear를 사용하여 "Have you (ever) heard about ~?"(~을 들어본 적이 있니?) 또는 "Did you hear about ~?"이라고 하기도 한다. hear를 사용할 때는 know를 사용했을 때보다는 다소 부드러운 느낌을 줄 수 있다.

■ 그 외에 알고 있는지를 물어볼 때는 aware, realize 등을 사용해서 "Are you aware of ~?"(~을 알고 있니?), "Are you aware that ~?" 또는 "Do you realize ~?" 등을 사용하여 상대방이 알고 있는지를 물어볼 수 있다.

알고 있는지 묻기

- You know that ~, don't you? 너 ~알지, 그렇지 않니?
- Do you know about/that ~? ~을 아십니까?
- Have you (ever) heard (about) ~? (한번이라도) ~를(에 대해서) 들어본 적이 있습니까?
- Have you been told about ~? ~에 대해 들어본 적 있어?
- Are you aware of/that ~? ~을 알고 있니?
- Do you realize that ~? ~을 알고 있니?

핵심 Check

1. 다음 우리말에 해당하는 영어 문장을 빈칸에 쓰시오.

> B: _____? (Jian, mosquito needle을 들어본 적이 있니?)
>
> G: A mosquito needle? Can you explain it to me?
>
> B: Some scientists made this new needle by imitating a mosquito's mouth.
>
> G: That's interesting. So how will that help?
>
> B: You know mosquito bites are not very painful, don't you? The new needle will also cause less pain.

관심 표현하기

I'm fascinated by this noodle cooling fan. 나는 이 국수 냉각팬에 매료되었어.

- "I'm fascinated by …"는 "나는 …에 매료되었다."라는 뜻으로 "be fascinated by ~"는 관심이 많은 것을 나타내는 표현이다. "fascinate"(마음을 사로잡다) 이외에도 "impress"(인상을 주다)를 사용하여 "… impress(es) me a lot."(…가 나에게는 깊은 인상을 준다.), "… is really impressive"(…은 정말로 인상적이다.), "I'm (really) impressed by …"(나는 정말로 ~에 의해서 인상을 받았다.)라고 할 수도 있다.

- 상대방의 말에 관심을 나타낼 때 사용하는 표현으로는 "interest"를 사용하여 나타낼 수 있다. "interest"는 명사로 "흥미, 관심"이라는 뜻이 있고, 동사로 "관심을 끌다, 관심을 보이다"의 뜻이다. "That interests me a lot."는 글자 그대로 "저것이 나의 관심을 끈다."의 뜻이다. 이 표현은 "그것 참 재미있네요." 또는 "그것 참 흥미롭네요." 정도로 해석할 수 있다.

- 관심을 나타내는 말로 "I am interested in~ "(나는 ~에 관심이 있다.), 또는 "I have an interest in ~"(나는 ~에 관심이 있다.)라고 할 수 있고, "be into ~" (~에 관심이 있다)와 같은 표현을 사용하여 "I am into ~."(나는 ~에 관심이 있다.)라고 할 수도 있다.

관심 표현하기

- I'm fascinated by ~. 나는 ~에 매료되었다.
- It is really impressive. 그것은 정말로 인상적이다.
- I am interested in ~. 나는 ~에 관심이 있다.
- My main interest is ~. 나의 주된 관심은 ~이다.
- That impresses me a lot. 저것은 나에게 깊은 인상을 준다.
- That interests me. 그것 참 흥미롭습니다.
- I have an interest in ~. 나는 ~에 관심이 있다.
- I enjoy/like/love ~ 나는 ~하는 것을 즐긴다. / 좋아한다.

핵심 Check

2. 다음 밑줄 친 말 대신 쓰기에 적절하지 <u>않은</u> 것은?

> B: <u>I'm fascinated by this noodle cooling fan.</u>
> G: A noodle cooling fan? I've never heard of it.
> B: This little fan will cool noodles when they're very hot.
> G: That looks funny but useful.

① This noodle cooling fan impresses me a lot.

② This noodle cooling fan is really impressive.

③ I'm interested in this noodle cooling fan.

④ I'm eager to use this noodle cooling fan.

⑤ I have an interest in this noodle cooling fan.

Listen & Speak 1 A

> **G:** ❶You know that Leonardo da Vinci painted the *Mona Lisa*, don't you?
>
> **B:** Sure. I think he was a really great artist.
>
> **G:** He was also a great inventor.
>
> **B:** What did he invent?
>
> **G:** ❷He dreamed of flying like a bird. ❸So, he drew a flying machine that looked like a bird.
>
> **B:** Did he also make that machine?
>
> **G:** No, but his creative idea inspired many other inventors.

소녀: 레오나르도 다빈치가 모나 리자를 그린 것을 알지, 그렇지 않니?
소년: 몰론. 그는 정말로 위대한 미술가라고 생각해.
소녀: 그는 또한 위대한 발명가였어.
소년: 그가 무엇을 발명했니?
소녀: 그는 새처럼 나는 것을 꿈꿨어. 그래서 그는 새처럼 보이는 나는 기계를 그렸어.
소년: 그가 그 기계도 만들었니?
소녀: 아니. 하지만 그의 창의적인 생각은 많은 발명가에게 영감을 주었어.

❶ "You know that ~, don't you?"는 "너는 ~을 알지?"라는 뜻으로 상대에게 아는지를 묻는 말이다.
❷ "dream of"는 "~을 꿈꾸다"의 의미이다.
❸ that은 a flying machine을 선행사로 하는 주격 관계 대명사이다.

Check(√) True or False

(1) Leonardo da Vinci was a great artist who painted the *Mona Lisa*.　　T ☐ F ☐

(2) Leonardo da Vinci was a dreamer who wanted to fly like a bird.　　T ☐ F ☐

(3) Leonardo da Vinci was a great inventor who made a flying machine.　　T ☐ F ☐

Real Life Communication A

> **Henry:** What are you doing, Mina?
>
> **Mina:** I'm reading an article about a bug robot.
>
> **Henry:** A bug robot? Is it interesting?
>
> **Mina:** Yes. ❶I'm really fascinated by this thing.
>
> **Henry:** Can you tell me more about it?
>
> **Mina:** ❷You know that some bugs can slip into narrow spaces, don't you?
>
> **Henry:** Yeah. ❸That's why it's hard to catch them.
>
> **Mina:** A bug robot can do the same. It can help to find survivors after earthquakes or big fires.
>
> **Henry:** That's really fascinating!

Henry: 미나야, 뭐 하고 있니?
Mina: 나는 bug robot에 관한 기사를 읽고 있어.
Henry: "bug robot"이라고? 재미있니?
Mina: 응, 나는 이것에 정말로 매료되었어.
Henry: 그것에 대해 좀 더 말해 줄 수 있니?
Mina: 너는 몇몇 곤충이 좁은 공간에 미끄러져 들어갈 수 있는 것을 알지?
Henry: 알아. 그것이 그들을 잡기 어려운 이유이지.
Mina: bug robot도 똑같이 할 수 있어. 그것은 지진이나 대형 화재 이후에 생존자들을 찾는 것을 도와줄 수 있어.
Henry: 그거 정말 흥미롭다!

❶ "I'm really fascinated by ~"는 "나는 정말로 ~에 매료되었다."라는 뜻으로 관심이 많은 것을 나타내는 말이다.
❷ "You know that ~, don't you?"는 "너는 ~을 알지?"라는 뜻으로 상대에게 아는지를 묻는 말이다.
❸ "That's why ~."는 "That's the reason why ~."에서 선행사 the reason을 생략한 형태로 글자 그대로 "그것이 ~한 이유이다."라고 해석할 수 있지만, "그런 이유로 ~하다."라고 해석하기도 한다.

Check(√) True or False

(4) A bug robot can slip into narrow spaces like some bugs.　　T ☐ F ☐

(5) Some bugs can fly to a distant place with ease.　　T ☐ F ☐

(6) A bug robot can help to find survivors during earthquakes or big fires.　　T ☐ F ☐

Listen & Speak 1 B

B: ❶Have you heard of a mosquito needle, Jian?

G: A mosquito needle? Can you explain it to me?

B: Some scientists made this new needle ❷by imitating a mosquito's mouth.

G: That's interesting. So how will that help?

B: You know mosquito bites are not very painful, don't you? The new needle will also cause less pain.

G: That's great. ❸How come it's less painful?

B: Like a mosquito's mouth, it makes less contact with our skin.

G: Wow, I think that there's nothing useless in the world!

❶ "Have you heard of ∼?"는 "∼을 들어본 적이 있니?"에 해당하는 말로 상대가 알고 있는지를 묻는 말이다.
❷ 전치사 by의 목적어로 동명사가 쓰였다.
❸ "How come ∼?"은 "어째서 ∼?"라는 뜻으로 이유를 묻는 말이다.

 Listen & Speak 2 A-1

B: ❶I'm fascinated by this noodle cooling fan.

G: A noodle cooling fan? I've never heard of it.

B: This little fan will cool noodles when they're very hot.

G: That looks funny but useful.

❶ "I'm fascinated by ∼"는 관심이 있는 것을 나타내는 표현이다.

 Listen & Speak 2 A-2

G: ❶This candle holder can make candles last twice as long.

B: Really? How's that possible?

G: When a candle burns, it melts into the tube below the holder to form a new candle.

B: Wow, ❷I am so fascinated by the idea! Now we can use candles longer.

❶ 동사 make는 사역동사이므로 목적격보어로 원형부정사 last가 쓰였다.
❷ "I am so fascinated by ∼"는 "나는 ∼에 매우 매료되었다."는 뜻으로 관심을 나타내는 표현이다.

 Listen & Speak 2 A-3

B: You know what? I'm really fascinated by the special door in Juwon's room.

G: ❶What makes the door so special?

B: Juwon and I played table tennis on it.

G: How could you play table tennis on a door?

B: The door ❷can be changed into a table.

G: That's cool!

❶ "What makes ∼?"는 "무엇이 ∼하게 만드는가?"의 뜻으로 이유를 묻는 말이다.
❷ "can be changed into ∼"는 "조동사 can+be+과거분사"의 수동태이다.

 Listen & Speak 2 B

W: Today, we have a special guest, Thomas Thwaites, the Goat Man. Hello, Thomas.

M: Hello, Anna. Great to be here.

W: Thomas, ❶I'm so fascinated by the fact that you lived like a goat in the Alps for three days. Why did you do that?

M: One day, ❷I saw goats playing on the mountain. They looked so peaceful that I wanted to live like them.

W: Didn't you have any problems being a goat?

M: ❸Walking on all four legs was very difficult for me.

W: Do you have any plans to live like a goat again?

M: Sure. I'm planning my second visit to the Alps.

W: I can't wait to hear about your next adventure. Thank you, Thomas, for your time.

❶ "the fact that ∼"은 동격을 나타내는 명사절이 사용되었다.
❷ 지각동사 saw의 목적격보어로 현재분사가 쓰였다.
❸ "Walking ∼"은 문장의 주어로 쓰인 동명사로 단수 취급한다.

● 다음 우리말과 일치하도록 빈칸에 알맞은 말을 쓰시오.

Listen & Speak 1 A

G: You _____ that Leonardo da Vinci _____ the *Mona Lisa*, _____ you?

B: Sure. I _____ he was a really _____ artist.

G: He was _____ a great _____.

B: _____ did he _____?

G: He _____ _____ flying like a bird. So, he _____ a _____ machine that _____ _____ a bird.

B: _____ he _____ _____ that _____?

G: No, but his _____ _____ _____ many other _____.

G: 레오나르도 다빈치가 모나리자를 그린 것을 알지, 그렇지 않니?
B: 몰론. 그는 정말로 위대한 미술가라고 생각해.
G: 그는 또한 위대한 발명가였어.
B: 그가 무엇을 발명했니?
G: 그는 새처럼 나는 것을 꿈꿨어. 그래서 그는 새처럼 보이는 나는 기계를 그렸어.
B: 그가 그 기계도 만들었니?
G: 아니, 하지만 그의 창의적인 생각은 많은 발명가들에게 영감을 주었어.

Listen & Speak 1 B

B: _____ _____ heard of a mosquito _____, Jian?

G: A mosquito needle? _____ you _____ _____ to me?

B: Some scientists _____ _____ new needle by _____ a mosquito's _____.

G: That's interesting. So _____ _____ that help?

B: You _____ mosquito _____ are not _____ _____, don't you? The new _____ will also _____ _____ _____.

G: That's great. _____ _____ it's less painful?

B: Like a mosquito's mouth, it makes _____ _____ with our skin.

G: Wow, I _____ that there's nothing _____ in the world!

B: Jian, mosquito needle을 들어본 적이 있니?
G: mosquito needle이라고? 그것 좀 설명해 줄 수 있니?
B: 몇몇 과학자들이 모기의 입을 모방하여 이 새로운 바늘을 만들었어.
G: 흥미롭군. 그럼 그것이 어떻게 도움이 될까?
B: 모기가 무는 것은 별로 고통스럽지 않다는 건 알지? 이 새로운 주사바늘도 역시 통증을 줄여 줄 거야.
G: 대단한데. 어째서 덜 고통스럽지?
B: 모기의 입처럼 그것은 우리의 피부에 덜 닿아.
G: 와, 세상에 쓸모없는 것은 아무것도 없는 것 같아!

Listen & Speak 2 A-2

G: This candle _____ can make _____ _____ twice as long.

B: Really? How's that _____?

G: When a candle _____, it _____ into the _____ below the holder to _____ a new candle.

B: Wow, I am so _____ by the idea! Now we can _____ candles _____.

G: 이 양초 받침이 양초를 두 배나 오래 지속되도록 만들 수 있어.
B: 정말? 어떻게 그것이 가능해?
G: 양초가 탈 때 그것은 받침 아래에 있는 관으로 녹아들어 새로운 양초를 만들어.
B: 와, 나는 그 아이디어에 매료되었어! 이제 우리는 양초를 더 오래 사용할 수 있어.

Listen & Speak 2 A3

B: You know _____? I'm really _____ by the _____ door in Juwon's room.

G: _____ makes the door so _____?

B: Juwon and I _____ table tennis on it.

G: _____ could you play table tennis on a _____?

B: The door can _____ _____ into a _____.

G: That's _____!

Listen & Speak 2 B

W: Today, we _____ a special _____, Thomas Thwaites, the Goat Man. Hello, Thomas.

M: Hello, Anna. _____ to _____ here.

W: Thomas, I'm so _____ by the _____ that you _____ like a _____ in the Alps for _____ days. _____ did you _____ that?

M: One day, I _____ goats _____ on the mountain. They _____ so _____ that I wanted to _____ like them.

W: Didn't you _____ any _____ being a goat?

M: _____ on all four legs _____ very _____ for me.

W: Do you have _____ plans to live _____ a goat again?

M: Sure. I'm _____ my second _____ to the Alps.

W: I can't _____ to hear about your next _____. Thank you, Thomas, for your time.

Real Life Communication

Henry: _____ are you _____, Mina?

Mina: I'm reading an _____ about a bug robot.

Henry: A bug robot? Is it _____?

Mina: Yes. I'm _____ fascinated by this thing.

Henry: _____ you tell me _____ about it?

Mina: You _____ that some _____ can _____ into _____ spaces, don't you?

Henry: Yeah. That's _____ it's _____ to catch them.

Mina: A bug robot can do the same. It can _____ to find _____ after earthquakes or big fires.

Henry: That's really _____!

해석

B: 너 그거 알아? 나는 주원이네 방의 특별한 문에 매료되었어.

G: 왜 그 문이 그리 특별하니?

B: 주원이와 내가 그 위에서 탁구를 쳤어.

G: 어떻게 문 위에서 탁구를 칠 수 있어?

B: 문이 탁구대로 바뀔 수 있어.

G: 멋있는데!

W: 오늘 우리는 특별 손님인 염소 인간 Thomas Thwaites를 모시게 되었습니다. 안녕하세요, Thomas.

M: 안녕하세요, Anna. 여기 오게 되어 기쁩니다.

W: Thomas, 나는 당신이 3일 동안 알프스에서 염소처럼 살았다는 사실에 매료되었습니다. 왜 그렇게 했나요?

M: 어느 날, 나는 염소들이 산에서 노는 것을 보았어요. 그들이 너무 평화로워 보여서 나는 그들처럼 살고 싶었습니다.

W: 염소가 되는 데 아무 문제가 없었나요?

M: 네 발로 걷는 것이 나에게는 매우 어려웠어요.

W: 당신은 다시 염소처럼 살 계획이 있나요?

M: 물론이죠. 나는 알프스를 다시 방문할 계획을 하고 있어요.

W: 당신의 다음 모험에 대해 빨리 듣고 싶어요. 시간 내주셔서 감사합니다, Thomas.

Henry: 미나야, 뭐 하고 있니?

Mina: 나는 bug robot에 관한 기사를 읽고 있어.

Henry: "bug robot"라고? 재미있니?

Mina: 응, 나는 이것에 정말로 매료되었어.

Henry: 그것에 대해 좀 더 말해줄 수 있니?

Mina: 너는 몇몇 곤충이 좁은 공간에 미끄러져 들어갈 수 있는 것을 알지?

Henry: 알아. 그것이 그들을 잡기 어려운 이유이지.

Mina: bug robot이 똑같이 할 수 있어. 그것은 지진이나 대형 화재 이후에 생존자들을 찾는 것을 도와줄 수 있어.

Henry: 그거 정말 흥미롭다!

[01~02] 다음 대화의 빈칸에 들어갈 말로 알맞은 것은?

01

> B: I'm _____ by Sophia, a robot girl.
> G: What's so special about her?
> B: She is able to show more than 60 facial expressions.
> G: That's amazing. What else can she do?
> B: She has many other abilities. She looks, talks, and even thinks like a human.
> G: That's fascinating!

① fascinated   ② pleased   ③ annoyed

④ disappointed   ⑤ nervous

02

> B: You know what? I'm really fascinated by the special door in Juwon's room.
> G: _____
> B: Juwon and I played table tennis on it.
> G: How could you play table tennis on a door?
> B: The door can be changed into a table.
> G: That's cool!

① Where did you play table tennis?

② Who can play table tennis better?

③ What can you make with the door?

④ What makes the door so special?

⑤ Who made the door special?

03 다음 대화에 이어지기에 순서가 바르게 배열된 것을 고르시오.

> G: This candle holder can make candles last twice as long.
> (A) Wow, I am so fascinated by the idea! Now we can use candles longer.
> (B) Really? How's that possible?
> (C) When a candle burns, it melts into the tube below the holder to form a new candle.

① (A) – (C) – (B)   ② (B) – (A) – (C)

③ (B) – (C) – (A)   ④ (C) – (A) – (B)

⑤ (C) – (B) – (A)

[01~03] 다음 대화를 읽고 물음에 답하시오.

G: You know that Leonardo da Vinci painted the *Mona Lisa*, don't you? (A)

B: Sure. I think he was a really great artist.

G: He was also a great inventor. (B)

B: What did he invent? (C)

G: He dreamed of flying like a bird. (D)

B: Did he also make that machine? (E)

G: No, but his (가)_____ idea inspired many other inventors.

01 (A)~(E) 중에서 다음 문장이 들어가기에 가장 적절한 곳은?

So, he drew a flying machine that looked like a bird.

① (A)   ② (B)   ③ (C)   ④ (D)   ⑤ (E)

02 빈칸 (가)에 들어가기에 적절한 것은?

① creative   ② artistic

③ usual   ④ common

⑤ ordinary

03 위 대화를 읽고 대답할 수 없는 것은?

① What did Leonardo da Vinci paint?

② What did Leonardo da Vinci dream of?

③ How did Leonardo da Vinci make the flying machine?

④ What did the flying machine look like?

⑤ What inspired many other inventors?

[04~05] 다음 대화를 읽고 물음에 답하시오.

B: (A)Have you heard of a mosquito needle, Jian?

G: A mosquito needle? Can you explain it to me?

B: Some scientists made this new needle by imitating a mosquito's mouth.

G: That's interesting. So how will that help?

B: You know mosquito bites are not very painful, don't you? The new needle will also cause less pain.

G: That's great. How come it's less painful?

B: Like a mosquito's mouth, it makes less contact with our skin.

G: Wow, I think that there's nothing useless in the world!

04 다음 중 밑줄 친 (A) 대신 쓰기에 적절한 것은?

① You know about a mosquito needle, don't you, Jian?

② Do you know that there's nothing useless in the world, Jian?

③ Jian, you said about a mosquito needle, didn't you?

④ Do you believe scientists are imitating a mosquito's mouth, Jian?

⑤ I know a mosquito needle is useful, Jian.

05 위 대화의 내용과 일치하지 않는 것은?

① The girl hasn't heard of a mosquito needle.

② Some scientists imitated a mosquito's mouth.

③ Mosquito bites are not very painful.

④ The new needle will cause more pain.

⑤ The new needle makes less contact with our skin.

[06~08] 다음 대화를 읽고 물음에 답하시오.

W: Today, we have a special guest, Thomas Thwaites, the Goat Man. Hello, Thomas.

M: Hello, Anna. Great to be here.

W: Thomas, (가)_____ that you lived like a goat in the Alps for three days. (A)

M: One day, I saw goats playing on the mountain. (B) They looked so peaceful that I wanted to live like them. (C)

W: Didn't you have any problems being a goat? (D)

M: Walking on all four legs was very difficult for me. (E)

W: Do you have any plans to live like a goat again?

M: Sure. I'm planning my second visit to the Alps.

W: (나)I can't wait to hear about your next adventure. Thank you, Thomas, for your time.

06 대화의 내용으로 보아, 빈칸 (가)에 들어가기에 적절하지 않은 것은?

① I'm so fascinated by the fact
② I'm interested in the fact
③ it is really impressive
④ I have an interest in the fact
⑤ I'm aware of the fact

07 (A)~(E) 중에서 다음 문장이 들어가기에 가장 적절한 곳은?

Why did you do that?

① (A) ② (B) ③ (C) ④ (D) ⑤ (E)

08 밑줄 친 (나)가 의도하는 것은?

① 감사 표현하기   ② 만족 표현하기
③ 관심 표현하기   ④ 의무 말하기
⑤ 기대 표현하기

[09~11] 다음 대화를 읽고 물음에 답하시오.

Henry: What are you doing, Mina?

Mina: I'm reading an article about a bug robot.

Henry: A bug robot? Is it interesting?

Mina: Yes. I'm really (A)_____ this thing.

Henry: Can you tell me more about it?

Mina: You know that some bugs can slip into narrow spaces, don't you?

Henry: Yeah. That's (B)_____ it's hard to catch them.

Mina: A bug robot can do the same. It can help to find survivors after earthquakes or big fires.

Henry: That's really (C)_____!

09 빈칸 (A)에 들어가기에 적절한 것은?

① worried about
② relieved by
③ wondering about
④ satisfied with
⑤ fascinated by

10 다음 중 (B)에 들어갈 말과 같은 말이 들어갈 수 있는 것은?

① I read the book _____ he had written.
② This is the house _____ he designed.
③ Do you know _____ will help her?
④ Tell me _____ you were late for class.
⑤ I know _____ he lives.

11 위 대화의 내용으로 보아 (C)에 들어가기에 어색한 것은?

① fascinating   ② interesting
③ cool   ④ wonderful
⑤ disappointing

[01~03] 다음 대화를 읽고 물음에 답하시오.

B: (A)_____ Sophia, a robot girl.(나는 로봇 소녀, Sophia에 매혹되었어.)
G: (B)_____'s so special about her?
B: She is able to show more than 60 facial expressions.
G: That's amazing. What else can she do?
B: She has no other abilities. She looks, talks, and even thinks like a human.
G: That's fascinating!

중요
01 빈칸 (A)를 우리말에 어울리는 영어 표현을 넣어 문장을 완성하시오. (by를 포함할 것)
➡ _____

02 빈칸 (B)에 알맞은 의문대명사를 쓰시오.
➡ _____

고난이도
03 위 대화에서 흐름상 어색한 것을 찾아 적절한 것으로 고치시오.
➡ _____

[04~05] 다음 대화를 읽고 물음에 답하시오.

G: (가)너 Leonardo da Vinci가 the *Mona Lisa*를 그린 것을 알지, 그렇지 않니? (do)
B: Sure. I think he was a really great artist.
G: He was also a great inventor.
B: What did he invent?
G: He dreamed of flying like a bird. So, he drew a flying machine that looked like a bird.
B: Did he also make that machine?
G: No, but his creative idea inspired many other inventors.

04 밑줄 친 (가)의 우리말을 주어진 단어를 이용하여 영어로 옮기시오.
➡ _____
_____

중요
05 위 대화의 내용에 어울리도록 아래 빈칸에 적절한 말을 쓰시오.

Leonardo da Vinci _____ of flying like a bird, but he didn't _____ a flying machine.

[06~07] 다음 대화를 읽고 물음에 답하시오.

B: (A)Have you heard of a mosquito needle, Jian? (aware)
G: A mosquito needle? Can you explain it to me?
B: Some scientists made this new needle by imitating a mosquito's mouth.
G: That's interesting. So how will that help?
B: You know mosquito bites are not very painful, don't you? The new needle will also cause less pain.
G: That's great. (B)_____ _____ it's less painful?
B: Like a mosquito's mouth, it makes less contact with our skin.
G: Wow, I think that there's nothing useless in the world!

06 밑줄 친 (A)를 주어진 단어를 이용하여 같은 의미가 되도록 바꿔 쓰시오.
➡ _____

중요
07 내용상 빈칸 (B)에 들어가기에 적절한 두 단어를 쓰시오.
➡ _____

Grammar

① not only A but also B

> • The fastener was **not only** strong **but also** easy to use. 그 고정 장치는 튼튼할 뿐만 아니라 사용하기도 쉬웠다.
> • He is **not only** poor **but also** lazy. 그는 가난할 뿐만 아니라 게으르다.

■ 형태: not only A but also B
　의미: A뿐만 아니라 B도

■ 'not only A but also B'는 'A뿐만 아니라 B도'라는 뜻으로 두 단어가 짝을 이루어 하나의 접속사 역할을 하는 상관접속사로, 두 개의 단어, 구, 절을 연결하며, A와 B의 품사는 같아야 한다.

　• She was **not only** intelligent **but also** very musical. 그녀는 이지적일뿐 아니라 음악성도 대단했다.

　• She **not only** wrote the text **but also** selected the illustrations.
　　그녀는 그 본문을 썼을 뿐만 아니라 삽화들을 선별하기도 했다.

■ 'Not only A but also B'가 주어로 쓰일 경우 수의 일치는 B에 맞춘다.

　• **Not only** you **but also** she is pretty. 너뿐만 아니라 그녀도 예뻐.

■ 'not only A but also B'는 'B as well as A'로 바꾸어 쓸 수 있다. 이때도 동사의 수는 B에 맞춘다.

　• They sell **not only** newspapers **but also** books.
　　= They sell books **as well as** newspapers. 그들은 신문뿐만 아니라 책도 판다.

핵심 Check

1. 다음 괄호 안에서 알맞은 것을 고르시오.

　(1) He not only read the book, but also (remembers / remembered) what he had read.

　(2) It makes sense not only politically but also (economical / economically).

　(3) The documentary was not only funny (but / and) also very informative.

② 간접의문문

- Do you know **where the key is**? 열쇠가 어디 있는지 아니?
- I'm wondering **what you were talking about**. 네가 무슨 얘기를 하고 있었는지 궁금한데.

■ 형태: 의문사+주어+동사
  의미: ~인지/일지

■ 간접의문문은 의문문이 다른 문장에 포함되어 그 문장의 일부가 되는 것이며 의문사가 있는 경우 '의문사+주어+동사'의 어순이 된다.
  - Do you know? + What did he do today? (의문사+동사+주어)
  = Do you know **what he did today**? (의문사+주어+동사) 오늘 그가 뭘 했는지 알아?

■ 의문사가 주어인 경우에는 의문사 뒤에 바로 동사가 이어진다.
  - Can you tell me? + What happened? (의문사(= 주어)+동사)
  = Can you tell me **what happened**? (의문사(= 주어)+동사) 어떻게 된 건지 말해 줄래?

■ 'how often, how much, how many people, what kind of food'처럼 하나의 의미 단위로 쓰이는 의문사구는 하나의 의문사로 취급한다.
  - Do you know? + How much time did we spend? (의문사구+조동사+주어+동사원형)
  = Do you know **how much time we spent**? (○) 우리가 얼마나 많은 시간을 보냈는지 아니?
    Do you know how time we spent much? (×)

■ 간접의문문이 believe, imagine, suppose, consider, expect, think, guess 등의 목적어로 쓰인 경우 의문사를 맨 앞으로 보낸다.
  - Do you think? + When will you be finished?
  = **When** do you think **you'll be finished**? 언제쯤 끝날 것 같아요?

■ 의문사가 없는 의문문은 의문사 대신 if나 whether를 쓰고 'if[whether]+주어+동사'의 어순이 된다. 이때 'if[whether]'는 '…인지 아닌지'의 뜻을 갖는다.
  - I wonder. + Will there be a pay raise next year? (동사+주어) 내년에 임금이 인상될지 궁금하네.
  = I wonder **if[whether] there will be a pay raise next year**. (접속사+주어+동사)

핵심 Check

2. 다음 괄호 안에서 알맞은 것을 고르시오.

(1) Let me know (who is he / who he is) meeting with.

(2) I wonder whether (may I ask you a question / I may ask you a question).

(3) She asked me (how old I was / how I was old).

01 다음 두 문장을 하나의 문장으로 만들 때 빈칸에 알맞은 것은?

- I don't know.
- Where did she buy this pen?
- → I don't know _____ .

① where did she buy this pen
② where she bought this pen
③ did she where buy this pen
④ she bought where this pen
⑤ she bought this pen where

02 다음 두 문장을 하나의 문장으로 만들 때 알맞은 것은?

- He is smart.
- He is kind, too.

① He is not smart but kind.
② He is only smart also kind.
③ He is not only smart but also kind.
④ He is not smart but also kind.
⑤ He is not only smart also kind.

03 다음 우리말에 맞게 괄호 안에 주어진 단어를 바르게 배열하시오.

(1) 난 지금까지 네가 얼마나 많은 책을 읽었는지 궁금해.

(you, I'm, books, now, many, wondering, read, have, how, until)

➡ _____

(2) 왜 코끼리는 긴 코가 있는지 아니?

(you, trunk, elephant, why, has, know, do, a, an)

➡ _____

(3) 소미는 음악 감상뿐만 아니라 그림 그리는 것도 즐긴다.

(Somi, pictures, music, listening, enjoys, only, painting, also, not, but, to)

➡ _____

(4) 그는 개뿐만 아니라 고양이도 있다.

(he, dog, cat, but, not, a, a, has, also, only)

➡ _____

05 다음 주어진 빈칸에 괄호 안의 문장을 알맞은 형태로 바꾸어 쓰시오.

> Do you know _____?
> (Why won't this computer turn on?)

06 다음 문장을 as well as를 이용하여 바꾸어 쓰시오.

(1) I want to learn not only taekwondo but also tennis.

➡ _____

(2) He treated me not only to lunch but also to cake.

➡ _____

(3) She not only likes playing the guitar but also composes good songs.

➡ _____

_____

(4) Not only Mark but also his brothers want to go to the concert.

➡ _____

_____

07 다음 중 어법상 어색한 문장을 찾아 바르게 고쳐 다시 쓰시오.

> a. Do you know what he bought at the store?
> b. I am wondering if I can use your pen.
> c. He wondered how the bird could fly high.
> d. Tell me where the key is.

➡ _____

08 다음 문장을 어법에 맞게 고쳐 쓰시오.

(1) The director as well as actors are invited to the party.

➡ _____

_____

(2) He looks not only smart but also friend.

➡ _____

(3) Cathy is not only a smart girl but also has a warm heart.

➡ _____

_____

(4) How do you know old he is?

➡ _____

(5) Do you believe what is causing this symptom?

➡ _____

09 다음 문장을 두 문장으로 나누려고 한다. 빈칸에 알맞은 문장을 쓰시오.

(1) Do you know? + _____

➡ Do you know where the key is?

(2) He wants to know. + _____

_____

➡ He wants to know how that happened.

(3) I wonder. + _____

➡ I wonder if we could go there.

(4) Do you think? + _____

_____

➡ What do you think is wrong with the computer?

Nature's Inspiration

From flying birds to self-cleaning plants, the way nature works
현재분사(birds 수식)   = how
fascinates us. Some people not only use nature but also imitate it
                        not only A but also B 병렬 (use와 병렬 관계)
to find solutions to their problems. Leonardo da Vinci (1452-1519)
was one such person. He wondered how birds could fly. He closely
      그러한   간접의문문(의문사+주어+동사)
watched birds, made notes, and drew pictures of them. Even though his
                                              양보절을 이끄는 부사절 접속사
invention was not successful, he imitated a bird's wings to try to make
                                            to부정사의 부사적 용법 중 목적(~하기 위해서)
a flying machine. Since then, more and more people have successfully
                              더욱 더 많은
imitated the surprising abilities of nature's genius. Let's explore some
of them.
the surprising abilities of nature's genius

Learning from a Bird: Moving Fast and Quietly

The high-speed train was first made in Japan. But it had one problem.
When the train entered a tunnel, the sudden increase in air pressure
             타동사(전치사 없이 목적어를 취함)
created a very loud sound. It often woke people up and caused
                   a very loud sound   wake up: ~을 깨우다
headaches. A team of engineers tried to solve the problem, but they
didn't know how they could reduce the noise. One day, one of the
              간접의문문(의문사+주어+동사)
engineers was watching a bird in search of a meal. He saw the bird
      one of+복수명사: 단수취급   지각동사+목적어+V(ing)(목적어와 목적격 보어가 능동 관계에 있을 때)
quickly and quietly diving into the water. He wondered how the bird
entered the water so gracefully.
간접의문문(의문사+주어+동사)

inspiration: 영감
self-clean: 자정 작용을 하다
work: 작동하다
fascinate: 매료시키다
imitate: 모방하다
closely: 가까이에서, 면밀히
invention: 발명품
suprising: 놀라운
genius: 천재
enter: ~로 들어가다
increase: 증가하다
pressure: 압력
sudden: 갑작스러운
cause: 야기하다
headache: 두통
reduce: 줄이다
in search of: ~을 찾아
gracefully: 우아하게

📎 **확인문제**

● 다음 문장이 본문의 내용과 일치하면 T, 일치하지 않으면 F를 쓰시오.

1 Humans are fascinated by the way nature works. ☐

2 Leonardo da Vinci looked into birds to understand how they flies. ☐

3 The high-speed train that was first made in Japan satisfied all the passengers. ☐

4 Engineers knew how to solve the problem the train had. ☐

So, he studied more about the bird and discovered its long, narrow
<u>the bird's</u>
beak. He redesigned the front of the train by imitating the bird's beak.
<u>by+Ving: V함으로써</u>
It was successful. Now the new train travels not only more quietly but
<u>not only 부사 but also 부사</u>
also 10% faster with 15% less electricity.

Learning from Burrs: Inventing an All-Purpose Fastener

One day, a Swiss engineer, George de Mestral, was hiking in the
<u>a Swiss engineer와 동격</u>
woods with his dog. On his way home, he saw that burrs were
<u>집에 오는 길에</u>   <u>명사절 접속사 that</u>
stuck to his clothes and his dog's hair. He wanted to know how that
<u>stick의 과거분사</u>   <u>간접의문문(의문사+주어+동사)</u>
happened. He took a closer look at the burrs and noticed that the ends
<u>명사절 접속사 that</u>
of the burr needles were not straight. He wondered if he could apply
<u>의문사가 없는 의문문의 간접의문문을 만들 때 쓰임(~인지 아닌지)</u>
that to make something useful. After a lot of testing, he finally
<u>-thing으로 끝나는 부정대명사는 형용사의 수식을 뒤에서 받음</u>
invented two new materials. One had many tiny needles like those
of burrs and the other had a hairy surface. When they were pressed
<u>둘 중의 하나는 one. 나머지 하나는 the other</u>
together, they became a very good fastener. It was not only strong but
<u>not only 형용사 but also 형용사</u>
also easy to use. Since then, many people have used his invention in
many different ways. It is often used for clothing, shoes, and bags.
Some people use it to play a number of different games. In space, it
<u>= many</u>
keeps things from floating away.
<u>keep A from Ving: A가 V하지 못하게 막다</u>
There is nothing useless in nature. We just have to become curious
<u>-thing으로 끝나는 부정대명사는 형용사의 수식을 뒤에서 받음</u>
and ask questions.

discover: 발견하다
narrow: 좁은
redesign: 외관을 고치다. 다시 설계하다
beak: 부리
successful: 성공적인
electricity: 전기
burr: 가시 식물
all-purpose: 만능의
on one's way home: 집으로 가는 길에
happen: 발생하다
straight: 곧은
useful: 유용한
hairy: 털이 많은
fastener: 고정 장치
surface: 표면
float away: 떠다니다
useless: 쓸모없는
curious: 호기심 있는

확인문제

● 다음 문장이 본문의 내용과 일치하면 T, 일치하지 <u>않으면</u> F를 쓰시오.

1 The train was redesigned like the bird's beak. ☐

2 The new train travels faster than the old one. ☐

3 George de Mestral was interested in burrs because it looked beautiful. ☐

4 The two new materials were easy to use but not strong. ☐

5 Everything in nature is useful. ☐

● 우리말을 참고하여 빈칸에 알맞은 말을 쓰시오.

Nature's Inspiration

1 _____ flying birds _____ self-cleaning plants, the way nature _____ _____ _____.

2 Some people _____ _____ use nature _____ _____ imitate _____ to find _____ to their problems.

3 Leonardo da Vinci (1452-1519) was _____ _____ _____.

4 He wondered _____ _____ _____ _____ _____.

5 He _____ watched birds, _____ notes, and drew pictures of them.

6 _____ _____ his invention was not _____, he _____ a bird's wings _____ _____ _____ _____ a flying machine.

7 _____ then, more and more people _____ successfully _____ the _____ _____ of nature's genius.

8 _____ _____ some of them.

Learning from a Bird: Moving Fast and Quietly

9 The _____ _____ was first made in Japan. But it _____ one problem.

10 When the train _____ a tunnel, the _____ _____ in air pressure _____ a very loud sound.

11 It often _____ _____ _____ and _____ headaches.

12 A team of engineers tried _____ _____ the problem, but they didn't know _____ _____ _____ _____ the noise.

13 One day, one of _____ _____ _____ watching a bird _____ _____ _____ a meal.

14 He _____ the bird quickly and quietly _____ _____ the water.

15 He wondered _____ _____ _____ _____ the water so gracefully.

---

1 나는 새에서 자정 작용을 하는 식물까지, 자연이 기능하는 방식은 우리를 매료시킵니다.

2 몇몇 사람들은 그들의 문제에 대한 해결책을 찾기 위해 자연을 이용할 뿐만 아니라 자연을 모방하기까지 합니다.

3 레오나르도 다빈치(1452-1519)가 이러한 사람들 중 한 사람이었습니다.

4 그는 새들이 어떻게 날 수 있는지 궁금했습니다.

5 그는 새를 자세히 관찰했고, 기록했으며, 그림으로 그렸습니다.

6 그의 발명은 비록 성공하지 못했지만, 그는 나는 기계를 만들어 보려고 새의 날개를 모방했습니다.

7 그 후로, 점점 더 많은 사람들이 자연 속 천재의 놀라운 능력을 성공적으로 모방해 오고 있습니다.

8 그들 중 몇 가지를 알아봅시다.

새에게서 배우기: 빠르고 조용하게 움직이기

9 고속 열차는 일본에서 처음 만들어졌습니다. 하지만 그것은 한 가지 문제점이 있었습니다.

10 열차가 터널에 들어갔을 때, 갑작스러운 기압의 상승은 매우 시끄러운 소리를 발생시켰습니다.

11 그것은 종종 사람들의 잠을 깨웠고 두통을 일으켰습니다.

12 한 공학자 팀이 그 문제를 해결하려 했지만, 그들은 어떻게 소음을 줄일 수 있을지 몰랐습니다.

13 어느 날, 공학자들 중 한 사람이 먹이를 찾고 있는 새를 관찰하고 있었습니다.

14 그는 새가 빠르고 조용하게 물속으로 뛰어드는 것을 보았습니다.

15 그는 새가 어떻게 그렇게 우아하게 물속으로 들어가는지 궁금했습니다.

07 What was the problem of the first high-speed train?

① It made people sit uncomfortably.

② It was not fast enough.

③ It created too much smoke.

④ It was too expensive for people to use.

⑤ It was too noisy when entering a tunnel.

08 다음 중 위 글을 읽고 답할 수 있는 것은?

① When was the high-speed train made?

② Who invented the high-speed train?

③ Why did people in the train have headaches?

④ Where did the man see the bird?

⑤ How far did the train travel at a time?

[09~13] 다음 글을 읽고 물음에 답하시오.

Learning from Burrs: Inventing an All-Purpose Fastener

(A) One had many tiny needles like those of burrs and the other had a hairy surface. When they were pressed together, they became a very good fastener.

(B) He wanted to know how that happened. He took a closer look at the burrs and noticed ⓐthat the ends of the burr needles were not straight.

(C) One day, a Swiss engineer, George de Mestral, was hiking in the woods with his dog. On his way home, he saw that burrs were stuck to his clothes and his dog's hair.

(D) He wondered if he could apply that to make something useful. After a lot of testing, he finally invented two new materials.

It was not only strong but also easy to use. Since then, many people have used his invention in many different ways. It is often

used for clothing, shoes, and bags. Some people use it to play a number of different games. In space, it keeps things from floating away.

There is nothing useless in nature. We just have to become curious and ask questions

서답형

09 자연스러운 글이 되도록 (A)~(D)를 바르게 나열하시오.

➡ _____

서답형

10 다음과 같이 풀이되는 말을 위 글에서 찾아 쓰시오.

being interested in something and wanting to know more about it

➡ _____

서답형

11 For what is George's invention often used? Answer in English with a full sentence.

➡ _____

12 다음 중 밑줄 친 ⓐ와 쓰임이 같은 것은?

① She made that to make you happy.

② The boy that you met is my brother.

③ The fruit that he bought looks fresh.

④ Did you hear that he stole it?

⑤ Making the pie wasn't that difficult.

13 다음 중 위 글의 내용과 일치하는 것은?

① George de Mestral was hiking alone.

② George was a Swiss engineer.

③ Burrs were stuck to George's hair.

④ George failed to invent something new.

⑤ What George invented was strong but hard to use.

[14~17] 다음 글을 읽고 물음에 답하시오.

From flying birds to self-cleaning plants, the way nature works fascinates us. (①) Some people not only use nature but also imitate it to find solutions to their problems. (②) He wondered how birds could fly. He closely watched birds, made notes, and drew pictures of them. (③) Even though his invention was not successful, he imitated a bird's wings to try to make a (A)flying machine. (④) Since then, more and more people have successfully imitated the surprising abilities of nature's genius. (⑤) Let's explore some of them.

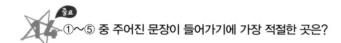

①~⑤ 중 주어진 문장이 들어가기에 가장 적절한 곳은?

> Leonardo da Vinci (1452-1519) was one such person.

①   ②   ③   ④   ⑤

15 다음 중 밑줄 친 (A)와 쓰임이 다른 하나는?

① I need some sleeping pills.
② Please lend me your camping car.
③ Do you see the crying baby over there?
④ I am here in the waiting room.
⑤ Did she buy a washing machine?

16 다음 중 위 글에 이어질 내용으로 가장 적절한 것은?

① examples of failed inventions
② what Leonardo da Vinci invented
③ how to draw birds well
④ examples of successful imitation of nature
⑤ some geniuses who destroy nature

17 위 글의 내용과 일치하도록 빈칸에 알맞은 말을 쓰시오.

> We are _____ by the way nature works.

[18~21] 다음 글을 읽고 물음에 답하시오.

Learning from a Bird: (A)_____

The high-speed train was first made in Japan. But it had one problem. When the train entered a tunnel, the sudden increase in air pressure created a very loud sound. It often woke people up and caused headaches. A team of engineers tried to solve the problem, but they didn't know how they could reduce the noise. One day, one of the engineers was watching a bird in search of a meal. He saw the bird quickly and quietly diving into the water. He wondered how the bird entered the water so gracefully. So, he studied more about the bird and discovered its long, narrow beak. He redesigned the front of the train by imitating the bird's beak. It was successful. Now the new train travels not only more quietly but also 10% faster with 15% less electricity.

18 다음 중 빈칸 (A)에 들어갈 말로 가장 적절한 것은?

① Moving As Slow As It Can
② Flying Fast and High
③ The Most Grace Animal
④ Flying in Search of Its Meal
⑤ Moving Fast and Quietly

19 What happened when the high-speed train entered the tunnel? Answer in English with eleven words.

➡ _____

_____

20 Choose the one that is TRUE about the new train.

① It makes people suffer from headaches.
② Its front looks like a bird tail.
③ The front of the train is long and wide.
④ It uses less electricity than the old one.
⑤ It doesn't travel as fast as the old one.

21 위 글의 내용에 맞게 빈칸에 알맞은 말을 쓰시오.

> After watching a bird, the engineer studied more about the bird to figure out
>
> _____ .

[22~26] 다음 글을 읽고 물음에 답하시오.

Learning from Burrs: Inventing an All-Purpose Fastener

One day, a Swiss engineer, George de Mestral, was hiking in the woods with his dog. On his way home, he saw that burrs were stuck to his clothes and his dog's hair. He wanted to know how that happened. He took a closer look at the burrs and noticed that the ends of the burr needles were not straight. He wondered (A)_____ he could apply that to make something useful. After a lot of testing, he finally invented two new materials. One had many tiny needles like (B)those of burrs and the other had a hairy surface. When they were pressed together, they became a very good fastener. It was not only strong but also easy to use. Since then, many people have used his invention in many different ways. It is often used for clothing, shoes, and bags. Some people use it to play a number of different games. In space, it keeps things from floating away.

There is nothing useless in nature. We just have to become curious and ask questions.

22 다음 중 빈칸 (A)에 들어갈 말과 같은 말이 들어가는 것은?

① Can you tell me _____ old you are?
② Do you know _____ invited you?
③ I wonder _____ she came from.
④ Tell me _____ your birthday is.
⑤ Let me know _____ she is hungry.

23 밑줄 친 (B)가 가리키는 것을 위 글에서 찾아 쓰시오.

➡ _____

24 Choose the one that is NOT true about what George de Mestral invented.

① It is divided into two parts.
② One has a hairy surface.
③ It is easy to use but not strong.
④ It has been used in various ways.
⑤ To be used as a fastener, it should be pressed together.

25 How is the fastener used in space? Answer in English with nine words.

➡ _____

26 다음 중 위 글을 읽고 답할 수 있는 것은?

① When did George hike with his dog?
② What did George see when he was hiking?
③ What did burrs' needles look like?
④ How long did it take George to invent a very good fastener?
⑤ How many tests did George take?

[01~04] 다음 글을 읽고 물음에 답하시오.

From flying birds to self-cleaning plants, the way nature works fascinates us. Some people not only use nature but also imitate it to find solutions to their problems. Leonardo da Vinci (1452-1519) was one such person. (A)_____ He closely watched birds, made notes, and drew pictures of them. Even though his invention was not successful, he imitated a bird's wings to try to make a flying machine. Since (B)then, more and more people have successfully imitated the surprising abilities of nature's genius. Let's explore some of them.

01 주어진 단어를 바르게 나열하여 빈칸 (A)에 들어갈 말을 쓰시오.

(wondered / fly / birds / could / how / he)

➡ _____

02 What did Leonard da Vinci do to find out how birds could fly?

➡ _____

_____

03 밑줄 친 (B)가 의미하는 것을 위 글에서 찾아 우리말로 쓰시오.

➡ _____

_____

04 What did Leonardo da Vinci try to make? Answer in English with a full sentence.

➡ _____

_____

[05~09] 다음 글을 읽고 물음에 답하시오.

Learning from Burrs: Inventing an All-Purpose Fastener

One day, a Swiss engineer, George de Mestral, was hiking in the woods with his dog. On his way home, he saw that burrs were stuck to his clothes and his dog's hair. He wanted to know how (A)that happened. He took a closer look at the burrs and noticed that the ends of the burr needles were not straight. (B)그는 유용한 무언가를 만드는 데 그것을 적용할 수 있을지 궁금했습니다. After a lot of testing, he finally invented two new materials. One had many tiny needles like those of burrs and the other had a hairy surface. When they were pressed together, they became a very good fastener. It was not only strong but also easy to use. Since then, many people have used his invention in many different ways. It is often used for clothing, shoes, and bags. Some people use it to play a number of different games. In space, (C)it keeps floating away from things.

There is nothing useless in nature. We just have to become curious and ask questions.

05 밑줄 친 (A)가 의미하는 것을 우리말로 쓰시오.

➡ _____

06 주어진 단어를 바르게 나열하여 밑줄 친 우리말 (B)를 영어로 쓰시오. 하나의 단어를 추가하시오.

(he / he / that / useful / make / wondered / something / could / to / apply)

➡ _____

_____

07 밑줄 친 (C)는 문맥상 어색한 문장이다. 단어를 재배열하여 문맥에 맞는 문장으로 고쳐 쓰시오.

➡ _____

08 When George took a closer look at the burrs, what did he notice? Answer in English with a full sentence.

➡ _____
_____

09 What do we have to do in order to learn from nature? Answer in English with a full sentence.

➡ _____

[10~14] 다음 글을 읽고 물음에 답하시오.

Learning from a Bird: Moving Fast and Quietly

The high-speed train was first made in Japan. But it had one problem. When the train entered a tunnel, the sudden increase in air pressure created a very loud sound. It often woke people up and caused headaches. A team of engineers tried to (A)_____ the problem, but they didn't know how they could (B)_____ the noise. One day, one of the engineers was watching a bird in search of a meal. He saw the bird quickly and quietly diving into the water. He wondered how the bird entered the water so gracefully. So, he studied more about the bird and discovered its long, narrow beak. He redesigned the front of the train by (C)_____ the bird's beak. It was successful. Now the new train travels not only more quietly but also 10% faster with 15% less electricity.

10 주어진 단어를 글의 흐름과 어법에 맞게 빈칸 (A)~(C)에 쓰시오.

(imitate / reduce / solve)

➡ (A)_____ (B)_____ (C)_____

11 What did the engineer wonder when he watched a bird in search of a meal? Answer in English.

➡ _____
_____

12 What did the bird's beak look like? Answer in English. Use the word 'have.' (6 words)

➡ _____

13 다음 물음에 〈조건〉에 맞추어 답하시오.

Q: How does the new train differ from the old train?

┌─ 조건 ─┐
1. 두 개의 문장으로 된 영어로 답할 것.
2. First, Second를 사용하여 답하시오.

➡ _____
_____

14 위 글의 내용에 맞게 빈칸에 알맞은 말을 쓰시오.

The high-speed train first made in _____ had one problem. When it entered a tunnel, it made a very loud sound because _____ _____ suddenly _____ in the tunnel.

Real Life Communication C

You know that some bugs have many eyes, don't you?
<small>부가의문문으로 상대에게 확인하기 위하여 묻는 형식이다.</small>

Some of them have thousands of eyes. I was fascinated by that and designed
<small>"Some of them"은 "그 중의 몇몇"이라는 뜻으로 복수 취급한다.　　　　　동사 was와 병렬구조를 이루는 과거 동사이다.</small>

Bug Eye Robot. It has many eyes to see things better. It will help people who
<small>who는 주관 관계대명사로 선행사는 people이다.</small>

can't see well.

구문해설 · thousands of 수천의 · be fascinated by ~에 매료되다, design 디자인하다, 설계하다

해석

너 곤충이 많은 눈을 가지고 있는 것을 알지? 그 중에 몇몇은 수 천 개의 눈을 가지고 있어. 나는 그것에 매료가 되어서 **Bug Eye Robot**을 만들었어. 그것은 더 잘 보기 위하여 많은 눈을 가지고 있어. 그것은 잘 볼 수 없는 사람을 도와 줄 거야.

Culture & Life

Polar Bears, North Pole

Polar bears survive the cold because they have black skin to easily absorb the
<small>　　　　　the+형용사: 추상명사　　　　　　　　　　　형용사적 용법의 to 부정사</small>

heat from the sun. Each of their hairs has an air space. This also helps them
<small>　　　　　each가 주어일 경우 단수 동사　　　　　앞 문장의 내용</small>

stay warm.
<small>help의 목적격보어로 동사원형</small>

구문해설 · survive: 생존하다 · absorb: 흡수하다

북극곰, 북극

북극곰은 태양열을 쉽게 흡수할 수 있는 검은 피부를 가지고 있기 때문에 추위에서 생존한다. 북극곰 털 하나하나에는 공기층이 있다. 이것 또한 따뜻함을 유지하는 데 도움이 된다.

Culture & Life

Sahara Desert Ants, North Africa

The Sahara Desert is not only the driest but also the hottest place on earth. But
<small>　　　　　not only A but also B: A뿐만 아니라 B도　　　　　지구상에서</small>

even at the hottest time of day, Sahara Desert ants go hunting. Do you know
<small>　　　　　go Ving: V하러 가다</small>

how they survive the heat? Their bodies are covered with unique hairs that
<small>간접의문문(의문사+주어+동사)　　　　　주격 관계대명사(선행사: hairs)</small>

reflect the heat from the sun.

구문해설 · desert: 사막 · dry: 건조한 · survive: 생존하다, 살아남다 · be covered with: ~으로 덮여 있다 · reflect: 반사하다

사하라 사막 개미들, 북아프리카

사하라 사막은 지구상에서 가장 건조할 뿐만 아니라 가장 뜨거운 곳이다. 하지만 하루 중 가장 뜨거운 시간에도 사하라 사막 개미들은 사냥을 간다. 그들이 어떻게 그 열기에서 살아남는지 아는가? 개미들의 몸은 태양으로부터의 열기를 반사해내는 독특한 털로 덮여 있다.

Culture & Life Project

You know horses run very fast, don't you? One of the reasons is that they have
<small>　　　　　부가의문문　　　　　one of+복수 명사+단수 동사</small>

strong feet. Our group designed shoes by imitating a horse's foot. When you
<small>　　　　　전치사+동명사</small>

wear them, you will not only run faster but also look taller.
<small>　　　　　A뿐만 아니라 B도　　　　　look+형용사 보어</small>

구문해설 · imitate: 모방하다

여러분은 말이 빨리 달리는 것을 알고 있습니다, 그렇죠? 그 이유 중의 하나는 그들이 튼튼한 발을 가지고 있다는 겁니다. 우리 모둠은 말의 발을 모방해서 신발을 만들었습니다. 여러분이 그것을 신으면, 여러분은 빨리 달릴 뿐만 아니라 키가 더 커 보일 겁니다.

Words & Expressions

01 다음 두 문장에 공통으로 알맞은 것을 고르시오.

> • You have to make contact _____ us.
> • The window was covered _____ snow.

① to   ② for   ③ with
④ by   ⑤ about

02 다음 주어진 단어의 적절한 형태를 고르시오.

> He will get angry with this _____.
> (decide)

① decisive   ② decided
③ deciding   ④ to decide
⑤ decision

03 다음 영영풀이에 해당하는 단어를 고르시오.

> a passage that goes under the ground

① tunnel   ② path
③ subway   ④ transport
⑤ vehicle

04 다음 밑줄 친 부분의 우리말 뜻이 알맞지 <u>않은</u> 것은?

① Boys try to <u>imitate</u> stars. (모방하다)
② We will <u>increase</u> the price. (인상하다)
③ His music will <u>inspire</u> children. (관심을 가지다)
④ His speech won't <u>last</u> long. (지속하다)
⑤ She has a very <u>inventive</u> idea. (창의적인)

Conversation

[05~06] 다음 우리말과 일치하도록 빈칸에 알맞은 말을 쓰시오.
(05: 7단어, 06: 11단어)

05

> A: _____
> (나는 식물들이 할 수 있는 것에 매혹되었어.)
> B: What do you mean?
> A: For example, some plants never get wet or dirty.
> B: That's interesting!

06

> A: _____
> _____
> (북극곰이 수영을 잘하는 거 알지, 그렇지 않니?)
> B: Sure. They can swim more than 60 miles without rest.

07 다음 대화의 빈칸에 들어가기에 적절한 것은?

> G: This candle holder can make candles last twice as long.
> B: Really? _____
> G: When a candle burns, it melts into the tube below the holder to form a new candle.
> B: Wow, I am so fascinated by the idea! Now we can use candles longer.

① Where is the holder?
② What's on the holder?
③ How's that possible?
④ Why are you fascinated?
⑤ What's the problem?

[08~10] 다음 대화를 읽고 물음에 답하시오.

B: (A)너는 mosquito needle에 관하여 들어본 적이 있지, Jian?

G: A mosquito needle? Can you explain it to me?

B: Some scientists made this new needle by (B)_____ a mosquito's mouth.

G: That's interesting. So how will that help?

B: You know mosquito bites are not very painful, don't you? The new needle will also cause less pain.

G: That's great. How come it's more painful?

B: Like a mosquito's mouth, it makes less contact with our skin.

G: Wow, I think that there's nothing useless in the world!

08 밑줄 친 (A)의 우리말에 해당하는 영어 문장으로 적절한 것은?

① Did you tell about a mosquito needle, Jian?

② Have you studied a mosquito needle, Jian?

③ Will you ask about a mosquito needle, Jian?

④ Did you think about a mosquito needle, Jian?

⑤ Have you heard of a mosquito needle, Jian?

09 빈칸 (B)에 들어가기에 적절한 것은?

① drawing   ② making

③ imitating   ④ finding

⑤ increasing

10 위 대화에서 내용상 <u>어색한</u> 부분이 있는 문장을 찾아 자연스러운 문장으로 고쳐 쓰시오.

➡ _____

[11~13] 다음 대화를 읽고 물음에 답하시오.

G: (A)You know that Leonardo da Vinci painted the *Mona Lisa*, don't you?

B: Sure. I think he was a really great artist.

G: He was also a great inventor.

B: What did he invent?

G: He dreamed of flying like a bird. So, he drew (B)_____ that looked like a bird.

B: Did he also make that machine?

G: No, but his creative idea inspired many other inventors.

11 밑줄 친 (A)와 같은 의미의 문장으로 적절한 것은?

① Did you say that Leonardo da Vinci painted the *Mona Lisa*?

② Have you told Leonardo da Vinci painted the *Mona Lisa*?

③ Are you sure that Leonardo da Vinci painted the *Mona Lisa*?

④ Are you excited that Leonardo da Vinci painted the *Mona Lisa*?

⑤ Are you aware that Leonardo da Vinci painted the *Mona Lisa*?

12 빈칸 (B)에 들어가기에 적절한 것은?

① a robot bird   ② a bug robot

③ a cooling fan   ④ a new plane

⑤ a flying machine

13 위 대화를 통해서 알 수 있는 것이 <u>아닌</u> 것은?

① Leonardo da Vinci was very inventive.

② Leonardo da Vinci was an artist.

③ Leonardo da Vinci drew a flying machine.

④ Leonardo da Vinci's flying machine looked like a bird.

⑤ He was a great inventor and invented many flying machines.

Grammar

14 다음 중 어법상 <u>어색한</u> 문장을 고르시오.

① Do you think who you're talking to?

② I'm wondering when the library opens.

③ Can you guess where our bananas come from?

④ Can you tell me how the accident came about?

⑤ I don't know if he'll get better soon.

15 두 문장의 뜻이 같도록 빈칸에 들어갈 말을 차례대로 바르게 쓴 것은?

> • He works on weekends as well as on weekdays.
> = He works _____ on weekdays _____ on weekends.

① either – or

② neither – nor

③ not – but

④ not only – but also

⑤ as – as

16 다음 두 문장을 한 문장으로 바르게 옮긴 것은?

> • I don't know.
> • What was he doing at that time?

① I don't know if he was doing at that time.

② I don't know if what he was doing at that time.

③ I don't know what he was doing at that time.

④ I don't know what was he doing at that time.

⑤ What I don't know he was doing at that time.

17 다음 중 어법상 <u>어색한</u> 문장을 고르시오.

① He as well as you has to take part in the meeting.

② Charlotte as well as her sisters like to go hiking.

③ Not only he but also I remember the accident.

④ Not only the teacher but also the students were enjoying the game.

⑤ Not only men but also women want to live long.

18 다음 우리말을 주어진 어휘를 이용하여 영작하시오.

(1) 그녀는 얼굴뿐 아니라 마음씨도 곱다. (a pretty face, a warm heart, have, also)

➡ _____

(2) 성공은 재능뿐만 아니라 노력에 의해서도 결정된다. (depend, talent, also, effort, on)

➡ _____

_____

(3) 염소는 나뭇잎뿐만 아니라 과일도 먹는다. (a goat, leaves, fruit, as)

➡ _____

(4) Chris가 점심으로 무엇을 먹었는지 아니? (had, for lunch)

➡ _____

(5) 나는 그가 곧 돌아올지 궁금하다. (wondering, soon, come back)

➡ _____

(6) 그가 언제 집을 나왔다고 생각하니? (think, left home)

➡ _____

19 다음 중 어법상 <u>어색한</u> 문장의 개수로 알맞은 것은?

> ⓐ I wonder how much this skirt costs.
> ⓑ Do you know did who make this cake?
> ⓒ Do you think who is suitable for the new project?
> ⓓ Not only my friends but also my teacher like my idea.
> ⓔ A frog can not only jump but also swim.
> ⓕ So he got a good score in not only the English test but also in the math test.

① 1개 ② 2개 ③ 3개 ④ 4개 ⑤ 5개

Reading

[20~22] 다음 글을 읽고 물음에 답하시오.

From flying birds to self-cleaning plants, the way nature works fascinates us. Some people not only use nature but also imitate it to find solutions to their problems. Leonardo da Vinci (1452-1519) was one (a)<u>such person</u>.

(A) Even though his invention was not successful, he imitated a bird's wings to try to make a flying machine.

(B) He wondered how birds could fly. He closely watched birds, made notes, and drew pictures of them.

(C) Since then, more and more people have successfully imitated the surprising abilities of nature's genius. Let's explore some of (b)<u>them</u>.

---

20 자연스러운 글이 되도록 (A)~(C)를 바르게 나열하시오.

➡ _____

21 다음 중 밑줄 친 (a)가 의미하는 것으로 가장 적절한 것은?

① someone who liked to use technology
② someone who was interested in solving problems
③ someone who was into studying birds
④ someone who fascinated people
⑤ someone who copied nature successfully

22 다음 중 밑줄 친 (b)가 의미하는 것으로 가장 적절한 것은?

① some people who invented precious things
② people who have surprising abilities
③ things that have been treated carelessly
④ people who succeeded in their field
⑤ cases that people successfully imitated nature

[23~25] 다음 글을 읽고 물음에 답하시오.

A team of scientists questioned how certain animals climb walls so easily. (①) They have observed what their feet look like and how they stick to walls. (②) "The new material is not only strong but also easy to use," says one of the scientists. (③) In the movie Spider-Man, Spider-Man climbs a tall building with just his hands and feet. (④) Would (A)<u>that</u> ever be possible in the real world? (⑤) It doesn't sound impossible anymore!

23 ①~⑤ 중 다음 주어진 문장이 들어가기에 가장 적절한 곳은?

> As a result, they invented a new material that sticks to any surface.

①　　②　　③　　④　　⑤

24 밑줄 친 (A)가 의미하는 것을 10단어의 영어로 쓰시오.

➡ _____

_____

25 다음 중 위 글의 내용과 일치하는 것은?

① Some people climb walls with ease.
② Scientists don't care about climbing walls with just hands and feet.
③ The material scientists invented is not strong.
④ Spider-Man uses many gears to climb a tall building.
⑤ It is easy to use the new material scientists invented.

[26~27] 다음 글을 읽고 물음에 답하시오.

> Wolves are great hunters. Their wide ①feet help them ②travel a long way in the snow. (A)_____ is also important for their survival. The lead wolf decides ③when the group will travel and hunt. It also ④decides where to go and ⑤know what to do when there is danger.

26 다음 중 빈칸 (A)에 들어갈 말로 가장 적절한 것은?

① Friendship　　② Parentship
③ Leadership　　④ Ownership
⑤ Citizenship

27 ①~⑤ 중 어법상 바르지 않은 것은?

①　　②　　③　　④　　⑤

[28~29] 다음 글을 읽고 물음에 답하시오.

> The high-speed train was first made in Japan. But it had one problem. When the train entered a tunnel, the sudden increase in air pressure created a very loud sound. (A)It often woke people up and caused headaches. A team of engineers tried to solve the problem, but they didn't know how they could reduce the noise. One day, one of the engineers was watching a bird in search of a meal. He saw the bird quickly and quietly diving into the water. He wondered how the bird entered the water so gracefully. So, he studied more about the bird and discovered its long, narrow beak. He redesigned the front of the train by imitating the bird's beak. It was successful. Now the new train travels not only more quietly but also 10% faster with 15% less electricity.

28 밑줄 친 (A)가 의미하는 것을 우리말로 쓰시오.

➡ _____

29 Choose the one that is NOT true.

① It was in Japan that the first high-speed train was made.
② The first high-speed train couldn't pass a tunnel without making a loud sound.
③ Engineers tried to find out how to decrease the noise.
④ The engineer redesigned the tail of the train by imitating a bird.
⑤ The new train travels faster with less energy.

출제율 90%

01 짝지어진 단어의 관계가 같도록 빈칸에 알맞은 말을 쓰시오.

creative : inventive = g_____ : graciously

출제율 90%

02 다음 빈칸에 들어갈 말로 적절한 것은?

The traditions of other cultures often _____ people.

① fascinate ② reduce
③ ignore ④ observe
⑤ reflect

출제율 95%

03 다음 빈칸에 공통으로 들어가기에 적절한 것은?

- _____ come you are so angry this morning?
- _____ about going for lunch?

① What ② Whether
③ When ④ How
⑤ Which

출제율 100%

04 다음 〈보기〉의 단어로 자연스러운 문장을 만들 수 없는 것은?

보기
pressure redesign reflect reduce

① They are trying very hard to _____ the city.
② Let's check your blood _____ first.
③ Dark surface doesn't usually _____ much light.
④ Do you have any creative _____?
⑤ Use ice to _____ the pain.

[05~07] 다음 대화를 읽고 물음에 답하시오.

B: (가)Have you heard of a mosquito needle, Jian?
G: A mosquito needle? Can you explain it to me?
B: Some scientists made this new needle by imitating a mosquito's mouth.
G: That's interesting. So (A)_____ will that help?
B: You know mosquito bites are not very painful, don't you? The new needle will also cause less pain.
G: That's great. (B)_____ come it's less painful?
B: Like a mosquito's mouth, it makes less contact with our skin.
G: Wow, I think that there's nothing useless in the world!

출제율 90%

05 밑줄 친 (가) 대신 쓰기에 적절하지 않은 것은?

① Do you know about a mosquito needle, Jian?
② Are you aware of a mosquito needle, Jian?
③ Did you ask about a mosquito needle, Jian?
④ Have you been told about a mosquito needle, Jain?
⑤ Jian, you know about a mosquito needle, don't you?

출제율 95%

06 빈칸 (A)와 (B)에 들어가기에 알맞은 것으로 짝지어진 것은?

	(A)	(B)
①	what	Why
②	how	What
③	why	What
④	how	How
⑤	which	What

07 위 대화를 읽고 알 수 <u>없는</u> 것은?

① Some scientists made a new needle called a mosquito needle.

② Some scientists imitated a mosquito's mouth to make a new needle.

③ The new needle will cause less pain.

④ The new needle makes less contact with our skin.

⑤ The reason why it causes less pain isn't known to us.

[08~09] 다음 대화를 읽고 물음에 답하시오.

W: Today, we have a special guest, Thomas Thwaites, the Goat Man. Hello, Thomas.

M: Hello, Anna. Great to be here.

W: Thomas, I'm so fascinated by the fact (가) <u>that</u> you lived like a goat in the Alps for three days. Why did you do that?

M: One day, I saw goats playing on the mountain. They looked so peaceful that I wanted to live like them.

W: Didn't you have any problems being a goat?

M: Walking on all four legs was very pleasing to me.

W: Do you have any plans to live like a goat again?

M: Sure. I'm planning my second visit to the Alps.

W: I can't wait to hear about your next adventure. Thank you, Thomas, for your time.

08 밑줄 친 (가)와 같은 용법으로 쓰인 것은?

① Have you met <u>that</u> boy before?

② The car <u>that</u> he bought is very good.

③ Do you know <u>that</u> was his idea?

④ I agree with his idea <u>that</u> we should delay our picnic.

⑤ Is it the house <u>that</u> he designed?

09 위 대화를 읽고 알 수 <u>없는</u> 것은?

① The name of the hostess is Anna.

② The guest is called the Goat Man.

③ Thomas lived like a goat in the Alps.

④ Anna saw goats playing on the mountain.

⑤ Thomas is planning a second visit to the Alps.

10 다음 문장에서 어법상 <u>어색한</u> 부분을 찾아 바르게 고쳐 다시 쓰시오.

> Can you explain to me how this machine costs much?

➡ _____

11 다음 빈칸에 적절한 말을 주어진 단어를 알맞은 형태로 바꾸어 써 넣으시오.

(1) The baby not only is healthy but also looks very _____. (love)

(2) He works _____ as well as very hard. (efficient)

12 다음 우리말을 괄호 안의 어휘를 이용하여 영작하시오.

(1) 너는 학교 축제가 언제 시작됐는지 아니? (your school festival, know, start)

➡ _____

(2) 그녀는 달리기뿐만 아니라 수영하는 것을 즐긴다. (merely, running, also, swimming)

➡ _____

13 다음 주어진 문장을 잘못 바꾼 것을 고르시오.

> Kevin wants to study Greek. He wants to study Latin, too.

① Kevin wants to study Greek and Latin.

② Kevin wants to study Latin as well as Greek.

③ Kevin wants to study not only Greek but also study Latin.

④ Kevin wants to study not only Greek but also Latin.

⑤ Kevin wants to study not only Greek but Latin as well.

14 다음 두 문장을 한 문장으로 고쳐 쓰시오.

(1) • I'm wondering.

　　• Have you read the notice about the contest?

　　➡ ＿＿＿＿＿＿＿＿＿＿＿＿＿

　　＿＿＿＿＿＿＿＿＿＿＿＿＿

(2) • Do you suppose?

　　• What will you do?

　　➡ ＿＿＿＿＿＿＿＿＿＿＿＿＿

15 다음 빈칸에 공통으로 알맞은 것은?

> • This is ＿＿＿＿ she wants to eat.
> • I wonder ＿＿＿＿ she wants to eat.

① how　　② when　　③ why

④ that　　⑤ what

16 다음 괄호 안에 주어진 단어의 형태가 바르게 짝지어진 것은?

> Vivian is good at (read) as well as (write) in Korean.

① to read – to write　　② reading – writing

③ to read – writing　　④ reads – writes

⑤ read – write

[17~20] 다음 글을 읽고 물음에 답하시오.

Learning from Burrs: (A)＿＿＿＿＿＿

One day, a Swiss engineer, George de Mestral, was hiking in the woods with his dog. On his way home, he saw that burrs were stuck to his clothes and his dog's hair. He wanted to know how that happened. He took a closer look at the burrs and noticed that the ends of the burr needles were not straight. He wondered (B) [that / if] he could apply that to make something useful. After a lot of testing, he finally invented two new materials. One had many tiny needles like (C)[that / those] of burrs and (D)[the other / another] had a hairy surface. When they were pressed together, they became a very good fastener. It was not only strong but also easy to use. Since then, many people have used his invention in many different ways. It is often used for clothing, shoes, and bags. Some people use it to play a number of different games. In space, it keeps things from floating away.

There is nothing useless in nature. We just have to become curious and ask questions.

17 빈칸 (A)에 들어갈 말로 가장 적절한 것은?

① Making Lives Difficult

② How It Flies Far Away

③ The Mother of Needs

④ Inventing an All-Purpose Fastener

⑤ Making Invention Easy

출제율 100%

18 다음 중 위 글을 읽고 답할 수 있는 것은?

① How often did George hike?

② How old was George?

③ How long did George hike?

④ What was stuck to George's clothes?

⑤ How many times did George test to invent the final material?

출제율 95%

19 (B)~(D)에서 어법상 옳은 것을 골라 쓰시오.

➡ (B)_____ (C)_____ (D)_____

출제율 90%

20

What should be done in order for two new materials to be used as a very good fastener? Answer in English with five words.

➡ _____

[21~22] 다음 글을 읽고 물음에 답하시오.

The Sahara Desert is not only the driest but also the hottest place on earth. But even at the hottest time of day, Sahara Desert ants go hunting. Do you know (A)(the / how / survive / heat / they)? Their bodies are covered with unique hairs that reflect the heat from the sun.

출제율 90%

21 괄호 (A) 안의 단어를 바르게 나열하시오.

➡ _____

출제율 100%

22 다음 중 위 글을 읽고 알 수 없는 것은?

① No other desert in the world is drier than the Sahara Desert.

② The Sahara Desert is hotter than any other desert on Earth.

③ Sahara Desert ants go hunting even when it is the hottest time of day.

④ Sahara Desert ants like to go hunting at noon.

⑤ The unique hairs of the ants send back the heat from the sun.

[23~24] 다음 글을 읽고 물음에 답하시오.

From flying birds to self-cleaning plants, the way nature works fascinates us. (①) Some people not only use nature but also imitate it to find solutions to their problems. (②) Leonardo da Vinci (1452-1519) was one such person. (③) He closely watched birds, made notes, and drew pictures of them. (④) Even though his invention was not successful, he imitated a bird's wings to try to make a flying machine. (⑤) Since then, more and more people have successfully imitated the surprising abilities of nature's genius. Let's explore some of them.

출제율 95%

23 ①~⑤ 중 주어진 문장이 들어가기에 가장 적절한 곳은?

He wondered how birds could fly.

①   ②   ③   ④   ⑤

출제율 100%

24 What is the passage mainly talking about?

① the life of Leonardo da Vinci

② many interesting things in nature

③ fascinating inventions in the world

④ nature's inspiration for people

⑤ surprising abilities of Leonardo da Vinci

[01~03] 다음 대화를 읽고 물음에 답하시오.

> B: I'm fascinated by Sophia, a robot girl.
> G: (가)그녀가 뭐가 그리 특별한데? (so, about)
> B: She is able to show more than 60 facial expressions.
> G: That's amazing. (A)_____ else can she do?
> B: She has many other abilities. She looks, talks, and even thinks like a human.
> G: That's (B)(fascinate)!

01 (가)의 우리말에 해당하는 영어 문장을 괄호 안의 말을 이용하여 쓰시오.

➡ _____

02 빈칸 (A)에 들어가기에 적절한 한 단어를 쓰시오.

➡ _____

03 (B)에 주어진 단어를 적절한 형태로 바꾸어 쓰시오.

➡ _____

04 다음 그림을 보고 괄호 안에 주어진 어휘를 이용하여 빈칸을 채우시오.

➡ This fish _____
_____. (swim well, can glide over water, as)

05 다음 문장을 두 문장으로 나누려고 한다. 빈칸에 알맞은 문장을 쓰시오.

(1) A team of scientists questioned how certain animals climb walls so easily.
= A team of scientists questioned. +
_____

(2) What do you believe is the most important thing in life?
= Do you believe? + _____
_____

(3) I'm not sure if he was sleepy or drunk.
= I'm not sure. + _____

06 다음 문장에서 어색한 부분을 바르게 고쳐 다시 쓰시오.

(1) Do you know why is she crying?

➡ _____

(2) Do you think what she expected to happen as a result of her visit?

➡ _____
_____

(3) They not only made the cake but also eating it a lot.

➡ _____
_____

(4) You as well as your sister has to clean the room.

➡ _____
_____

단원별 모의고사

01 다음 짝지어진 두 단어의 관계가 같도록 빈칸에 알맞은 말을 쓰시오.

> explore : exploration = fascinate : _____

02 다음 영영풀이에 해당하는 단어로 적절한 것은?

> the hard usually pointed parts that over a bird's mouth

① robot
② beak
③ burr
④ solution
⑤ needle

03 다음 문장의 빈칸에 알맞은 것을 〈보기〉에서 찾아 쓰시오.

> ┤ 보기 ├
> dive   front   genius   fasteners

(1) He is a great _____ with patience.
(2) Even astronauts use Velcro _____.
(3) Many dolphins can _____ to depths of 200 meters.
(4) He was sitting in _____ of the fire.

04 다음 빈칸에 들어갈 말로 적절한 것은?

> The loud noise _____ the baby from sleeping.

① kept
② took
③ made
④ got
⑤ fascinated

[05~07] 다음 대화를 읽고 물음에 답하시오.

Henry: What are you doing, Mina?
Mina: I'm reading an article about a bug robot.
Henry: A bug robot? Is it interesting?
Mina: Yes. I'm really fascinated by this thing.
Henry: Can you tell me more about it?
Mina: You know that some bugs can slip into narrow spaces, don't you?
Henry: Yeah. That's why (A)_____.
Mina: (B)A bug robot can do the same. It can help to find survivors after earthquakes or big fires.
Henry: That's really fascinating!

05 빈칸 (A)에 적절한 것은?

① it can be a useful machine
② it's hard to catch them
③ it's fascinating us
④ it's very interesting to watch
⑤ it's very difficult to imitate a bug

06 밑줄 친 (B)를 다음과 같이 바꾸어 쓸 때 빈칸에 적절한 단어를 쓰시오.

➡ A bug robot can do the same.
   = The bug robot can _____ _____ narrow spaces.

07 위 대화의 내용과 일치하지 않는 것은?

① Mina is reading an article about a bug robot.
② Mina is fascinated by the bug robot.
③ Henry doesn't know the fact that some bugs can slip into narrow spaces.
④ It is not easy to catch bugs because they can slip into narrow spaces.
⑤ A bug robot can be used to find survivors after earthquakes.

[08~09] 다음 대화를 읽고 물음에 답하시오.

B: Have you heard of a mosquito needle, Jian?

G: A mosquito needle? (A)

B: Some scientists made this new needle by imitating a mosquito's mouth. (B)

G: That's interesting. (C) So how will that help?

B: You know mosquito bites are not very painful, don't you? (D) The new needle will also cause less pain.

G: That's great. (E) How come it's less painful?

B: Like a mosquito's mouth, it makes less contact with our skin.

G: Wow, I think that there's nothing useless in the world!

08 (A)~(E) 중에서 다음 문장이 들어가기에 적절한 곳은?

Can you explain it to me?

① (A)　② (B)　③ (C)　④ (D)　⑤ (E)

09 위 대화의 내용과 일치하는 것은?

① The boy didn't hear of a mosquito needle.

② The girl explains about a mosquito needle.

③ Some scientists imitated a mosquito needle.

④ A mosquito needle causes less pain.

⑤ A mosquito's mouth is useless.

10 다음 중 어법상 올바른 문장을 고르시오.

① Do you know what does this mean?

② I wonder you could point me in the right direction for the bus station.

③ What do you suppose I should do?

④ I'm not sure if she is our new leader in the near future.

⑤ Why do you know Jonathan left so early?

11 다음 중 어법상 어색한 문장을 고르시오.

① It is not only dirty but also rusty.

② I like not only studying but also go hiking.

③ Mike is a troublemaker not only at the office but also at home.

④ Inho is not only fun but also creative.

⑤ Kate is not only a smart but also a kind girl.

12 다음 우리말을 영어로 바르게 옮기지 않은 것은?

그 새로운 물질은 튼튼할 뿐만 아니라 사용하기도 쉽습니다.

① The new material is not only strong but also easy to use.

② The new material is not only strong but easy to use.

③ The new material is not only strong but easy to use as well.

④ The new material is easy to use as well as strong.

⑤ The new material is not strong but easy to use.

13 우리말과 일치하도록 할 때, 빈칸에 알맞은 것은?

내가 올 수 있을지 모르겠지만 노력은 해 볼게.
→ I don't know _____ I can come, but I'll try.

① if   ② that   ③ what
④ which   ⑤ how

14 그림을 보고 주어진 어휘를 이용하여 문장을 완성하시오.

➡ Yuna likes _____.
(listen to music, as, running)

15 다음 문장에서 'where'가 들어갈 위치로 알맞은 것을 고르시오.

Do ① you ② know ③ the toilet ④ is ⑤?

①   ②   ③   ④   ⑤

16 두 문장이 같은 의미가 되도록, 빈칸에 알맞은 말을 쓰시오.

(1) Siyeong is eating not only salad but also steak.
  = Siyeong is eating steak _____ _____ _____ salad.
(2) Leonardo da Vinci invented not only a moving bridge but also a flying machine.
  = Leonardo da Vinci invented a flying machine _____ _____ _____ a moving bridge.
(3) Please tell me. + _____
  = Please tell me what she does.
(4) I don't know. + Where should I go?
  = _____

[17~20] 다음 글을 읽고 물음에 답하시오.

The high-speed train was first made in Japan.
(A) He saw the bird quickly and quietly ① diving into the water. He wondered how the bird entered the water so gracefully. So, he studied more about the bird and discovered ② its long, narrow beak.
(B) A team of engineers tried to solve the problem, but they didn't know ③how could they reduce the noise. One day, one of the engineers was watching a bird in search of a meal.
(C) He redesigned the front of the train by imitating the bird's beak. It was successful. Now the new train travels not only ④more quietly but also 10% faster with 15% less electricity.
(D) But it had one problem. When the train ⑤entered a tunnel, the sudden increase in air pressure created a very loud sound. It often woke people up and caused headaches.

17 자연스러운 글이 되도록 (A)~(D)를 바르게 나열하시오.

➡ _____

18 위 글의 내용에 맞게 빈칸에 알맞은 말을 쓰시오.

Because of a very loud sound, people used to _____ _____ and _____ _____ when the train went into a tunnel.

19 ①~⑤ 중 어법상 바르지 않은 것은?

① ② ③ ④ ⑤

20 다음 중 위 글의 내용과 일치하는 것은?

① Japan was famous for its noisy train.
② The engineers fixed the problem right away as soon as they detected it.
③ The front of the train was redesigned by copying the train of another country.
④ The new train travels as fast as the old one.
⑤ The old train used more electricity than the new one.

[21~22] 다음 글을 읽고 물음에 답하시오.

Is Spider-Man Possible in Real Life?

  A team of scientists questioned how ⓐcertain animals climb walls so easily. ⓑThey have observed what ⓒtheir feet look like and how ⓓthey stick to walls. (A)_____, ⓔthey invented a new material that sticks to any surface. "The new material is not only strong but also easy to use," says one of the scientists.

  In the movie Spider-Man, Spider-Man climbs a tall building with just his hands and feet. Would that ever be possible in the real world? It doesn't sound impossible anymore!

21 빈칸 (A)에 들어갈 말로 가장 적절한 것은?

① On the contrary   ② For example
③ As a result   ④ However
⑤ That is to say

22 ⓐ~ⓔ 중 같은 것을 지칭하는 것끼리 바르게 묶으시오.

➡ _____

[23~24] 다음 글을 읽고 물음에 답하시오.

  From flying birds to self-cleaning plants, the way nature works ①fascinates us. Some people not only use nature but also ②create it to find solutions to their problems. Leonardo da Vinci (1452-1519) was one such person. He wondered how birds could fly. He ③closely watched birds, made notes, and drew pictures of them. Even though his invention was not successful, he imitated a bird's wings to try to make ④a flying machine. Since then, more and more people have ⑤successfully imitated the surprising abilities of nature's genius. Let's explore some of them.

23 ①~⑤ 중 글의 흐름상 어색한 것은?

① ② ③ ④ ⑤

24 다음 중 위 글의 내용과 일치하지 않는 것은?

① There are plants which can self-clean.
② Leonardo da Vinci wanted to know how birds could fly.
③ Leonardo da Vinci studied birds hard.
④ Leonardo da Vinci copied birds' wings to try to make a flying machine.
⑤ People aren't interested in imitating nature's genius.

Lesson 4

I Don't See It That Way

🎤 의사소통 기능

- 만족이나 불만족 묻기
  How do you like the story?
- 이유 묻기
  Why do you think so?

🎤 언어 형식

- 과거완료
  The pig **had built** his house of bricks.
- 감정형용사+to부정사
  I'm **sorry to trouble** you.

Words & Expressions

Key Words

- **actually** [ǽktʃuəli] 부 실제로
- **advantage** [ədvǽntidʒ] 명 장점
- **apologize** [əpɑ́lədʒàiz] 동 사과하다
- **apology** [əpɑ́lədʒi] 명 사과
- **artwork** [ɑ́rtwərk] 명 예술 작품
- **bathroom** [bǽθrùːm] 명 화장실
- **beak** [biːk] 명 부리
- **borrow** [bɑ́rou] 동 빌리다
- **bother** [bɑ́ðər] 동 괴롭히다
- **brick** [brik] 명 벽돌
- **character** [kǽriktər] 명 등장인물
- **compare** [kəmpέər] 동 비교하다
- **complain** [kəmpléin] 동 불평하다
- **completely** [kəmplíːtli] 부 완전하게
- **creative** [kriéitiv] 형 창조적인
- **crime** [kraim] 명 범죄
- **decide** [disáid] 동 결정하다
- **deserve** [dizə́ːrv] 동 ~을 받을 만하다
- **drawing** [drɔ́ːiŋ] 명 그림
- **explain** [ikspléin] 동 설명하다
- **frame** [freim] 동 테를 두르다, 누명을 씌우다
- **frightening** [fráitniŋ] 형 무서운
- **grab** [græb] 동 붙잡다
- **hairy** [hέəri] 형 털이 많은
- **impolite** [impəláit] 형 무례한
- **independent** [indipéndənt] 형 자립심이 강한, 독립적인
- **invite** [inváit] 동 초대하다
- **lend** [lend] 동 빌려주다
- **mean** [miːn] 동 의미하다 형 인색한, 사나운
- **object** [ɑ́bdʒikt] 명 물건, 물체
- **original** [ərɑ́dʒənl] 형 원래의, 원본의
- **palace** [pǽlis] 명 궁전
- **peacefully** [píːsfəli] 부 평화롭게
- **performance** [pərfɔ́ːrməns] 명 성과, 공연
- **prefer** [prifə́ːr] 동 선호하다
- **response** [rispɑ́ns] 명 반응, 응답
- **responsible** [rispɑ́nsəbl] 형 책임이 있는
- **retelling** [riːtéliŋ] 명 다시 만든 이야기
- **rude** [ruːd] 형 무례한
- **scared** [skεərd] 형 겁먹은
- **shocked** [ʃɑkt] 형 충격을 받은
- **similar** [símələr] 형 비슷한, 유사한
- **skinny** [skíni] 형 마른
- **sneeze** [sniːz] 동 재채기하다
- **steadily** [stédili] 부 꾸준히
- **stepmother** [stépmʌðər] 명 계모
- **stork** [stɔːrk] 명 황새
- **straw** [strɔː] 명 짚, 지푸라기
- **support** [səpɔ́ːrt] 동 부양하다, 지지하다
- **sweat** [swet] 명 땀 동 땀을 흘리다
- **trouble** [trʌ́bl] 동 귀찮게 하다
- **turtle** [tə́ːrtl] 명 거북이
- **unfortunately** [ʌnfɔ́rtʃənətli] 부 불행하게도, 안타깝게도
- **unique** [juːníːk] 형 독특한

Key Expressions

- **at least** 적어도
- **be afraid of** ~을 두려워하다
- **be made of** ~로 만들어지다
- **be responsible for** ~에 책임이 있다
- **be taken to** 끌려가다
- **blow down** 바람을 불어 넘어뜨리다
- **break into** 침입하다
- **fall in love with** ~와 사랑에 빠지다
- **I can't wait to** ~ 너무 ~하고 싶다
- **instead of** ~ 대신에
- **go perfectly with** 매우 잘 어울리다
- **keep -ing** 계속해서 ~하다
- **look for** ~을 찾다
- **make money** 돈을 벌다
- **make sense** 의미가 통하다, 이해가 되다
- **on one's own** 스스로
- **point of view** 관점, 견해
- **run out of** ~이 다 떨어지다
- **take a look at** ~을 살펴보다

2 이유 묻기

Why do you think so? 왜 그렇게 생각하니?

■ 상대방이 왜 그렇게 말하는지, 혹은 왜 그렇게 생각하는지 등에 대해 이유를 물을 때는 'Why do you think so?(왜 그렇게 생각해?)' 또는 'Why do you say that?(왜 그렇게 말하니?)'과 같은 표현을 사용하여 물을 수 있다.

■ 상대방의 생각이나 말의 이유를 물을 때는 'What makes you say that?', 'What makes you think so?'와 같은 표현을 쓸 수도 있다. 이는 '무엇 때문에 그런 말을 하니/그렇게 생각하니?'의 의미로 상대방이 한 말의 이유를 확인하거나 상대방의 생각에 대한 부연 설명을 듣고 싶을 때 쓰는 표현이다. 이런 질문에 대답할 때는 단순히 자기 생각이나 이유를 말하면 되고, Because를 붙여서 말해도 된다.

■ 의문사로 시작하는 이유를 묻는 말 앞에 'Can you tell me'나 'I'd like to know', 'I wonder' 등을 붙여, 간접의문문의 형식으로 좀 더 격식을 갖춰 물어볼 수도 있다. 이유를 말할 때에는 문장 앞에 'I think'나 'In my opinion' 등을 덧붙일 수도 있다.

이유 묻기

- Why do you think so? 왜 그렇게 생각하니?
- I wonder what makes you say that. 무엇 때문에 그런 말을 하는지 궁금해.
- Why is that? 왜 그렇지?
- Can you tell me (the reason) why ~? ~한 이유를 설명해 주겠니?

이유 대답하기

- I did it because ~ ~ 때문에 그렇게 했어요.
- (Because) ~ 왜냐하면 ~ 때문이야.
- That's because ~ 그것은 ~ 때문입니다.

핵심 Check

2. 다음 밑줄 친 (A)를 대신해서 쓰기에 가장 적절한 것은?

> W: You look worried, Juwon.
> B: I think we will lose the soccer game tomorrow, Ms. Kim.
> W: (A)Why do you think so?
> B: We will have a match against Class 3. They have the strongest players in the school.

① What makes you think so?　② Why do you make so?
③ What do you make?　④ What did you have?
⑤ How do you think so?

Listen and Speak 1 A

G: Have you finished the book, Taeho?

B: Yes. I finished ❶it yesterday, Anna.

G: How did you like ❶it?

B: It was interesting.

G: What is the book about?

B: You know the story of Heungbu, right? In the book, Nolbu tells the story from his ❷point of view.

G: What does ❸he say?

B: Well, ❸he says he didn't help Heungbu for a reason. ❸He wanted Heungbu to ❹make money ❺on his own and be independent.

G: Wow, it's a unique story! ❻I can't wait to read the book. Thanks, Taeho.

G: 책 다 읽었니, 태호야?
B: 응. 어제 다 읽었어, Anna.
G: 어땠니?
B: 재미있었어.
G: 그 책은 무슨 내용이니?
B: 너 흥부 이야기 알지, 그렇지? 책에서는 놀부가 자신의 관점에서 이야기해.
G: 놀부가 뭐라고 하는데?
B: 음, 놀부는 이유가 있어서 흥부를 도와주지 않았다고 말하고 있어. 그는 흥부가 스스로 돈을 벌고 자립할 수 있기를 바랐거든.
G: 와, 독특한 이야기구나! 그 책을 빨리 읽고 싶어. 고마워 태호야.

❶ it은 the book을 가리킨다. ❷ point of view: 관점 ❸ he는 모두 'Nolbu'를 가리킨다. ❹ make money: 돈을 벌다 ❺ on one's own: 스스로 ❻ I can't wait to ~: 너무 ~하고 싶다

Check(√) True or False

(1) Taeho finished the book about Heungbu yesterday.   T ☐ F ☐

(2) Taeho wanted Heungbu to make money on his own.   T ☐ F ☐

 Listen and Speak 2 A

W: You ❶look worried, Juwon.

B: I think we will lose the soccer game tomorrow, Ms. Kim.

W: ❷Why do you think so?

B: We will have a match ❸against Class 3. They have ❹the strongest players in the school.

W: Look on the bright side. They might have strong players, but your class has the best teamwork.

B: You're right. I didn't think about it that way. I'll go and practice!

W: 걱정스러워 보이는구나, 주원아.
B: 내일 축구 경기에서 질 것 같아요, 김 선생님.
W: 왜 그렇게 생각하니?
B: 저희는 3반과 경기가 있거든요. 3반에는 학교에서 가장 잘하는 선수들이 있어요.
W: 긍정적으로 생각하렴. 3반에 잘하는 선수들이 있을지 모르지만, 너희 반은 팀워크가 가장 좋잖아.
B: 선생님 말씀이 맞아요. 저는 그렇게는 생각하지 못했어요. 가서 연습할게요!

❶ look+형용사: ~하게 보이다 ❷ 이유를 묻는 표현으로 'What makes you say so?' 등으로 바꾸어 표현할 수 있다.
❸ against는 전치사로 '~에 맞서, 반대하여'를 뜻한다. ❹ the+최상급: 가장 ~한

Check(√) True or False

(3) Juwon looks worried because his team lost the soccer game.   T ☐ F ☐

(4) Juwon is one of the strongest players in his school.   T ☐ F ☐

Listen and Speak 1 B

B: ❶How did you like the movie *Good Friends*, Yura?

G: I liked ❷it. It was fun to ❸compare the movie with the original book.

B: Which did you like better, the movie or the book?

G: Well, I liked the movie, but I think I enjoyed the book more. The book ❹helped me understand the characters better.

B: That's interesting. To me, the movie was better because ❺it was easier to understand the story.

G: That's true. I guess ❻they both have their own advantages.

B: You're right.

❶ How do[did] you like ~?: 너는 ~이 어때[어땠어]?, 너는 ~이 좋아[좋았어]/마음에 드니?
❷ it은 the movie *Good Friends*를 가리킨다.
❸ compare: 비교하다
❹ help는 준사역동사로 목적격보어로 원형부정사를 취할 수 있기 때문에 understand가 이어졌다.
❺ it은 the movie를 가리킨다. ❻ they는 책과 영화를 가리킨다.

Listen and Speak 2 B

M: What do you think about my drawing, Prince?

B: Wow, this picture is very ❶frightening!

M: Why do you think so?

B: I mean the picture shows a snake ❷that ate an elephant.

M: You're right. Actually, many people thought it was a picture of a hat.

B: Really? That's interesting.

M: I know. ❸That's why I decided to become a pilot ❹instead of a painter.

B: Haha. ❺At least I can understand what you mean.

M: Thank you, Prince.

❶ frightening: 무서운   ❷ 주격 관계대명사로 which로 바꾸어 쓸 수 있다.
❸ That's why ~.: 그것이 ~한 이유이다.   ❹ instead of: ~ 대신에
❺ at least: 적어도

Real Life Communication

Ms. Parker: Now, ❶take a look at this work of art. How do you like ❷it?

Jinho: Well, is it even art?

Henry: To me, it isn't more than a ❸toilet.

Ms. Parker: It is not just art. I think it is the greatest piece of art of the 20th century.

Mina: Why do you think so?

Ms. Parker: It is a perfect example of a different ❹point of view. The artist used ❺real-life objects to create art.

Claire: So, he didn't create something new?

Ms. Parker: That's right. He simply wanted people to look at the objects in a different way.

Mina: Thank you so much, Ms. Parker. I learned a lot today!

❶ take a look at ~을 살펴보다   ❷ it은 the work of art를 가리킨다.
❸ toilet: 변기   ❹ point of view 관점, 견해
❺ real-life object: 실생활 물건

Let's Check

B: Do you know the story *The Rabbit and the Turtle*?

G: Of course, I do.

B: I think the turtle in the story is ❶mean.

G: Why do you think so?

B: The turtle sees the rabbit ❷sleeping but doesn't wake ❸him up. It is not ❹fair.

G: I don't see it that way. Why should the turtle ❺be responsible for the rabbit? I don't think he should be.

B: That's interesting.

❶ mean: 인색한, 못된   ❷ 현재분사로 동작의 진행을 나타낸다.
❸ him은 the rabbit을 가리킨다.   ❹ fair: 공정한
❺ be responsible for: ~에 책임이 있다

● 다음 우리말과 일치하도록 빈칸에 알맞은 말을 쓰시오.

Listen & Speak 1 A

G: Have you _____ the book, Taeho?

B: Yes. I finished it yesterday, Anna.

G: _____ _____ _____ _____ it?

B: It was _____.

G: _____ is the book _____?

B: You know the story of Heungbu, right? In the book, Nolbu tells the story from his _____ _____ _____.

G: What does he say?

B: Well, he says he didn't help Heungbu for a _____. He wanted Heungbu to _____ _____ on his own and be _____.

G: Wow, it's a _____ story! I _____ _____ _____ read the book. Thanks, Taeho.

Listen & Speak 1 B

B: _____ did you _____ the movie *Good Friends*, Yura?

G: I liked it. It was fun to _____ the movie _____ the original book.

B: _____ did you like _____, the movie or the book?

G: Well, I liked the movie, but I think I _____ the book _____. The book helped me _____ the _____ better.

B: That's interesting. To me, the movie was _____ because it was _____ to understand the story.

G: That's true. I guess they _____ have their own _____.

B: You're right.

Listen & Speak 2 A

W: You look worried, Juwon.

B: I think we will _____ _____ _____ _____ tomorrow, Ms. Kim.

W: Why do _____ _____ _____?

B: We will have a _____ _____ Class 3. They have the _____ players in the school.

W: Look on the _____ _____. They might have strong players, but your class has the best _____.

B: You're right. I didn't think about it _____ _____. I'll go and practice!

해석

G: 그 책 다 읽었니, 태호야?
B: 응. 어제 다 읽었어, Anna.
G: 어땠니?
B: 재미있었어.
G: 그 책은 무슨 내용이니?
B: 너 흥부 이야기 알지, 그렇지? 책에서는 놀부가 자신의 관점에서 이야기해.
G: 놀부가 뭐라고 하는데?
B: 음, 놀부는 이유가 있어서 흥부를 도와주지 않았다고 말하고 있어. 그는 흥부가 스스로 돈을 벌고 자립할 수 있기를 바랐거든.
G: 와, 독특한 이야기구나! 그 책을 빨리 읽고 싶어. 고마워, 태호야.

B: 'Good Friends' 영화 어땠니, 유라야?
G: 좋았어. 영화를 원작과 비교하는 게 재미있었어.
B: 너는 영화와 책 중 어떤 것이 더 좋았니?
G: 글쎄, 영화가 좋았지만 책이 더 재미있었던 것 같아. 책이 등장인물을 더 잘 이해하게 해줬거든.
B: 그거 흥미롭구나. 나는 이야기를 이해하기 더 쉬워서 영화가 더 좋았어.
G: 그건 맞아. 책과 영화 둘 다 각각의 장점들이 있는 것 같아.
B: 맞아.

W: 걱정스러워 보이는구나, 주원아.
B: 내일 축구 경기에서 질 것 같아요, 김 선생님.
W: 왜 그렇게 생각하니?
B: 저희는 3반과 경기가 있거든요. 3반에는 학교에서 가장 잘하는 선수들이 있잖아요.
W: 긍정적으로 생각하렴. 3반에 잘하는 선수들이 있을지 모르지만, 너희 반은 팀워크가 가장 좋잖아.
B: 선생님 말씀이 맞아요. 저는 그렇게는 생각하지 못했어요. 가서 연습할게요!

Listen & Speak 2 B

M: _____ do you _____ about my drawing, Prince?

B: Wow, this picture is very _____!

M: _____ do you _____ _____?

B: I mean the picture shows a _____ that _____ an elephant.

M: You're right. Actually, many people thought it was a picture of a _____.

B: Really? That's _____.

M: I know. That's why I _____ to become a _____ _____ _____ a painter.

B: Haha. _____ _____ I can understand _____ _____ _____.

M: Thank you, Prince.

Real Life Communication

Ms. Parker: Now, take a look at this work of art. _____ _____ you _____ it?

Jinho: Well, is it even art?

Henry: _____ _____, it isn't more than a _____.

Ms. Parker: It is not just art. I think it is the _____ piece of art of the 20th century.

Mina: _____ do you _____ _____?

Ms. Parker: It is a perfect example of a _____ _____ _____ _____. The artist used _____ _____ to create art.

Claire: So, he didn't create _____ _____?

Ms. Parker: That's _____. He simply wanted people to look at the _____ in a _____ way.

Mina: Thank you so much, Ms. Parker. I learned a lot today!

Let's Check

B: Do you know the story *The Rabbit and the Turtle*?

G: Of course, I do.

B: I think the _____ in the story is _____.

G: Why do you _____ _____?

B: The turtle sees the rabbit _____ but doesn't _____ _____. It is not _____.

G: I don't see it _____ _____. Why should the turtle _____ _____ _____ the rabbit? I don't think he should be.

B: That's interesting.

M: 왕자님, 제 그림에 대해 어떻게 생각하세요?

B: 우와, 이 그림은 너무 무섭군요!

M: 왜 그렇게 생각하죠?

B: 그림이 코끼리를 먹은 뱀을 보여주잖아요.

M: 왕자님 말이 맞아요. 사실 많은 사람들이 모자 그림이라고 생각했어요.

B: 정말요? 그거 재미있군요.

M: 맞아요. 그래서 제가 화가 대신에 비행사가 되기로 결심했던 거예요.

B: 하하. 적어도 나는 당신이 무엇을 의도한 건지 이해할 수 있어요.

M: 고마워요, 왕자님.

Ms. Parker: 자, 이 예술 작품을 보세요. 어떤가요?

Jinho: 글쎄요, 이것도 예술인가요?

Henry: 저한테는 변기 그 이상은 아닌데요.

Ms. Parker: 이건 그냥 예술이 아니에요. 나는 20세기의 가장 위대한 예술 작품이라고 생각해요.

Mina: 왜 그렇게 생각하세요?

Ms. Parker: 이것은 다른 관점에 대한 완벽한 예시예요. 작가는 작품을 만들기 위해 실생활 물건을 사용했어요.

Claire: 그러면 작가가 새로운 것을 만들지 않았다는 건가요?

Ms. Parker: 맞아요. 그는 그저 사람들이 다른 방식으로 사물을 보기를 원했어요.

Mina: 정말 감사합니다. Parker 선생님. 오늘 많은 걸 배웠어요!

B: 너는 '토끼와 거북이' 이야기를 아니?

G: 물론 알지.

B: 난 그 이야기 속의 거북이가 못됐다고 생각해.

G: 왜 그렇게 생각하니?

B: 거북이는 토끼가 자고 있는 것을 보지만 그를 깨우지 않잖아. 그건 공정하지 않아.

G: 나는 그렇게 보지 않아. 왜 거북이가 토끼에 대해 책임을 져야 해? 그가 그래야 한다고 생각하지 않아.

B: 흥미로운데.

Conversation 시험대비 기본평가

[01~02] 다음 대화를 읽고 물음에 답하시오.

Anna: Have you finished the book, Taeho?

Taeho: Yes. I finished it yesterday, Anna.

Anna: How did you like it?

Taeho: It was interesting.

Anna: What is the book about?

Taeho: You know the story of Heungbu, right? In the book, Nolbu tells the story from his point of view.

Anna: What does he say?

Taeho: Well, he says he didn't help Heungbu for a reason. He wanted Heungbu to make money on his own and be independent.

Anna: Wow, it's a unique story! (A)I can't wait to read the book. (forward) Thanks, Taeho.

01 위 대화의 밑줄 친 (A)와 의미가 같도록 주어진 단어를 사용하여 다시 쓰시오.

➡ _____

02 위 대화의 내용과 일치하지 <u>않는</u> 것은?

① 태호는 어제 그 책을 다 읽었다.

② 태호는 놀부의 관점에서 이야기하는 책을 읽었다.

③ Anna는 흥부 이야기에 대해 알고 있다.

④ 놀부는 흥부가 스스로 돈을 벌고 자립할 수 있기를 바랐다.

⑤ 놀부는 아무런 이유 없이 흥부를 돕지 않았다.

03 다음 대화가 자연스럽게 이어지도록 순서대로 배열하시오.

Jack: Do you know the story *The Rabbit and the Turtle?*

(A) Why do you think so?

(B) I think the turtle in the story is mean.

(C) Of course, I do.

(D) I don't see it that way. Why should the turtle be responsible for the rabbit? I don't think he should be.

(E) The turtle sees the rabbit sleeping but doesn't wake him up. It is not fair.

Jack: That's interesting.

➡ _____

22 What is TRUE about the passage?

① The news is about food chain.

② The wolf is resting in his house now.

③ The reporter is talking on the news.

④ The wolf wasn't arrested by the police yet.

⑤ The wolf will explain what happened to the pigs.

[23~24] 다음 글을 읽고 물음에 답하시오.

Pig: Yes. My brothers and I thought it was time to build our own houses, so we built houses with straw, sticks, and bricks. One day, the wolf came and completely blew down my brothers' houses. He almost blew down my house, but it was made of bricks, so he couldn't.

Reporter: How are your brothers doing now?

Pig: They are shocked (A)to lose their houses. They are resting in my house.

23 다음 중 밑줄 친 (A)와 쓰임이 다른 하나는?

① David was sad to hear the news.

② Yumi was excited to see them dancing.

③ Nora was glad to speak in front of so many people.

④ June felt bored to read the book so long.

⑤ Julian must be diligent to wake up early in the morning.

24 What is the pig mainly talking about?

① how he made his house with bricks

② why he wants to make his own house

③ how long it took to build his own house

④ the accident the wolf blew down his brothers' houses

⑤ the friendship between him and the wolf

[25~26] 다음 글을 읽고 물음에 답하시오.

Reporter: Thank you, Mr. Pig. Now, let's ①meet our second guest, the wolf. Mr. Wolf, could you tell us what happened?

Wolf: This whole "Big Bad Wolf" thing is ②right. The real story is about a sneeze from a terrible cold and a cup of sugar.

Reporter: What do you mean?

Wolf: Back then, I was making a birthday cake for my dear old grandmother. I ran out of sugar. I walked down the street to ③ask my neighbor for a cup of sugar. When I knocked on the door, it ④fell down. Then I called, "Little pig, are you in?" I had just grabbed the broken door when I felt a sneeze coming on. I ⑤sneezed a great sneeze and you know what? The whole straw house fell down. I was very surprised by what had happened. Unfortunately, the same thing happened to the second little pig's house.

25 ①~⑤ 중 글의 흐름상 어색한 것은?

①   ②   ③   ④   ⑤

26 다음 중 위 글을 읽고 답할 수 <u>없는</u> 것은?

① Who is the second guest?

② What did the wolf need to make the cake?

③ For what did the wolf want to ask his neighbor?

④ What happened when the wolf knocked on the door?

⑤ When was the wolf making the cake?

01 출제율 95%

주어진 우리말에 맞게 빈칸을 채우시오. (철자가 주어진 경우 그 철자로 시작할 것)

(1) 그 미술가는 작품을 만들기 위해 실생활 물건을 사용했다.

➡ The artist used real-life o_____ to create art.

(2) 왜 거북이 토끼에 대해 책임을 져야 하지?

➡ Why should the turtle be _____ for the rabbit?

(3) 나는 느리고 꾸준히 걷는 것을 더 좋아한다.

➡ I prefer to walk slowly and _____.

(4) Ward는 7살 때 그의 아빠와 계모로부터 도망쳤다.

➡ Ward ran away from his father and _____ when he was seven years old.

02 출제율 100%

다음 문장의 빈칸에 들어갈 말을 〈보기〉에서 골라 쓰시오.

┌─ 보기 ─┐
framed / straw / grabbed / trouble / sneeze
└─────┘

(1) I had just _____ the broken door when I felt a sneeze coming on.

(2) We built houses with _____, sticks, and bricks.

(3) Do you think you were _____?

(4) The real story is about a _____ from a terrible cold and a cup of sugar.

(5) I'm sorry to _____ you.

03 출제율 90%

다음 우리말과 일치하도록 주어진 단어를 모두 배열하여 영작하시오.

(1) 나의 집은 너무 약해서 늑대가 날려버릴 수 있었다.

(for / to / was / house / my / weak / too / down / wolf / the / blow)

➡ _____

(2) 함께 이 사진을 봅시다.

(a / look / together / let's / this / take / picture / at)

➡ _____

(3) 제 생각에 그것은 당신의 치마와 매우 잘 어울리네요.

(with / I / it / your / skirt / think / goes / perfectly)

➡ _____

[04~05] 다음 대화를 읽고 물음에 답하시오.

Jack: Do you know the story *The Rabbit and the Turtle*?

Sora: Of course, I do.

Jack: I think the turtle in the story is ⓐmean.

Sora: Why do you think so?

Jack: The turtle sees the rabbit ⓑsleeping but doesn't ⓒwake up him. It is not fair.

Sora: I don't see it ⓓthat way. Why should the turtle be ⓔresponsible for the rabbit? I don't think he should be.

Jack: That's interesting.

04 출제율 90%

위 대화의 밑줄 친 ⓐ~ⓔ 중 어법상 틀린 것을 찾아 바르게 고치시오.

➡ _____

05 위 대화를 읽고 대답할 수 <u>없는</u> 것은?

① What does Jack think about Sora's view on *The Rabbit and the Turtle*?

② Why does Jack think the turtle in the story is mean?

③ Who doesn't wake up the rabbit in the story?

④ Does Sora think the turtle should be responsible for the rabbit?

⑤ Who is fair in the story *The Rabbit and the Turtle*?

[06~07] 다음 대화를 읽고 물음에 답하시오.

Mike: What do you think about my drawing, Prince?

Prince: Wow, this picture is very ⓐfrightened!

Mike: Why do you think so?

Prince: I mean the picture shows a snake ⓑthat ate an elephant.

Mike: You're right. Actually, many people thought it was a picture of a hat.

Prince: Really? That's ⓒinteresting.

Mike: I know. That's why I decided to become a pilot ⓓinstead of a painter.

Prince: Haha. At least I can understand ⓔwhat you mean.

Mike: Thank you, Prince.

06 위 대화의 밑줄 친 ⓐ~ⓔ 중 어법상 어색한 것을 찾아 바르게 고치시오.

➡ _____

07 위 대화의 내용과 일치하지 <u>않는</u> 것은?

① 왕자는 Mike의 그림이 매우 무섭다고 생각한다.

② 왕자는 Mike의 그림이 코끼리를 먹은 뱀을 보여 준다고 생각한다.

③ 많은 사람들은 Mike의 그림이 모자를 그린 그림이라고 생각했다.

④ Mike는 화가 대신에 비행사가 되기로 결심했다.

⑤ 왕자는 Mike의 그림을 이해하기가 어려웠다.

[08~10] 다음 대화를 읽고 물음에 답하시오.

Brian: How did you like the movie *Good Friends*, Yura?

Yura: I liked it. It was fun ⓐto compare the movie with the original book.

Brian: ⓑWhich did you like better, the movie or the book?

Yura: Well, I liked the movie, but I think I enjoyed the book more. The book helped me ⓒunderstanding the characters better.

Brian: That's ⓓinteresting. To me, the movie was better ⓔbecause it was easier to understand the story.

Yura: That's true. I guess they both have their own advantages.

Brian: You're right.

08 위 대화의 밑줄 친 ⓐ~ⓔ 중 어법상 <u>어색한</u> 것을 찾아 바르게 고치시오.

➡ _____

09 위 대화의 내용과 일치하도록 빈칸을 완성하시오.

Brian and Yura talked about the movie *Good Friends*. They had different opinion about it. Yura preferred (A)_____ to (B)_____ because (C)_____ _____. On the other hand, Brian liked (D)_____ better because it was easier for him (E)_____. They agreed that both of them had their own advantages.

10 위 대화를 읽고 대답할 수 <u>없는</u> 것은?

① What movie did Yura watch?

② What did Yura compare with the movie?

③ Why did Yura enjoy the book more than the movie?

④ Why did Brian think the movie was better?

⑤ What did Yura think the movie's disadvantage was?

11 다음 그림을 참고하고, 괄호 안의 단어를 활용하여 빈칸을 알맞게 채우시오.

(1)　　　　(2)　　　　(3)

(1) I _____ my father. (enjoy, help)

(2) I made a plan about her idea that she _____ during our meeting. (tell)

(3) I _____ teach my grandmother how to use a cell phone. (happy)

12 괄호 안의 단어를 활용하여 우리말에 맞게 영작하시오.

(1) 나는 엄마에게 숙제를 끝냈다고 말했다. (tell, mother, finish)

➡ _____

_____

(2) 이모가 그녀의 딸에게 인형을 주고 싶었다고 쓰여 있었다. (it, that, my aunt, write, give, to)

➡ _____

_____

(3) 그는 맨체스터에서 뛰고 싶었다고 나에게 말했다. (tell, want)

➡ _____

_____

13 다음 중 어색한 문장을 고르시오.

① The Prince was happy to find Cinderella.

② I'm glad to meet you here.

③ I was shocked that see the building on fire.

④ My friends were sorry to hear the news.

⑤ I was excited to be invited to the party.

14 괄호 안의 단어를 활용하여 우리말에 맞게 영작하시오.

> 우리가 그 게임에서 진 것은 운이 없었다. (unfortunate, lose)

➡ _____

[15~17] 다음 글을 읽고 물음에 답하시오.

Reporter: Thank you, Mr. Pig. Now, let's meet our second guest, the wolf. Mr. Wolf, could you tell us what happened?

Wolf: This whole "Big Bad Wolf" thing is wrong. The real story is about (A)_____.

Reporter: What do you mean?

Wolf: Back then, I was making a birthday cake for my dear old grandmother. I ran out of sugar. I walked down the street to ask my neighbor for a cup of sugar. When I knocked on the door, it fell down. Then I called, "Little pig, are you in?" I had just grabbed the broken door when I felt a sneeze coming on. I sneezed a great sneeze and you know what? The whole straw house fell down. I was very surprised by (B)<u>what had happened</u>. Unfortunately, the same thing happened to the second little pig's house.

15 다음 중 빈칸 (A)에 들어갈 말로 가장 적절한 것은?

① a sneeze from three pigs and my grandmother

② throwing a dinner party for my grandmother

③ making a birthday cake for the three little pigs

④ a cup of sugar and learning how to make a strong house

⑤ a sneeze from a terrible cold and a cup of sugar

16 밑줄 친 (B)가 의미하는 것을 우리말로 쓰시오.

➡ _____

17 다음 중 위 글을 읽고 답할 수 있는 것은?

① What is the name of the reporter?

② How many animals is the reporter going to interview?

③ Why did the wolf's neighbor build his house with straw?

④ What happened when the wolf grabbed the broken door?

⑤ When was the wolf's grandmother's birthday?

[18~20] 다음 글을 읽고 물음에 답하시오.

Reporter: Then why did you go to the third little pig's house?

Wolf: I still needed that cup of sugar, so I went to the next house. The third little pig ① had built his house of bricks. I called out, "I'm sorry to trouble you, but are you in?" And do you know ②what he answered? "Go away. Don't bother me again!" ③How impolite! I thought I deserved an apology,

so I kept knocking. When the police came, of course they thought I was breaking into this pig's house.

Reporter: Do you think you were ④framed?

Wolf: Yes. The news reporters of the town thought a sick wolf going to borrow a cup of sugar didn't sound very exciting. So, they made me the "Big Bad Wolf." Could you maybe lend me a cup of sugar?

Reporter: Thank you for your time. Everyone, which do you think is the true story, ⑤ the pig or the wolf?

18 ①~⑤ 중 어법상 바르지 <u>않은</u> 것은?

①   ②   ③   ④   ⑤

19 What did the wolf do to get an apology from the third little pig? Answer in English with a full sentence.

➡ _____

20 다음 중 위 글의 내용으로 보아 알 수 <u>없는</u> 것은?

① The wolf wanted the pig to give him an apology.

② The police thought the wolf was breaking into the pig's house.

③ The news reporters wanted to make their news sound exciting.

④ The reporter interviewing the wolf believes what the wolf is saying.

⑤ The wolf was made the "Big Bad Wolf" by the news reporters.

[01~03] 다음 대화를 읽고 물음에 답하시오.

> Ms. Parker: Now, take a look at this work of art. How do you like it?
>
> Mina: Well, is it even art?
>
> Henry: To me, it isn't more than a toilet.
>
> Ms. Parker: It is not just art. I think it is the greatest piece of art of the 20th century.
>
> Mina: Why do you think so?
>
> Ms. Parker: It is a perfect example of a different point of view. The artist used real-life objects to create art.
>
> Claire: So, he didn't create something new?
>
> Ms. Parker: That's right. He simply wanted people to look at the objects in a different way.
>
> Mina: Thank you so much, Ms. Parker. I learned a lot today!

01 What does Ms. Parker think about the work of art?

➡ _____

_____

02 What did the artist use to create the work of art?

➡ _____

03 What did the artist want people to do?

➡ _____

_____

04 다음은 Suji에 대한 이야기이다. 주어진 〈Feeling〉과 〈Reason〉을 조합하여 문장을 완성하시오. (〈Feeling〉과 〈Reason〉에 나오는 단어 또는 어구는 한번 씩만 사용할 것.)

> <Feeling>
> bored   happy   excited   surprised

> <Reason>
> • receive a present that she hadn't think ever
> • see her brother enjoy the party
> • read a boring book
> • join a popular club in her school

(1) _____

(2) _____

_____

(3) _____

_____

(4) _____

_____

05 다음 그림을 보고 괄호 안의 단어를 사용하여 빈칸을 채우시오.

Last weekend I _____(go) to the souvenir shop. I _____(glad) see my new classmate there. He _____(tell) me that he _____(know) about me because he _____(see) me before.

Reporter: Welcome to Animal World News. Last Sunday, a wolf was taken to the police station for blowing down pigs' houses. Today, we have the third little pig and the wolf with us. Mr. Pig, (A) 당신과 당신 형제들에게 무슨 일이 일어났는지 설명해 주시겠어요?

Pig: Yes. My brothers and I thought it was time to build our own houses, so we built houses with straw, sticks, and bricks. One day, the wolf came and completely blew down my brothers' houses. He almost blew down my house, but it was made of bricks, so he couldn't.

Reporter: How are your brothers doing now?

Pig: They are shocked to lose their houses. They are resting in my house.

Reporter: Thank you, Mr. Pig. Now, let's meet our second guest, the wolf. Mr. Wolf, could you tell us what happened?

06 According to the dialogue, why were the pigs shocked? Answer in English and use the words 'they', and 'due to.'

➡ _____

07 주어진 단어를 활용하여 밑줄 친 (A)를 영어로 쓰시오.

| (could / explain / to) |

➡ _____
_____

Reporter: Then why did you go to the third little pig's house?

Wolf: I still needed that cup of sugar, so I went to the next house. The third little pig had built his house of bricks. I called out, "I'm sorry to trouble you, but are you in?" And do you know what he answered? "Go away. Don't bother me again!" How impolite! I thought I (A)_____ an apology, so I kept (B)_____. When the police came, of course they thought I was (C)_____ into this pig's house.

Reporter: Do you think you were framed?

Wolf: Yes. The news reporters of the town thought a sick wolf going to borrow a cup of sugar didn't sound very exciting. So, they made me the "Big Bad Wolf." Could you maybe lend me a cup of sugar?

08 주어진 단어를 내용과 어법에 맞게 빈칸 (A)~(C)에 쓰시오.

| knock / break / deserve |

➡ (A)_____ (B)_____ (C)_____

09 According to the passage, why did the wolf visit pigs' houses? Use the phrase 'in order to.'

➡ _____
_____

창의사고력 서술형 문제

01 다음 그림을 보고 대화의 내용과 일치하도록 빈칸을 완성하시오.

Ms. Parker: Now, take a look at this work of art. How do you like it?

Jinho: Well, is it even art?

Henry: To me, it isn't more than a toilet.

Ms. Parker: It is not just art. I think it is the greatest piece of art of the 20th century.

Mina: Why do you think so?

Ms. Parker: It is a perfect example of a different point of view. The artist used real-life objects to create art.

Claire: So, he didn't create something new?

Ms. Parker: That's right. He simply wanted people to look at the objects in a different way.

Mina: Thank you so much, Ms. Parker. I learned a lot today!

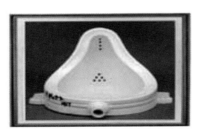

Title: Fountain

Artist: Marcel Duchamp

Special Point:

1) The artist used _____ _____ _____ to create art.

2) The artist wanted people to look at the objects _____
_____ _____ _____.

---

02 다음 내용을 바탕으로 재판에서 배심원에게 낭독할 글을 완성하시오.

The wolf says, "I blew down the first and the second pigs' houses because of a sneeze from a terrible cold." And according to the wolf's friend, he had seen the wolf going to a hospital that day.

What the wolf said is true.

The wolf said he (A)_____ the first and the second pigs' houses because of (B)_____. I think what he said is (C)_____. His (D)_____ said that he had seen (E)_____. I would be glad to hear your wise decision. Thank you.

단원별 모의고사

01 다음 영영풀이가 가리키는 것을 고르시오.

> by bad luck

① impolitely ② uniquely
③ steadily ④ unfortunately
⑤ peacefully

02 다음 중 밑줄 친 부분의 뜻풀이가 바르지 <u>않은</u> 것은?

① The noise was <u>frightening</u>. (무서운)
② If he continues to bother you, <u>simply</u> ignore him. (단순히)
③ I bought a <u>straw</u> hat at the market. (짚, 지푸라기)
④ Most of the buildings in the town are made of <u>bricks</u>. (벽돌)
⑤ I have to go back to the house and <u>grab</u> the car keys. (빌리다)

03 다음 우리말을 주어진 단어를 이용하여 영작하시오.

(1) 지난 일요일, 한 늑대가 경찰서에 끌려갔다. (take)
➡ Last Sunday, a wolf _____ _____ _____ the police station.

(2) 늑대는 돼지들의 집들을 바람을 불어 넘어뜨렸다. (blow)
➡ The wolf _____ _____ the pigs' houses.

(3) 그들은 내가 이 돼지의 집에 침입하고 있다고 생각했다. (break)
➡ They thought I was _____ _____ this pig's house.

(4) 당신은 늑대의 이야기가 이해가 되나요? (make)
➡ Does the wolf's story _____ _____ to you?

[04~06] 다음 대화를 읽고 물음에 답하시오.

Anna: Have you finished the book, Taeho?
Taeho: Yes. I finished it yesterday, Anna.
Anna: (A)[What / How] did you like it?
Taeho: It was interesting.
Anna: What is the book about?
Taeho: You know the story of Heungbu, right? In the book, Nolbu tells the story from his point of view.
Anna: What does he say?
Taeho: Well, he says he didn't help Heungbu for a reason. He wanted Heungbu to make money on his own and be (B)[dependent / independent].
Anna: Wow, it's a (C)[common / unique] story! I can't wait to read the book. Thanks, Taeho.

04 위 대화의 괄호 (A)~(C)에 알맞은 말이 바르게 짝지어진 것은?

	(A)	(B)	(C)
①	What	dependent	common
②	What	independent	unique
③	How	independent	common
④	How	independent	unique
⑤	How	dependent	common

05 위 대화를 읽고 대답할 수 <u>없는</u> 것은?

① What is the book Taeho read about?
② From whose point of view is the story in the book told?
③ Why didn't Nolbu help Heungbu in the book?
④ What did Nolbu want Heungbu to do in the book?
⑤ Did Heungbu want to make money for himself?

06 위 대화의 내용과 일치하도록 Anna의 일기를 완성하시오.

> Today, Taeho introduced an interesting book for me. He finished the book (A)_____ and explained the story. The book was about the story of Heungbu written from Nolbu's (B)_____. Taeho told me that Nolbu didn't help Heungbu (C)_____. Nolbu wanted Heungbu to (D)_____ on his own and be independent. It sounded so unique and interesting. I'm looking forward to (E)_____

[07~08] 다음 대화를 읽고 물음에 답하시오.

Brian: How did you like the movie *Good Friends*, Yura?

Yura: I liked it. It was fun to compare the movie with the original book.

Brian: Which did you like better, the movie or the book?

Yura: Well, I liked the movie, but I think I enjoyed the book more. The book helped me understand the characters better.

Brian: That's interesting. To me, the movie was better because it was easier to understand the story.

Yura: That's true. I guess they both have their own advantages.

Brian: You're right.

07 Which did Brian like better, the movie or the book and why?

➡ _____

_____

08 Why did Yura prefer the book?

➡ _____

_____

[09~10] 다음 대화를 읽고 물음에 답하시오.

Ms. Kim: You look worried, Juwon.

Juwon: I think we will lose the soccer game tomorrow, Ms. Kim.

Ms. Kim: (A)왜 그렇게 생각해?

Juwon: We will have a match against Class 3. They have the strongest players in the school.

Ms. Kim: Look on the bright side. They might have strong players, but your class has the best teamwork.

Juwon: You're right. I didn't think about it that way. I'll go and practice!

09 위 대화의 밑줄 친 (A)의 우리말을 주어진 말을 써서 영작하시오. (why, so)

➡ _____

10 위 대화의 내용과 일치하지 <u>않는</u> 것은?

① 주원이는 내일 축구 경기에 질 것 같다고 생각한다.
② 주원이네 반은 내일 3반과 축구 경기를 할 예정이다.
③ 3반에는 학교에서 가장 잘하는 선수들이 있다.
④ 주원이네 반은 팀워크가 가장 좋다.
⑤ 주원이는 자기네 반의 팀워크가 좋다고 생각하지 않는다.

[11~12] 다음 대화를 읽고 물음에 답하시오.

Ms. Parker: Now, take a look at this work of art. How do you like it?

Jinho: Well, is it even art?

Henry: To me, it isn't more than a toilet.

Ms. Parker: (A) It is not just art. I think it is the greatest piece of art of the 20th century.

Mina: (B) Why do you think so?

Ms. Parker: (C) The artist used real-life objects to create art.

Claire: (D) So, he didn't create something new?

Ms. Parker: (E) That's right. He simply wanted people to look at the objects in a different way.

Mina: Thank you so much, Ms. Parker. I learned a lot today!

11 위 대화의 (A)~(E) 중 주어진 문장이 들어가기에 적절한 곳은?

It is a perfect example of a different point of view.

① (A) ② (B) ③ (C) ④ (D) ⑤ (E)

12 위 대화를 읽고 대답할 수 없는 것은?

① What are they looking at now?

② What does Ms. Parker think about the work of art?

③ According to Ms. Parker, why is the work of art a perfect example of a different point of view?

④ What did the artist want people to do?

⑤ How did the artist use real-life objects to create art?

13 괄호 안의 단어를 활용하여 우리말에 맞게 영작하시오.

(1) 그들은 집을 잃어 충격에 빠졌다. (lose, shock)

➡ _____

(2) 재채기가 나오려 할 때 나는 부서진 문을 막 움켜잡았다. (grab, sneeze)

➡ _____
_____

14 다음 빈칸에 공통으로 들어갈 단어를 고르시오

• It is surprising _____ he should do such a thing.

• It is lucky _____ I live in Korea.

• I was happy _____ you will go to study abroad.

① to   ② for   ③ at

④ that   ⑤ in

15 다음 중 어법상 어색한 것은?

① I'm glad that you won the first prize.

② It is strange for your friend to come here.

③ Were you surprised to receive the news?

④ We are afraid that go to the hospital tomorrow.

⑤ She is proud of you.

16 다음 그림을 보고 〈보기〉에 있는 표현 중 적절한 것을 골라 빈칸을 알맞게 채우시오.

┌─ 보기 ┐
be sad to   be surprised to
be happy to   be sorry to
└─────────┘

➡ He _____ think that he will go on safari this summer vacation.

17 다음 그림은 Suji의 블로그에 올라온 Suji의 가족 사진으로 2년 전에 찍은 것이다. 각 문제에 알맞게 답하시오.

(1) 빈칸에 공통으로 들어갈 알맞은 것을 고르시오. (시간의 차이가 나도록 할 것.)

> I remembered that
> • I _____ the guitar, sitting on a chair beside the sofa.
> • my mom and my brother _____ Baduk.

① play
② playing
③ played
④ had played
⑤ to play

(2) 괄호 안의 단어를 사용하여 빈칸을 채우시오. (시간의 차이가 나도록 할 것.)

> I remembered that my lovely cat _____ (sit) on my grandmother's knee.

(3) 우리말에 맞게 괄호 안의 단어를 배열하시오.

> 나는 가족과 즐거운 시간을 보내서 행복했다.

(family, great, a, my, with, happy, was, to, I, have, time)

➡ _____

[18~21] 다음 글을 읽고 물음에 답하시오.

Pig: Yes. My brothers and I thought it was time to build our own houses, so we built houses with straw, sticks, and bricks. One day, the wolf came and completely blew down my brothers' houses. He almost blew down my house, but it was made of bricks, so he couldn't.

Reporter: How are your brothers doing Mnow?

Pig: They are shocked to lose their houses. They are resting in my house.

Reporter: Thank you, Mr. Pig. Now, let's meet our second guest, the wolf. Mr. Wolf, could you tell us what happened?

Wolf: This whole "Big Bad Wolf" thing is wrong. The real story is about a sneeze from a terrible cold and a cup of sugar.

Reporter: What do you mean?

Wolf: Back then, I was making a birthday cake for my dear old grandmother. I ran out of sugar. I walked down the street to ask my neighbor for a cup of sugar. When I knocked on the door, it fell down. Then I called, "Little pig, are you in?" I had just grabbed the broken door when I felt a sneeze coming on. I sneezed a great sneeze and you know what? The whole straw house fell down. I was very surprised by what had happened. Unfortunately, the same thing happened to the second little pig's house.

18 다음 중 위 글의 내용과 일치하지 <u>않는</u> 것은?

① The three pigs built their own houses.
② The reporter wonders what happened to both the pigs and the wolf.
③ The wolf sneezed because of a cold.
④ The wolf broke down the door on purpose.
⑤ The pig blames the wolf for destroying his brothers' houses.

19 Write the reason why the wolf couldn't blow down the third little pig's house. Answer in English and use the phrase 'It's because.'

➡ _____

20 다음은 위 글의 내용을 요약한 것이다. 빈칸에 알맞은 말을 쓰시오.

> The pig says the wolf came and completely _____ _____ _____ _____ _____. On the other hand, the wolf says the houses fell down because of _____ _____ _____ _____ _____ .

21 What did the wolf run out of when he was making a birthday cake for his grandmother? Answer in English with five words.

➡ _____

[22~25] 다음 글을 읽고 물음에 답하시오.

> **Reporter:** Then why did you go to the third little pig's house?
>
> **Wolf:** I still needed that ①cup of sugar, so I went to the next house.
>
> (A) And do you know what he answered? "Go away. Don't bother me again!" How impolite!
>
> (B) The third little pig had built his house ②of bricks. I called out, "I'm sorry ③to trouble you, but are you in?"
>
> (C) I thought I deserved an apology, ④so I kept knocking. When the police came, of course they thought I was breaking into this pig's house.
>
> **Reporter:** Do you think you were ⓐ_____?

> **Wolf:** Yes. The news reporters of the town thought a sick wolf going to borrow a cup of sugar didn't sound very ⑤excited. So, they made me the "Big Bad Wolf." Could you maybe lend me a cup of sugar?

22 ①~⑤ 중 어법상 바르지 않은 것은?

①   ②   ③   ④   ⑤

23 자연스러운 글이 되도록 (A)~(C)를 바르게 나열한 것은?

① (A)–(C)–(B)　　② (B)–(A)–(C)
③ (B)–(C)–(A)　　④ (C)–(A)–(B)
⑤ (C)–(B)–(A)

24 다음 중 빈칸 ⓐ에 들어갈 말로 가장 적절한 것은?

① guilty　　　　② desperate
③ wrong　　　　④ depressed
⑤ framed

25 다음 빈칸에 들어갈 말이 바르게 짝지어진 것은?

> **Q:** Why did the police think the wolf was breaking into the third pig's house?
>
> **A:** It's because he kept _____ on the pig's door. He thought he deserved a(n) _____ for the pig's _____ response.

① kicking – apology – rude
② knocking – forgiveness – impolite
③ kicking – forgiveness – polite
④ knocking – apology – rude
⑤ knocking – manners – impolite

MEMO

Lesson 5

Which Way to Go?

🎙 의사소통 기능

- 가능성 정도 묻기
  Is it possible to visit Mirror Maze Park?
- 길 묻기
  How do I get to the restaurant?

🎙 언어 형식

- 부정대명사 one
  Here is **one** as an example.
- 분사구문
  Looking at them closely, you may find the beauty of order and regularity.

Words & Expressions

Key Words

- **activity** [æktívəti] 명 활동
- **actually** [ǽktʃuəli] 부 실제로
- **beauty** [bjúːti] 명 미, 아름다움
- **careful** [kɛ́ərfəl] 형 조심스러운
- **certain** [sə́ːrtn] 형 어떤, 확실한
- **check** [tʃek] 동 확인하다
- **choice** [tʃɔis] 명 선택
- **closely** [klóusli] 부 자세히
- **compare** [kəmpɛ́ər] 동 비교하다
- **confusion** [kənfjúːʒən] 명 혼란, 혼동
- **connect** [kənékt] 동 연결하다, 이어지다
- **consider** [kənsídər] 동 여기다
- **convenient** [kənvíːnjənt] 형 편리한
- **dead end** 막다른 길
- **decide** [disáid] 동 결정하다
- **decision** [disíʒən] 명 결정, 결심
- **difference** [dífərəns] 명 차이
- **effective** [ifékiv] 형 효과적인
- **entrance** [éntrəns] 명 입구
- **escape** [iskéip] 동 탈출하다
- **especially** [ispéʃəli] 부 특히
- **exchange** [ikstʃéindʒ] 동 교환하다
- **exit** [égzit] 명 출구
- **floor** [flɔːr] 명 층, 바닥
- **frustrate** [frʌ́steit] 동 방해하다, 좌절시키다
- **hedge** [hedʒ] 명 산울타리

- **labyrinth** [lǽbərìnθ] 명 미궁
- **Mars** [mɑːrz] 명 화성
- **maze** [meiz] 명 미로
- **mean** [miːn] 동 의미하다
- **method** [méθəd] 명 방법
- **monster** [mánstər] 명 괴물
- **mythology** [miθálədʒi] 명 신화
- **notice** [nóutis] 동 주목하다, 알아차리다
- **order** [ɔ́ːrdər] 명 순서, 질서
- **origin** [ɔ́ːrədʒin] 명 기원
- **place** [pleis] 명 장소 동 두다
- **post office** 우체국
- **prison** [prízn] 명 감옥
- **reasonable** [ríːzənəbl] 형 (가격이) 적당한
- **regularity** [règjulǽrəti] 명 규칙성
- **reliable** [riláiəbl] 형 믿을 만한
- **remember** [rimémbər] 동 기억하다
- **schedule** [skédʒuːl] 명 스케줄
- **solution** [səlúːʃən] 명 해결책
- **spend** [spend] 동 보내다, 쓰다
- **suggest** [səgdʒést] 동 제안하다
- **trip** [trip] 명 여행
- **unfortunately** [ənfɔ́ːrtʃənətli] 부 불행하게도
- **willingly** [wíliŋli] 부 기꺼이
- **worth** [wəːrθ] 형 ~할 가치가 있는
- **yet** [jet] 부 아직

Key Expressions

- **a variety of** 다양한
- **come up with** ~을 생각해 내다
- **get out of** ~에서 나오다, 도망치다
- **get (to)** ~에 도착하다, 닿다
- **give it a try** 시도하다, 한번 해보다
- **in the order of** ~의 순서로
- **look forward to** ~을 기대하다
- **lose one's way** 길을 잃다

- **make a choice** 선택하다
- **make a decision** 결정하다
- **make a plan** 계획을 세우다
- **my pleasure** 도움이 되어 저도 기뻐요
- **set for** ~의 준비를 하다
- **That's why** ~. 그것이 ~ 한 이유이다.
- **turn around** 돌다, 돌아서다
- **Why don't you** ~? ~하는 게 어때?

Word Power

※ 서로 비슷한 뜻을 가진 어휘

- □ **actually** 실제로 – **really** 사실은
- □ **choice** 선택 – **selection** 선택
- □ **consider** 여기다 – **regard** 여기다
- □ **decide** 결정하다 – **determine** 결정하다
- □ **reasonable** 적당한 – **sensible** 합리적인

- □ **careful** 조심스러운 – **cautious** 조심스러운
- □ **closely** 자세히 – **intently** 주의 깊게
- □ **convenient** 편리한 – **handy** 편리한
- □ **prison** 감옥 – **jail** 감옥
- □ **reliable** 믿을 만한 – **dependable** 믿을 만한

※ 서로 반대의 뜻을 가진 어휘

- □ **beauty** 미, 아름다움 ↔ **ugliness** 추함
- □ **connect** 연결하다 ↔ **disconnect** 연결을 끊다
- □ **difference** 차이 ↔ **similarity** 닮은 점
- □ **order** 순서, 질서 ↔ **disorder** 무질서
- □ **reliable** 믿을 만한 ↔ **unreliable** 믿을 수 없는

- □ **careful** 조심스러운 ↔ **careless** 부주의한
- □ **convenient** 편리한 ↔ **inconvenient** 불편한
- □ **entrance** 입구 ↔ **exit** 출구
- □ **reasonable** 적당한 ↔ **unreasonable** 적절하지 못한
- □ **remember** 기억하다 ↔ **forget** 잊다

※ 동사 – 명사

- □ **act** 행동하다 – **action** 행동, **activity** 활동
- □ **compare** 비교하다 – **comparison** 비교
- □ **suggest** 제안하다 – **suggestion** 제안

- □ **choose** 선택하다 – **choice** 선택
- □ **solve** 해결하다 – **solution** 해결책

English Dictionary

- □ **connect** 연결하다, 이어지다
  - → to become joined or united or linked
  - 접합되거나 결합되거나 연결되다
- □ **entrance** 입구
  - → a door, gate, passage, etc. used for entering a room, building or place
  - 방, 건물, 장소에 들어가기 위해 사용되는 문, 통로 등
- □ **exchange** 교환하다
  - → to give things of a particular kind to each other at the same time
  - 동시에 서로에게 특별한 종류의 어떤 것을 주다
- □ **exit** 출구
  - → a way out of a public building or vehicle
  - 공공 건물이나 차량 등의 나가는 길
- □ **frustrate** 방해하다, 좌절시키다
  - → to make somebody feel annoyed or impatient because they cannot do or achieve what they want
  - 원하는 것을 하거나 이룰 수 없어서 짜증나거나 초조하게 느끼도록 만들다
- □ **hedge** 산울타리
  - → a row of bushes or small trees planted close together, usually along the edge of a field, garden, yard or road

보통 들판, 정원, 마당, 도로 등의 가장자리를 따라 조밀하게 줄지어 심겨진 덤불 또는 작은 나무

- □ **labyrinth** 미궁
  - → a complicated series of paths, which it is difficult to find your way through
  - 통과할 길을 찾기가 어려운 일련의 복잡한 통로
- □ **maze** 미로
  - → a system of paths separated by walls or hedges built in a park or garden that is designed so that it is difficult to find your way through
  - 공원이나 정원에 통과할 길을 찾기가 어렵도록 설계된 벽이나 울타리에 의해 분리된 통로 시스템
- □ **mythology** 신화
  - → ancient myths in general; the ancient myths of a particular culture, society, etc.
  - 일반적인 고대의 신화들; 특정 문화, 사회 등의 고대 신화들
- □ **prison** 감옥
  - → a building where criminals are kept as punishment or where people accused of a crime are kept before their trial
  - 처벌로서 범죄자를 가두거나 재판 받기 전 범죄로 고소된 사람들이 갇히는 건물
- □ **worth** ~할 가치가 있는
  - → having a specified value
  - 특정한 가치를 가지고 있는

서답형

01 다음 짝지어진 단어의 관계가 같도록 빈칸에 알맞은 말을 쓰시오.

> beauty : ugliness = _____ : exit

02 다음 주어진 문장의 밑줄 친 place와 같은 의미로 쓰인 것은?

> Don't place your hand on her shoulder.

① Do you know where the meeting place is?

② My mother asked me to place the bottles in the refrigerator.

③ We're looking for the place to eat something.

④ I can't remember all the places we visited in Canada.

⑤ This would be a good place for a picnic.

중요

03 다음 문장에 공통으로 들어갈 말을 고르시오.

> • He found it hard to _____ a choice.
> • I'd like to listen to your opinion before I _____ a decision.
> • Let's _____ a plan for summer vacation.

① have   ② take

③ go   ④ make

⑤ come

04 다음 영영풀이가 가리키는 것을 고르시오.

> a row of bushes or small trees planted close together, usually along the edge of a field, garden, yard or road

① method   ② hedge

③ monster   ④ prison

⑤ order

중요

05 다음 중 밑줄 친 부분의 뜻풀이가 바르지 않은 것은?

① Narcissus was a character from Greek mythology. (신화)

② What do you mean by that? (의미하다)

③ My friend willingly spends lots of money on her pet. (마지못해)

④ I need to connect the printer to the computer. (연결하다)

⑤ It's very convenient to pay with my samrtphone. (편리한)

서답형

06 다음 우리말에 맞게 빈칸에 알맞은 말을 쓰시오.

(1) 많은 사람들이 미로 공원에 기꺼이 방문하여 "계획된 혼란"을 즐긴다.

➡ Many people _____ visit _____ parks and enjoy the "planned _____."

(2) 모든 벽이 이어져 있지 않은 경우, 이 간단한 방법은 효과가 없을지도 모른다.

➡ When all of the walls are not _____, this simple _____ may not be _____.

(3) 미로는 벽과 방, 산울타리와 같은 많은 다양한 재료로 제작된다.

➡ _____ are made with a _____ of different materials, like walls, rooms, and _____.

01 다음 문장의 빈칸에 들어갈 말을 〈보기〉에서 골라 쓰시오.

> ┌ 보기 ┐
> compare / decide / regularity / worth / exchange

(1) The _____ of the design gets boring after a while.

(2) The museum is certainly _____ a visit.

(3) I usually _____ the prices when I buy products.

(4) Would you _____ this blue shirt for the red one?

(5) I _____ to study English and Chinese harder.

02 다음 우리말과 일치하도록 주어진 어구를 모두 배열하여 영작하시오.

(1) 이 간단한 방법은 어떤 종류의 미로에서는 효과가 없을지도 모른다.
(may / this / mazes / not / be / in / effective / simple / types / certain / method / of)

➡ _____

_____

(2) 미궁의 기원은 그리스 신화에서 찾을 수 있다.
(the origin / the labyrinth / you / Greek / mythology / find / can / of / in)

➡ _____

_____

(3) 도착한 순서로 줄을 서 주세요.
(Please / arrival / in / of / order / up / line / the)

➡ _____

03 다음 우리말에 맞게 빈칸에 알맞은 말을 쓰시오. (철자가 주어진 것도 있음.)

(1) 빠져나오기 위해서는, 당신은 단지 돌아서서 들어간 길대로 걸어 나오면 된다.
➡ To get out, you simply have to _____ _____ and walk back out the way you came in.

(2) 학교 갈 준비가 되었니?
➡ Are _____ s_____ _____ school?

(3) 방문객들은 축제에서 다양한 음식들을 즐겼다.
➡ Visitors enjoyed _____ v_____ _____ foods at the festival.

04 다음 우리말을 주어진 단어를 이용하여 영작하시오.

(1) 우리는 정말 너를 다시 보기를 기대하고 있다. (forward, really)
➡ _____

(2) 우리가 시도한 첫 번째 길은 막다른 길로 드러났다. (turned, street, dead, try)
➡ _____

(3) 지금은 우리가 결정할 때이다. (make, time, when)
➡ _____

(4) 그들은 한 달에 한 번씩 승마를 간다. (go, once, horseback riding)
➡ _____

(5) 저는 평계를 생각해 내야만 합니다. (must, an excuse, come)
➡ _____

교과서

Conversation

1 가능성 정도 묻기

Is it possible to visit Mirror Maze Park? 거울 미로 공원에 가는 것이 가능할까요?

- 'Is it possible to ~?'는 '~하는 것이 가능하니?' 또는 '~해도 되니?'라는 뜻으로 어떤 일이 일어날 가능성을 묻거나 상대방의 허락을 구할 때 쓰는 표현이다. 'Is it possible'에 이어지는 'to부정사' 대신에 명사절을 사용하여 'Is it possible that+주어+동사 ~?(~한 것이 가능하니?)'가 될 수도 있다. 가능성을 나타내는 조동사를 사용하여 'Can+주어+동사원형 ~?'도 가능성을 묻거나 허가를 구하는 표현이 될 수 있다.

- 가능성을 나타내는 형용사 'possible(가능한)' 대신 'probable(~가 있을 것 같은, 가능한), likely(~할 것 같은, ~할 것으로 예상되는)'와 같은 형용사를 사용하여 'Is it likely to ~?', 'Is it probable to ~?(~할 것 같니?)'와 같이 물어볼 수 있다. 또한 부정사 대신 명사절을 사용하여 'Is it likely that+주어+동사 ~?', 'Is it probable that+주어+동사 ~?'처럼 써도 같은 의미가 될 수 있다.

- 가능성이 있다는 것을 표현하는 경우에는 'It is possible to ~.', 'It is likely to ~.', 'It is probable to ~.'와 같이 나타내거나 'It is possible that+주어+동사 ~.', 'It is likely that+주어+동사 ~.', 'It is probable that+주어+동사 ~.'의 형태를 써서 '~하는 것이 가능하다.'라고 할 수 있다. 'Is there any chance to/that ~?(~할 가능성이 있습니까?)'도 가능성을 묻는 표현으로 쓰일 수 있다.

가능성 정도 묻기

- Is it possible to ~ / that+주어+동사 ~?
- Is it likely to ~ / that+주어+동사 ~?
- Is it probable to ~ / that+주어+동사 ~?

핵심 Check

1. 다음 밑줄 친 우리말에 해당하는 영어 문장을 possible을 이용하여 쓰시오.

> W: How may I help you?
>
> B: Hi! I bought these shoes yesterday. <u>그것을 빨간 신발로 교환할 수 있나요?</u>
>
> W: Oh, actually white is really popular these days.
>
> B: I know, and that's why I spent a long time making the decision yesterday. But I think that red will look better on me.
>
> W: Okay, no problem.

➡

길 묻기

How do I get to the restaurant? 어떻게 그 식당에 갈 수 있나요?

■ 'How do/can I get to 장소?'는 '내가 ~에 어떻게 가나요?'라는 뜻으로 길을 물을 때 쓰는 표현이다. 이 표현은 'Could/Would you tell me the way to ~?'로 바꿔 쓸 수 있다. to는 전치사로 뒤에는 가고자 하는 장소를 명사(구)로 나타낸다. 대화 중에 장소가 언급되었을 때는 'How do/can I get there?(어떻게 거기에 갈 수 있습니까?)'라고 한다.

■ 공손하게 길을 물어볼 때는 앞에 'Excuse me.'를 붙여서 말한다. 'Excuse me. Do you know where ~ is?(~가 어디 있는지 아십니까?)', 'Excuse me. Could you show[tell] me where ~ is?(~가 어디 있는지 알려주시겠습니까?)', 'Excuse me. Do you know how to get to ~?(어떻게 ~에 가는지 아십니까?)'와 같이 물어보기도 한다.

■ 대중교통을 이용하는 경우에는 'Excuse me. What line goes to ~?(실례합니다. 몇 호선이 ~에 가나요?)', 'Excuse me. what bus goes to ~?(실례합니다. 몇 번 버스가 ~로 갑니까?)', 'Excuse me. what bus should I take to get to ~?(~에 가려면 몇 번 버스를 타야 합니까?)'와 같이 물어보기도 한다.

■ 길을 알려줄 때는 'Go straight ~ blocks.(곧장 ~ 블록을 가세요.)', 'Turn right at ~.' 또는 'Make a right turn at ~.(~에서 우회전하세요.)', 'Turn left at ~.' 또는 'Make a left turn at ~.(~에서 좌회전 하세요)'처럼 안내한다. 건물에서 '그것이 ~층에 있다.'고 할 때는 'It's on ~ floor.'라고 한다. 'You can't miss it.'은 '찾기 쉬워요.'에 해당하는 말이다.

길 묻기

- How do/can I get to 장소?
- Excuse me. Do you know where ~ is?
- Excuse me. Do you know how to get to ~?
- Excuse me. I'm looking for ~. Do you know where it is?
- Could/Would you tell me the way to ~?
- Excuse me. Could you show[tell] me where ~ is?

핵심 Check

2. 다음 밑줄 친 (A)를 대신하여 쓰기에 가장 적절한 것은?

> A: (A)How do I get to City Hall?
> B: Go straight for two blocks and turn left. Then go straight for about 20 meters. You can see City Hall on your right.
> A: Thank you for your help.

① Could you show me City Hall?
② Could you tell me the way to City Hall?
③ Can I get to City Hall?
④ Would you tell me the way?
⑤ How can I get there?

Listen and Speak 1 A

W: How may I help you?

B: Hi! I bought these shoes yesterday. Is it possible to exchange ❶ them for the red shoes?

W: Oh, actually white is really popular ❷these days.

B: I know, and that's why I ❸spent a long time ❹making the decision yesterday. But I think that red will ❺look better on me.

W: Okay, no problem.

W: 무엇을 도와드릴까요?

B: 안녕하세요! 제가 어제 이 신발을 샀는데요. 이것을 빨간색 신발로 교환하는 것이 가능한가요?

W: 오, 사실은 하얀색이 요즘 정말 인기 있어요.

B: 저도 알아요. 그래서 제가 어제 결정하는 데 오랜 시간을 보냈어요. 하지만 빨간색이 제게 더 잘 어울릴 것 같아요.

W: 알았어요. 문제 없어요.

❶ them은 'these shoes'를 가리킨다. ❷ these days: 요즘 ❸ spend+시간+~ing: ~하는 데 시간을 보내다 ❹ make the decision: 결정하다
❺ look better on: ~에게 잘 어울리다

Check(√) True or False

(1) The boy bought the white shoes yesterday.   T ☐ F ☐

(2) The woman recommended the red shoes because it looked better on the boy.   T ☐ F ☐

Listen and Speak 2 A

M: Hi, do you need any help?

G: Yes, please. ❶Could you suggest a good Chinese restaurant in this building? I can't decide between the two.

M: Hmm... . ❷What about Pappa Chen's? Their food is good and the prices are ❸reasonable.

G: Sounds great! ❹How do I get to the restaurant?

M: It's on the fourth floor. You can use the elevator over there. Pappa Chen's is next to the elevator.

G: Great! Thank you very much for your help.

M: My pleasure. Enjoy your dinner.

M: 안녕하세요, 도움이 필요하신가요?

G: 네, 부탁드려요. 이 건물에서 좋은 중국 음식점을 추천해 주실 수 있나요? 두 개 중에 결정할 수가 없네요.

M: 음… 파파첸스는 어떠세요? 그곳 음식은 훌륭하고 가격이 합리적이에요.

G: 좋을 것 같은데요! 그 음식점에 어떻게 가나요?

M: 그것은 4층에 있습니다. 당신은 저기 있는 승강기를 탈 수 있고요. 파파첸스는 승강기 옆에 있습니다.

G: 아주 좋아요! 도와주셔서 정말 감사합니다.

M: 천만에요. 저녁 맛있게 드세요.

❶ 'Could you suggest ~?'는 무엇을 추천해 줄 것을 요청하는 표현으로 'Can you recommend ~?' 등으로 바꾸어 표현할 수 있다.
❷ 'What about ~?'은 '~는 어때?'를 의미하며 'How about ~?' 등으로 바꾸어 표현할 수 있다. ❸ resonable: 적당한, 합리적인 ❹ 'How do/
can I get to 장소?'는 '내가 ~에 어떻게 가나요?'라는 뜻으로 길을 물을 때 쓰는 표현이며 'Could/Would you tell me the way to ~?'로 바꿔
쓸 수 있다.

Check(√) True or False

(3) The man recommends Pappa Chen's because of the good food and the reasonable prices.   T ☐ F ☐

(4) The Pappa Chen's is on the opposite side of the elevator.   T ☐ F ☐

Listen and Speak 1 B

G: Mom, did you decide where to visit ❶during our family trip to Jeju?

W: Almost. Come here and see the plan ❷I made.

G: It looks good. Hmm... Mom, ❸is it possible to visit Mirror Maze Park on our second day?

W: It sounds exciting, but I remember you said you wanted to go ❹horseback riding.

G: I know, but I heard the park is a lot more fun. Please ... .

W: All right. Let's change our schedule for the second day.

G: Thank you! I'm very excited about the trip.

W: It's great to hear that you're ❺looking forward to the trip.

❶ 'during+명사(구)', 'while+주어+동사'
❷ 목적격 관계대명사 that 또는 which가 생략되었다.
❸ 'is it possible to ~?'는 '~하는 것이 가능하니?' 또는 '~해도 되니?'라는 뜻으로 어떤 일이 일어날 가능성을 묻거나 상대방의 허락을 구할 때 쓰는 표현이다.
❹ horseback riding: 승마
❺ look forward to+(동)명사: ~을 기대하다, 고대하다

Listen and Speak 2 B

B: Hey, Minju, where are you?

G: Oh, Andrew, I'm coming. I'm coming.

B: Good. I was worried that you were lost.

G: I think I'm okay. What about Mason and Jian?

B: ❶They are already here at my house.

G: Good! Oh, I see the post office. ❷How do I get to your place from here?

B: You are almost here. ❸Go straight for one more block. Then you will see Kim's Bakery.

G: Kim's Bakery? Okay ... .

B: Then turn right and go straight for ❹about 100 meters.

G: Turn right and go straight ... . Okay, thanks! I'll see you soon.

❶ They는 Mason과 Jian을 가리킨다.
❷ 'How do I get to 장소?'는 '내가 ~에 어떻게 가나요?'라는 뜻으로 길을 물을 때 쓰는 표현이며 'Would you tell me the way to your place from here?'로 바꾸어 쓸 수 있다.
❸ 명령문이므로 동사로 시작한다.
❹ about은 '약, 대략'을 나타낸다.

Real Life Communication

Mina: ❶Are you all set for the trip this weekend?

Jinho, Claire, & Henry: Yes!

Mina: Good! Don't be late! We're meeting at 11 a.m. ❷in front of the clock tower.

Jinho: You got it! How do we get to the airport? I don't think we've ❸decided yet.

Henry: Jinho is right. We have two choices, bus or subway.

Claire: ❹What about the subway? It's more ❺ reliable than the bus.

Henry: Is it possible to get to Terminal 2 by subway?

Claire: Yes, I already checked.

Mina: Good. Okay, then let's take the subway.

❶ Are you all set for ~?: '~할 준비가 되었니?'를 의미한다. ❷ in front of: ~ 앞에 ❸ decide: 결정하다 ❹ 'What about ~?'은 '~하는 게 어때?'라고 제안하는 표현이다. ❺ reliable: 믿을 만한

Let's Check 1

B: What are you reading, Alice?

G: It's about the origin of the ❶labyrinth.

B: Labyrinth? Wasn't that an old ❷mythological prison to keep the half-man, half-bull monster?

G: Oh, Juwon, you know about the story.

B: Not really. I forgot the name of the monster.

G: The Minotaur. The king of Crete was angry at ❸it and put ❸it in a labyrinth.

B: Interesting! Alice, is it possible to borrow the book after you're finished with ❹it?

G: Sure, no problem. Maybe this Friday.

❶ labyrinth: 미궁 ❷ mythological: 신화적인 ❸ it은 모두 'The Minotaur'를 가리킨다. ❹ it은 'the book'을 가리킨다.

● 다음 우리말과 일치하도록 빈칸에 알맞은 말을 쓰시오.

Listen & Speak 1 A

W: How may I help you?

B: Hi! I bought these shoes yesterday. Is it _____ to _____ them for the red shoes?

W: Oh, actually white is really popular _____ _____.

B: I know, and that's _____ I spent a long time _____ _____ _____ yesterday. But I think that red will _____ _____ on me.

W: Okay, no problem.

Listen & Speak 1 B

G: Mom, did you _____ where to visit _____ our family trip to Jeju?

W: Almost. Come here and see the plan I made.

G: It looks good. Hmm… Mom, _____ _____ _____ to visit Mirror Maze Park on our second day?

W: It sounds _____, but I remember you said you wanted to go _____ _____.

G: I know, but I heard the park is _____ _____ more fun. Please ….

W: All right. Let's change our _____ for the second day.

G: Thank you! I'm very _____ about the trip.

W: It's great to hear that you're _____ _____ _____ the trip.

Listen & Speak 2 A

M: Hi, do you need any help?

G: Yes, please. Could you _____ a good Chinese restaurant in this building? I can't _____ between the two.

M: Hmm…. What _____ Pappa Chen's? Their food is good and the prices are _____.

G: Sounds great! How do I _____ _____ the restaurant?

M: It's on the _____ floor. You can use the elevator over there. Pappa Chen's is _____ _____ the elevator.

G: Great! Thank you very much for your help.

M: My _____. Enjoy your dinner.

해석

W: 무엇을 도와드릴까요?

B: 안녕하세요! 제가 어제 이 신발을 샀는데요. 이것을 빨간색 신발로 교환하는 것이 가능한가요?

W: 오, 사실은 하얀색이 요즘 정말 인기 있어요.

B: 저도 알아요. 그래서 제가 어제 결정하는 데 오랜 시간을 보냈어요. 하지만 빨간색이 제게 더 잘 어울릴 것 같아요.

W: 알았어요, 문제없어요.

G: 엄마, 제주도 가족 여행 동안 어디 방문할지 정하셨어요?

W: 거의. 이리 와서 내가 만든 일정표를 보렴.

G: 좋아 보여요. 흠. 엄마, 우리 두 번째 날에 거울 미로 공원에 가는 것이 가능할까요?

W: 재미있을 거 같지만, 네가 말 타러 가고 싶다고 말한 것으로 기억하는데.

G: 저도 알아요, 근데 공원이 훨씬 더 재미있다고 들었어요. 제발요….

W: 알았다. 두 번째 날 우리의 일정을 변경하자.

G: 감사합니다! 전 이번 여행에 대해 너무 신이 나요.

W: 네가 이번 여행을 고대한다니 아주 좋구나.

M: 안녕하세요, 도움이 필요하신가요?

G: 네, 부탁드려요. 이 건물에서 좋은 중국 음식점을 추천해 주실 수 있나요? 두 개 중에 결정할 수가 없네요.

M: 음… 파파첸스는 어떠세요? 그곳 음식은 훌륭하고 가격이 합리적이에요.

G: 좋을 것 같은데요! 그 음식점에 어떻게 가나요?

M: 그것은 4층에 있습니다. 당신은 저기 있는 승강기를 탈 수 있고요. 파파첸스는 승강기 옆에 있습니다.

G: 아주 좋아요! 도와주셔서 정말 감사합니다.

M: 천만에요. 저녁 맛있게 드세요.

Listen & Speak 2 B

B: Hey, Minju, where are you?

G: Oh, Andrew, I'm _____. I'm _____.

B: Good. I was _____ that you were lost.

G: I think I'm okay. What about Mason and Jian?

B: They are already here at my house.

G: Good! Oh, I see the _____ _____. _____ _____ _____ _____ _____ your place from here?

B: You are almost here. _____ _____ _____ one more block. Then you will see Kim's Bakery.

G: Kim's Bakery? Okay ….

B: Then _____ _____ and _____ _____ for about 100 meters.

G: _____ _____ and _____ _____ …. Okay, thanks! I'll see you soon.

Real Life Communication

Mina: _____ _____ _____ _____ _____ _____ the trip this weekend?

Jinho, Claire, & Henry: Yes!

Mina: Good! Don't be late! We're meeting at 11 a.m. _____ _____ _____ the clock tower.

Jinho: You _____ _____! How do we _____ _____ the airport? I don't think we've _____ yet.

Henry: Jinho is right. We have two _____, bus or subway.

Claire: What about the subway? It's more _____ than the bus.

Henry: Is it _____ _____ get to Terminal 2 _____ _____?

Claire: Yes, I already checked.

Mina: Good. Okay, then let's _____ the subway.

Let's Check 1

B: What are you reading, Alice?

G: It's about the _____ of the _____.

B: _____? Wasn't that an old _____ _____ to keep the half-man, half-bull monster?

G: Oh, Juwon, you know about the story.

B: Not really. I forgot the name of the monster.

G: The Minotaur. The king of Crete was _____ at it and _____ it in a _____.

해석

B: 민주야, 너 어디야?
G: 오, Andrew, 나 가고 있어. 가고 있어.
B: 좋아. 네가 길을 잃었을까봐 걱정했어.
G: 괜찮은 것 같아. Mason이랑 지안이는?
B: 그들은 우리 집에 벌써 왔지.
G: 좋아! 오, 우체국이 보여. 여기서부터 너희 집까지 어떻게 가니?
B: 거의 다 왔네. 한 블록 더 직진해. 그럼 너는 킴스 빵집이 보일 거야.
G: 킴스 빵집? 알았어….
B: 그럼 오른쪽으로 돌아서 100m 정도 직진해.
G: 오른쪽으로 돌아서 직진이라…. 알았어, 고마워! 곧 보자.

Mina: 너희 모두 이번 주말에 여행갈 준비 됐니?
Jinho, Claire, & Henry: 응!
Mina: 좋아! 늦지 마! 우리는 시계탑 앞에서 오전 11시에 만날 거야.
Jinho: 알았어! 우리 공항까지 어떻게 가지? 우리가 아직 결정하지 않은 것 같은데.
Henry: 진호 말이 맞아. 우리는 버스랑 지하철, 두 가지 선택이 있어.
Claire: 지하철은 어때? 그것은 버스보다 더 믿을 만하잖아.
Henry: 2터미널까지 지하철로 가는 것이 가능하니?
Claire: 응, 내가 이미 확인해 봤어.
Mina: 좋아. 그래, 그럼 지하철을 타자.

B: 무엇을 읽고 있니, Alice?
G: 미궁의 기원에 관한 거야.
B: 미궁? 그건 반인반수 괴물을 가두기 위한 옛 신화 속 감옥 아니니?
G: 와, 주원아, 너 그 이야기에 대해 아는구나.
B: 그다지 잘 아는 건 아니야. 그 괴물의 이름을 잊어버렸어.
G: 미노타우루스야. 크레타의 왕이 그 괴물에 화가 나서 그것을 미궁에 가두었지.

[01~02] 다음 대화를 읽고 물음에 답하시오.

> Mike: Hi, do you need any help?
>
> Sora: Yes, please. Could you suggest a good Chinese restaurant in this building? I can't decide between the two.
>
> Mike: Hmm.... What about Pappa Chen's? Their food is good and the prices are (A)<u>reason</u>.
>
> Sora: Sounds great! (B)_____
>
> Mike: It's on the fourth floor. You can use the elevator over there. Pappa Chen's is next to the elevator.

01 위 대화의 밑줄 친 (A)를 알맞은 형으로 고치시오.

➡ _____

02 위 대화의 빈칸 (B)에 들어갈 말로 어색한 것은?

① Can I get to the restaurant?

② How do I get to the restaurant?

③ Would you tell me the way to the restaurant?

④ Do you know how to get to the restaurant?

⑤ Could you show me where the restaurant is?

[03~04] 다음 대화를 읽고 물음에 답하시오.

> Mina: Are you all set for the trip this weekend?
>
> Jinho, Claire, & Henry: Yes!
>
> Mina: Good! Don't be late! We're meeting at 11 a.m. in front ___ⓐ___ the clock tower.
>
> Jinho: You got it! How do we get ___ⓑ___ the airport? I don't think we've decided yet.
>
> Henry: Jinho is right. We have two choices, bus or subway.
>
> Claire: What about the subway? It's more reliable than the bus.
>
> Henry: (A)(it / subway / by / is / to / to / get / possible / Terminal 2)?
>
> Claire: Yes, I already checked.

03 위 대화의 빈칸 ⓐ와 ⓑ에 각각 알맞은 전치사를 쓰시오.

➡ ⓐ _____ ⓑ _____

04 위 대화의 괄호 (A)에 주어진 단어들을 모두 배열하여 영작하시오.

➡ _____

[01~02] 다음 대화를 읽고 물음에 답하시오.

Juwon: What are you reading, Alice?

Alice: It's about the origin of the labyrinth.

Juwon: Labyrinth? Wasn't that an old mythological prison to keep the half-man, half-bull monster?

Alice: Oh, Juwon, you know about the story.

Juwon: Not really. I forgot the name of the monster.

Alice: The Minotaur. The king of Crete was angry at it and put it in a labyrinth.

Juwon: Interesting! Alice, is it possible to borrow the book after you're finished with it?

Alice: Sure, no problem. Maybe this Friday.

서답형

01 위 대화에서 다음 영영풀이가 가리키는 것을 찾아 쓰시오.

> a building where criminals are kept as punishment or where people accused of a crime are kept before their trial

➡ _____

중요

02 위 대화의 내용과 일치하지 <u>않는</u> 것은?

① Alice는 미궁의 유래에 관한 책을 읽고 있다.

② 미궁은 반인반수 괴물을 가둬 놓기 위한 옛 신화 속의 감옥이다.

③ 미노타우루스는 반인반수 괴물이다.

④ 크레타의 왕이 괴물에게 화를 내서 괴물에 의해 감옥에 갇혔다.

⑤ 주원은 Alice가 책을 다 읽은 후 책을 빌릴 수 있을 것이다.

[03~05] 다음 대화를 읽고 물음에 답하시오.

Andrew: Hey, Minju, where are you?

Minju: Oh, Andrew, I'm coming. I'm coming.

Andrew: Good. I was ⓐworry that you were lost.

Minju: I think I'm okay. What ⓑabout Mason and Jian?

Andrew: They are already here ⓒat my house.

Minju: Good! Oh, I see the post office. How do I get ⓓto your place from here?

Andrew: You are almost here. Go straight ⓔfor one more block. Then you will see Kim's Bakery.

Minju: Kim's Bakery? Okay ….

Andrew: Then turn right and go straight for about 100 meters.

Minju: Turn right and go straight …. Okay, thanks! I'll see you soon.

서답형

03 위 대화의 밑줄 친 ⓐ~ⓔ 중 어법상 <u>틀린</u> 것을 찾아 바르게 고치시오.

➡ _____

서답형

04 Where is Andrew's place? Check ✓ on the map.

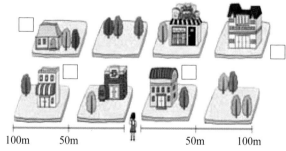

서답형

05 How can Minju get to Kim's Bakery from the post office?

➡ _____

[06~08] 다음 대화를 읽고 물음에 답하시오.

> Mike: Hi, do you need any help?
>
> Sora: Yes, please. Could you suggest a good Chinese restaurant in this building? I can't decide between the two.
>
> Mike: Hmm.... (A)_____ Their food is good and the prices are reasonable.
>
> Sora: Sounds great! (B)_____?
>
> Mike: It's on the fourth floor. You can use the elevator over there. Pappa Chen's is next to the elevator.
>
> Sora: Great! Thank you very much for your help.
>
> Mike: My pleasure. Enjoy your dinner.

06 위 대화의 빈칸 (A)에 들어갈 말로 나머지와 의도가 <u>다른</u> 것은?

① Why don't you try Pappa Chen's?

② What about Pappa Chen's?

③ I think you should try Pappa Chen's.

④ I recommend Pappa Chen's.

⑤ I'd like to visit Pappa Chen's.

서답형
07 위 대화의 빈칸 (B)에 들어갈 말을 <보기>에 주어진 단어들을 모두 배열하여 영작하시오.

> ┌ 보기 ┐
> I / the / restaurant / to / how / get / do

➡ _____

08 Where is Papa Chen's?

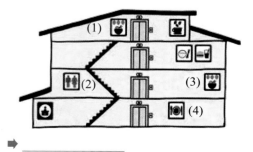

➡ _____

[09~12] 다음 대화를 읽고 물음에 답하시오.

> W: How may I help you?
>
> B: Hi! I bought these shoes yesterday. Is it possible to exchange them for the red shoes?
>
> W: Oh, actually white is really popular these days.
>
> B: I know, and that's why I spent a long time making the decision yesterday. But I think that red will look better on me.
>
> W: Okay, no problem.

서답형
09 What does the boy want to do?

➡ _____

_____

서답형
10 What color is popular these days?

➡ _____

서답형
11 Why does the boy want to exchange his shoes?

➡ _____

_____

서답형
12 위 대화의 내용과 일치하도록 빈칸을 완성하시오.

> I bought (A)_____ yesterday. They were so popular and I spent a long time _____. After coming back home, I thought (C)_____ _____. When I visited the shoe store and asked if I could have any chance to (D)_____ _____, I could do it. I love my red shoes now.

01 다음 대화가 자연스럽게 이어지도록 순서대로 배열하시오.

> How may I help you?

> (A) Okay, no problem.
> (B) Oh, actually white is really popular these days.
> (C) Hi! I bought these shoes yesterday. Is it possible to exchange them for the red shoes?
> (D) I know, and that's why I spent a long time making the decision yesterday. But I think that red will look better on me.

➡ _____

02 다음 대화의 내용과 일치하도록 빈칸을 완성하시오.

> **Gina:** Mom, did you decide where to visit during our family trip to Jeju?
> **Mom:** Almost. Come here and see the plan I made.
> **Gina:** It looks good. Hmm... Mom, is it possible to visit Mirror Maze Park on our second day?
> **Mom:** It sounds exciting, but I remember you said you wanted to go horseback riding.
> **Gina:** I know, but I heard the park is a lot more fun. Please … .
> **Mom:** All right. Let's change our schedule for the second day.
> **Gina:** Thank you! I'm very excited about the trip.
> **Mom:** It's great to hear that you're looking forward to the trip.

> Gina's family made a plan to visit Jeju soon. Gina and her mother talked about it. Everything looked fine, but Gina wanted to change the plan to (A)_____. Instead, she wanted to visit (B)_____ because (C)_____. Her mom decided to change their schedule for the second day, and Gina was excited about the trip.

[03~04] 다음 대화를 읽고 물음에 답하시오.

> **Mike:** Hi, do you need any help?
> **Sora:** Yes, please. Could you suggest a good Chinese restaurant in this building? I can't decide between the two.
> **Mike:** Hmm…. What about Pappa Chen's? Their food is good and the prices are reasonable.
> **Sora:** Sounds great! How do I get to the restaurant?
> **Mike:** It's on the fourth floor. You can use the elevator over there. Pappa Chen's is next to the elevator.
> **Sora:** Great! Thank you very much for your help.
> **Mike:** My pleasure. Enjoy your dinner.

03 Why does Mike recommend Pappa Chen's?

➡ _____

04 How can Sora get to Pappa Chen's? Fill the blanks with suitable words.

➡ She can use _____ in the building. Pappa Chen's is _____ the elevator on _____.

Grammar

1 부정대명사 one

> • Here is **one** as an example. 여기 그 예가 하나 있습니다.
> • The easiest and most reliable **one** is to place a hand on one wall from the very beginning. 가장 쉽고 믿을 만한 하나는 시작 지점부터 한쪽 벽에 손을 대는 것입니다.

■ one은 앞에서 언급된 명사와 같은 종류이지만 정해지지 않은 것을 가리킬 때 쓰며, 복수는 ones이다. 형용사+one, one+관계사절 등 앞과 뒤에서 꾸며주는 말과 함께 쓸 수 있다. 특정한 것을 가리킬 때는 it을 쓴다.

- Are you **the one** who answered the phone yesterday? 당신이 어제 전화를 받은 분인가요?
- They are **the ones** who sang and danced on TV. 저들이 TV에서 노래하고 춤추던 이들이에요.
- I don't like this color. Can you show me **a blue one**? 이 색깔이 맘에 들지 않아요. 파란 색으로 보여 주시겠어요?
- **A**: I have lost my pen. 펜을 잃어버렸어.

  B: Do you want me to buy **one** for you? 하나 사 줄까?

  A: No, thanks. But I should find the pen as it is my lucky pen. 고맙지만 아냐. 그것은 나의 행운의 펜이기 때문에 나는 그 펜을 꼭 찾아야 해

■ 둘 중 하나를 가리킬 때 첫 번째는 one, 나머지 하나는 the other이며, 셋 중 하나를 가리킬 때 첫 번째는 one, 그 다음 하나는 another, 마지막 남은 하나는 the other이다. 또한 여러 개 중 일부는 some, 그 외에 다른 일부는 others, 나머지 전부는 the others로 쓴다.

- **One** is mine and **the other** is hers. 하나는 내 것이고, 나머지 하나는 그녀의 것이다.
- There are three buildings I like in this town. **One** is the library, **another** is the hospital, and **the other** is the City Hall. 이 마을에서 내가 좋아하는 건물이 세 개 있다. 하나는 도서관, 다른 하나는 병원, 그리고 나머지 하나는 시청이다.
- **Some** like walking, and **others** prefer running. 몇몇은 걷기를, 다른 사람들은 달리기를 더 좋아한다.
- There are balls in the box. **Some** are red and **the others** are blue. 상자 안에 공들이 있다. 몇 개는 빨간색이고, 나머지는 파란색이다.

■ 둘 중 하나를 가리킬 때는 either, 둘 모두는 both, 둘 중 어느 것도 아닐 때는 neither, 셋 이상에서 어느 것도 아닐 때는 none을 각각 사용한다.

- **Either** of the two girls likes David. 그 두 소녀들 중 하나는 David을 좋아한다.
- **Neither** of the two girls likes David. 그 두 소녀들 중 누구도 David을 좋아하지 않는다.
- **Both** of the two girls like David. 그 두 소녀들 모두 David을 좋아한다.
- **None** of the girls likes David. (셋 이상의) 그 소녀들 중 누구도 David을 좋아하지 않는다.

핵심 Check

1. 다음 괄호 안에서 알맞은 말을 고르시오.

   (1) I need a pen. Can you buy me a new (it / one)?

   (2) Which (one / either) of the two men would you like to meet?

❷ 분사구문

> • **Looking at them closely**, you may find the beauty of order and regularity. 자세히 들
> 여다보면, 여러분은 질서와 규칙성이라는 아름다움을 발견할 수 있을지도 모릅니다.

■ 분사구문은 종속접속사가 이끄는 부사절을 분사를 이용하여 간략한 부사구로 바꾼 것이며, 다음과 같은 방법으로 만든다.

1) 접속사를 생략한다. (접속사의 의미를 강조할 경우, 접속사를 남겨둘 수 있다.)
2) 주절의 주어와 같은 주어는 생략한다. (주절과 다르면 주어를 남긴다. → 독립분사구문)
3) 능동은 'V-ing' 형태로, 수동은 'Being V-ed'에서 Being을 생략한 '과거분사' 형태로 쓴다.
4) 분사구문의 부정은 not이나 never를 분사 앞에 쓴다.
5) 종속절의 시제가 주절보다 앞선 경우, 완료분사구문을 사용한다.

■ 부사구와 주절의 관계에 따라 양보, 동시동작, 이유, 시간, 조건 등의 의미로 쓰인다.

(1) 양보: **Though she is short**, she jumps the highest in my class.

= **Being short**, she jumps the highest in my class. 비록 그녀가 작지만, 우리 반에서 가장 높이 뛴다.

(2) 동시동작(부대상황): **While he listened to the radio**, he read the report.

= **Listening to the radio**, he read the report. 라디오를 들으며, 그는 보고서를 읽었다.

(3) 이유: **As she didn't sleep enough**, she felt tired all day.

= **Not sleeping enough**, she felt tired all day. 잠을 충분히 못자서, 그녀는 종일 피곤했다.

(4) 시간: **When I heard the birds singing**, I felt delighted.

= **Hearing the birds singing**, I felt delighted. 새들의 노래 소리를 들었을 때, 나는 기뻤다.

(5) 조건: **If you walk in the rain**, you'll catch a cold.

= **Walking in the rain**, you'll catch a cold. 빗속에 걸으면 감기에 걸릴 것이다.

■ 주절과 종속절의 주어가 달라서 분사구문의 주어를 남겨 두는 것을 '독립분사구문'이라고 하며, 일반 인이 주어일 경우 생략하는 것을 '비인칭 독립분사구문'이라 부른다.

(1) 독립분사구문: **As it was** rainy, he couldn't walk his dogs.

= **It being** rainy, he couldn't walk his dogs. 비가 와서, 그는 개들을 산책시킬 수 없었다.

(2) 비인칭 독립분사구문: **generally speaking**(일반적으로 말해), **considering**(~를 고려하면)

■ 「with+목적어+분사」는 전치사 with 뒤에 나오는 목적어 입장에서의 능동/수동이 중요하다.

• Susan took a walk **with her arms folded**. (팔짱을 낀 채로)

핵심 Check

2. 다음 괄호 안에서 알맞은 말을 고르시오.

(1) With her eyes (closing / closed), Angela recalled her childhood.

(2) (Feeling / Felt) surprised, the teacher ran to the school to meet his old students.

Grammar 시험대비 기본평가

01 다음 빈칸에 들어갈 말로 알맞은 것은?

> Maria has two kitties. One is white and _____ is brown.

① another ② other ③ two
④ next ⑤ the other

02 다음 부사절을 분사구문으로 바꿔 쓸 때, 빈칸에 들어갈 말로 가장 적절한 것은?

> When you are in a maze, you have many choices to make.
> ➡ _____ in a maze, you have many choices to make.

① When you being ② You being
③ Your being ④ Having been
⑤ Being

03 다음 대화의 밑줄 친 부분 중 어법상 어색한 부분을 고르시오.

> A: How do we get to the city museum?
> B: Which ①one is better? Taking the subway or riding a bike?
> A: ②Both sound great.
> B: ③One will be convenient and ④another will be fun.
> A: Then, we should choose ⑤one with more fun.

04 다음 분사구문을 접속사가 이끄는 부사절로 만들 때, 빈칸에 알맞은 말을 써 넣으시오.

(1) Not feeling well, he couldn't go out with his friends.
  ➡ As _____ _____ _____ well, he couldn't go out with his friends.

(2) Being late for school, they started to run.
  ➡ Because _____ _____ _____ _____ _____, they started to run.

(3) Listening to the radio, Sean took photos.
  ➡ While he _____ _____ the radio, Sean took photos.

(4) Eating much, Sarah doesn't gain any weight.
  ➡ _____ _____ _____ _____, Sarah doesn't gain any weight.

 01 밑줄 친 부분의 용법이 나머지와 <u>다른</u> 것을 고르시오.

① <u>Being</u> interested in the magic let her become a magician.

② <u>Knowing</u> her name, I could find her seat at the conference.

③ Not <u>feeling</u> good, she left work earlier.

④ <u>Being</u> sick, Mina didn't go to school.

⑤ <u>Crossing</u> the street packed with cars, she didn't care about the traffic.

[02~03] 다음 중 어법상 옳은 것을 고르시오.

02 ① My daddy bought me a pencil but Jin took one away.

② Each of the men are going to Busan.

③ Did you buy the blue pen or the purple one?

④ I like neither coffee or coke.

⑤ I don't like the bag. I need a bigger it.

03 ① Don't knowing when to move, she asked for help.

② Being too hot, they had to cancel the race.

③ Opened the drawer, he took out a letter.

④ Being tired of running in the ground, she signed up for the gym.

⑤ Caught a cold, Mina was absent from the party.

[04~05] 다음 우리말을 어법상 알맞게 영작한 것을 고르시오.

04
두 학생 모두 장학금을 신청했지만, 누구도 받을 수 없다.

① Both students have applied for the scholarship, but anyone can get it.

② Either one of the students applied for the scholarship, but neither can get it.

③ Each students have applied for the scholarship, but both can't get it.

④ Both students have applied for the scholarship, but neither one can get it.

⑤ Both students have applied for the scholarship, but either one can get it.

 05
수지는 눈을 감은 채 산책했다.

① Suji took a walk her eyes closing.

② Suji closed her eyes and took a walk.

③ Suji took a walk with closed her eyes.

④ Suji took a walk closed her eyes with.

⑤ Suji took a walk with her eyes closed.

서답형 06 다음 문장에서 어법상 어색한 단어 두 개를 찾아서 고치시오.

Tiring of taking care of infectious diseases all day long, neither she or her fellow doctor had the power to open the boxes filled with the gifts of encouragement from the citizens.

➡ _____

서답형

07 다음 그림을 보고 자연스러운 문장이 되도록 괄호 안에 주어진 단어를 바르게 배열하여 빈칸을 완성하시오.

(1) (it, from, to, reading, left, right, "evil", reads)

➡ _____,

but it becomes "live" in opposite direction.

(2) (the duck, the water, under, from, seeing)

➡ _____,

you will find its feet never stop paddling.

중요

08 다음 밑줄 친 단어의 용법이 나머지와 같지 <u>않은</u> 것을 고르시오.

① Sam has only small shirts. He needs a bigger <u>one</u> for the game.
② Only <u>one</u> fifth of the students answered the question correctly.
③ Charlie lost his cell phone, so he needed to buy <u>one</u>.
④ Martin broke his guitar yesterday, so his friend might lend <u>one</u> to him.
⑤ Jin sold her car and bought a used <u>one</u> from her cousin.

09 다음 각 문장에 쓰인 분사구문을 접속사를 이용한 부사절로 전환할 때, 의미상 〈보기〉와 같은 것이 <u>아닌</u> 것은?

┤ 보기 ├

Being tired from the hard exercise, all the animals in the circus took a nap for an hour.

① Finishing the projects, Kane was able to watch the movie after a long time.
② Not knowing how much Tom liked the animals, I couldn't understand his attitude toward the cats.
③ Not having anything special to do, they just walked around the town.
④ Being old enough, you can marry without your parents' agreement now.
⑤ Living in Daegu for over 20 years, Robert still can't get the meaning of the Daegu words.

[10~12] 다음 빈칸에 알맞은 것을 고르시오.

10

Dad bought me a laptop for my birthday, but I don't like _____ at all.

① one   ② another   ③ other
④ the other   ⑤ it

중요

11

Cindy's dress was too old and worn to put on, so her mom would like to make new _____ for her graduation party.

① one   ② another   ③ other
④ ones   ⑤ it

12

_____ of her three children goes to a different school.

① Both   ② Each   ③ All
④ Either   ⑤ Some

[13~14] 다음 중 어법상 옳지 않은 문장을 고르시오.

13 ① Bill liked the pen but his girl friend broke it.

② I'm tired of always wearing the same jacket. I need to get a new one.

③ Dinner at the restaurant was excellent, but we won't order it again.

④ All of the boys want to go out.

⑤ David lost his wedding ring, so he bought a similar it.

14 ① Either of the two girls is going to do the job of guiding the customers.

② All of us know the results in the general election this week.

③ Both of them has watched the drama twice a week since March.

④ Each of the books has a great effect on children in Africa.

⑤ No one is coming to the party because of the disease.

서답형

[15~16] 우리말과 일치하도록 괄호 안에 주어진 단어들을 바르게 배열하시오.

15

또 후회하고 싶지 않았지만, 그는 경솔하게 아무에게나 투표했다. (it, to, not, again, wanting, regret), he voted for anyone at random.

➡ _____

16

마스크를 쓰지 않고 친구들과 놀았기 때문에, 그 여자가 많은 사람들에게 질병을 퍼뜨릴 가능성이 있다. (with, without, the girl, wearing, having, her friends, played, a mask), there is a possibility that she will spread the disease to many people.

➡ _____

　_____

17 다음 주어진 분사구문을 접속사를 이용한 부사절로 만들 때 가장 적절한 것은?

Feeling tired, Ken didn't attend the morning soccer match.

① Although he felt tired, Ken didn't attend the morning soccer match.

② If he felt tired, Ken didn't attend the morning soccer match.

③ As soon as he felt tired, Ken didn't attend the morning soccer match.

④ As he felt tired, Ken didn't attend the morning soccer match.

⑤ Even if he felt tired, Ken didn't attend the morning soccer match.

18 다음 빈칸에 들어갈 알맞은 말을 고르시오.

The princess Elsa made a snowman called Olaf, and she decided to make many _____.

① another   ② other ones
③ one   ④ those
⑤ the others

01 다음 우리말과 일치하도록 괄호 안에 주어진 어구를 바르게 배열하여 문장을 완성하시오.

(1) Sarah는 그 디자인 샘플들 중에서 첫 번째 것을 고르고, 그 다음 하나 더 선택했지만, 어느 것도 그녀의 마음에 들지 않았다. (the first, another, Sarah, then, one, neither, but, chose)

➡ Among those design samples, _____ _____ was to her satisfaction.

(2) 이 청바지는 조금 작네요. 약간 더 큰 것을 보여 주실 수 있으세요? (slightly, a, show, you, one, me, could, bigger)

➡ These jeans are a bit small. _____

(3) Jane은 새 바이올린이 필요하지만, 그녀는 한 대를 구입할 충분한 돈이 없다. (enough, doesn't, for, she, one, have, money)

➡ Jane needs a new violin, but _____ .

(4) 어떤 사람들은 반려동물로 고양이를 좋아하지만, 반면에 다른 사람들은 고양이를 무서워한다. (cats, are, while, others, of, afraid)

➡ Some people like cats as pets, _____ .

02 다음 〈보기〉에 있는 접속사를 한 번씩만 사용하여, 분사구문을 부사절로 바꾸시오. (단, 진행형 표현은 쓸 수 없다.)

┤ 보기 ├
while because when if though

(1) Fixing his computer, Jerry listened to the radio show.

➡ _____

(2) Having nothing to worry about, the little boy plays well with the toys.

➡ _____

(3) Looking at the mazes closely, you may find the beauty of order and regularity.

➡ _____

(4) Being sick all day long, Benny finally completed the difficult assignment.

➡ _____

03 다음 밑줄 친 부분을 부정대명사를 활용하여 어법에 맞게 고쳐 다시 쓰시오.

(1) Should Mina buy the red grapes or the green those?

➡ _____

(2) Frank didn't catch some fish in the lake last weekend.

➡ _____ _____

(3) Each of the student have been to Bulguksa in Gyoungju.

➡ _____ _____

(4) She has two pets and it is bigger than another.

➡ _____ _____

04 다음 그림을 보고 괄호 안의 단어를 배열하여 알맞게 영작하시오.

(1) (she, the map, the maze, stuck, calmly, in, reviewed)

➡ _____

(2) (music, cross, listening to, really, the street, it, dangerous, is, to)

➡ _____

05 다음 문장에서 어법상 <u>어색한</u> 단어를 하나씩만 찾아 바르게 고치시오.

(1) Both of my cats is overweight.

➡ _____

(2) Neither of the girls are going to learn Chinese in the high school.

➡ _____

(3) Some of the islands are crowded with visitors while another are not.

➡ _____

(4) Sunny lost a lot of her dolls, so she needs to buy new one.

➡ _____

(5) Either of Mr. Brown's kids have to answer the question.

➡ _____

(6) Jason's organization will not use their material for another furniture.

➡ _____

06 다음 그림을 보고 괄호 안의 단어를 배열하여 빈칸을 알맞게 채우시오. (어법에 맞게 동사의 중복 사용 가능.)

(a honeybee, a ladybug, a spider, other, another, one, the, is)

➡ There are three insects on the spider web; _____

_____ .

07 주어진 우리말을 〈조건〉에 맞게 영작하시오.

┌─── 조건 ────
1. 'one 또는 ones'를 사용할 것.
2. 같은 품사들이 병렬구조가 되어 순서가 크게 상관없을 때에는 주어진 단어들이 제시된 순서대로 사용할 것.
3. 접속사는 언제나 문장 중간에 넣을 것.
4. 주어진 단어를 활용하되, 괄호 안의 글자 수 조건과 시제에 맞출 것. (동사 변형 가능)
└──────────

(1) 어떤 이들은 붉은 장미들을 좋아하고, 다른 이들은 흰 장미들을 좋아한다. (and, like, red, some, love, white, roses, 현재시제, 9 단어)

➡ _____

(2) Harry는 그의 컴퓨터를 팔고 새것을 하나 장만했다. (and, sell, new, Harry, his computer, purchase, a, 과거시제, 9 단어)

➡ _____

(3) 그들 중 하나가 뭔가 도움이 되는 것을 해야 한다. (have to, something, do, helpful, of, them, either, 현재시제, 9 단어)

➡ _____

Enjoy the "Planned Confusion"

Comparing the two pictures below, you can easily notice some
분사구문(= If/When you compare the two pictures below)
differences. For example, the picture on the left is called a labyrinth
수동태(~라고 불리다)
and only has an entrance. The picture on the right is called a maze and
is와 병렬 관계
has both an entrance and an exit.
both A and B: A와 B 둘 다

You can find the origin of the labyrinth in Greek mythology. It is said
to be a prison that you cannot escape. But you may notice that the
목적격 관계대명사(선행사: a prison)   명사절 접속사(notice의 목적어를 이끎)
labyrinth has only a single path. There are no dead ends. This means
뒤에 오는 명사에 수의 일치   means (that) ~
you don't have to worry about getting out of it when you enter it. If
~할 필요가 없다(= need not)   조건을 이끄는 부사절 접속사(현재시제로 미래시제를 대신함)
you follow the path all the way to the end, you will reach the center. To
get out, you simply have to turn around and walk back out the way you
to부정사의 부사적 용법 중 목적(~하기 위해서)
came in.

When you are in a maze, it's a different story. There are many choices
to make and dead ends to frustrate you. You have to keep making
to부정사의 형용사적 용법 (choices 수식)   to부정사의 형용사적 용법 (dead ends 수식)   keep Ving: 계속해서 V하다
decisions about which way to go. If you are not careful, you can easily
의문형용사+명사+to부정사(전치사의 목적어)
lose your way.

These days, mazes are often considered left-brain puzzles.
(= people often consider mazes left-brain puzzles.)

---

confusion: 혼란
notice: 알아차리다
labyrinth: 미궁
entrance: 입구
maze: 미로
exit: 출구
mythology: 신화
path: 통로, 길
dead end: 막다른 길
turn around: 돌아서다. 돌다
frustrate: 좌절시키다
make a decision: 결정하다
lose one's way: 길을 잃다

📎 확인문제

● 다음 문장이 본문의 내용과 일치하면 T, 일치하지 않으면 F를 쓰시오.

1 There are a few differences between a labyrinth and a maze. ☐

2 There is only one way to enter a labyrinth. ☐

3 Like a labyrinth, a maze also doesn't have dead ends. ☐

4 It is easy to lose your way in a maze unless you are careful. ☐

5 To get out of a labyrinth, you have to turn around and walk back out the way you
   came in. ☐

Many people willingly visit maze parks and enjoy the "planned confusion." And some of them came up with their own solutions.
미로 공원에 기꺼이 방문하는 사람들을 지칭

The easiest and most reliable one is to place a hand on one wall from
= solution   to부정사의 명사적 용법(보어)
the very beginning. Then you just keep following that wall. It's like
전치사(~와 같은)
walking in a dark room. Unfortunately, this simple method may not be
추측의 조동사
effective in certain types of mazes, especially when all of the walls are not connected.

Mazes are made with a variety of different materials, like walls and
be made with: ~으로 만들어지다
rooms, hedges, bricks, mirrors, and even snow. In fact, they can also be
= mazes
printed or drawn on paper. Here is one as an example. This is called a
정해지지 않은 것 하나를 가리킬 때 쓰는 대명사(종이에 인쇄되거나 그려질 수 있는 미로를 가리킴)
number maze. You start from point A and have to go in the order of 1
→ 9 → 8 → 5 → 1 → 9 → .... Why don't you give it a try? You have
Why don't you 동사원형 (제안하는 말)   give it a try: 시험 삼아 해보다
30 seconds to escape!

Labyrinths and mazes are truly fun, but that's not the end of the
story. Looking at them closely, you may find the beauty of order and
분사구문(= If/When you look at them closely)
regularity. They may also show you how creative human beings are.
labyrinths와 mazes 지칭   간접의문문(의문사+주어+동사)

If there is a maze park on your next trip, why don't you stop and take
some time to enjoy it? It will surely be worth visiting!
be worth Ving: V할 가치가 있다

come up with: ~을 생각해 내다
reliable: 믿을 만한
effective: 효과적인
a variety of: 다양한
hedge: 산울타리
in the order of: ~의 순서로
escape: 탈출하다, 벗어나다
regularity: 규칙성
worth: ~할 가치가 있는

📎 **확인문제**

● 다음 문장이 본문의 내용과 일치하면 T, 일치하지 않으면 F를 쓰시오.

1 Some people succeeded in finding their own solutions to get out of a maze. ☐

2 The simple method to escape a maze works on every type of maze. ☐

3 You can enjoy mazes on paper. ☐

4 The number maze has a regular pattern. ☐

5 Labyrinths and mazes doesn't have the beauty of order and regularity. ☐

6 The writer suggests visiting a maze park. ☐

● 우리말을 참고하여 빈칸에 알맞은 말을 쓰시오.

Enjoy the "Planned Confusion"

1 _____ the two pictures _____, you can easily _____ some _____.

2 _____ _____, the picture _____ _____ _____ is _____ a labyrinth and only _____ an entrance.

3 The picture _____ _____ _____ is _____ a maze and _____ _____ an entrance _____ an exit.

4 You can find _____ _____ _____ the labyrinth in Greek _____.

5 It _____ _____ _____ _____ a prison _____ you cannot escape.

6 But you may _____ _____ the labyrinth has only _____ _____ _____.

7 There are _____ _____ _____.

8 This means you _____ _____ _____ getting out of it when you _____ _____.

9 If you follow the path _____ _____ _____ _____ _____, you will reach the center.

10 _____ _____ _____, you simply _____ _____ _____ and walk back out the way you _____ _____.

11 When you are _____ a maze, it's a _____ story.

12 There are many choices _____ _____ and _____ to frustrate you.

13 You have to keep _____ decisions about _____ _____ _____ _____.

14 _____ you _____ _____ _____, you can easily _____ your way.

15 These days, mazes _____ often _____ _____ puzzles.

'계획된 혼란'을 즐겨라

1 아래 두 그림을 비교하면 몇 가지 차이를 쉽게 알아차릴 수 있습니다.

2 예를 들면, 왼쪽 그림은 미궁이라 불리고 입구만 있습니다.

3 오른쪽 그림은 미로라 불리며 입구와 출구가 둘 다 있습니다.

4 미궁의 기원은 그리스 신화에서 찾을 수 있습니다.

5 그것은 여러분이 빠져나올 수 없는 감옥으로 알려져 있습니다.

6 하지만 여러분이 알아차릴 수 있듯, 미궁은 통로가 하나입니다.

7 막다른 길이 없습니다.

8 이것은 여러분이 거기에 들어갈 때 빠져나올 것을 걱정하지 않아도 된다는 것을 의미합니다.

9 통로를 따라 끝까지 가면, 여러분은 미궁의 중앙에 도착할 것입니다.

10 빠져나오기 위해서는, 여러분은 단지 돌아서 들어간 길대로 걸어 나오면 됩니다.

11 미로 안에 있을 때에는 완전히 상황이 다릅니다.

12 결정할 많은 선택지가 있고 여러분을 좌절하게 만들 막다른 길들이 있습니다.

13 어느 길로 갈지 계속 선택을 해야만 합니다.

14 조심하지 않으면 길을 잃기 쉽습니다.

15 오늘날, 미로는 흔히 좌뇌형 퍼즐로 간주됩니다.

16 Many people _____ _____ maze parks and _____ the "_____ _____."

17 And some of _____ _____ _____ _____ their own solutions.

18 The easiest and _____ _____ _____ is _____ place a hand _____ one wall from _____ _____ _____.

19 Then you just keep _____ _____ _____.

20 It's _____ _____ in a dark room.

21 _____, this simple method may not be _____ in _____ _____ of mazes, especially when all of the walls _____ _____ _____.

22 Mazes _____ _____ _____ a variety of _____ _____, like walls and rooms, _____, bricks, mirrors, _____ even snow.

23 _____ _____, they can also _____ _____ or _____ on paper.

24 _____ _____ one as an example. This is _____ a number maze.

25 You start _____ point A and have to go _____ _____ _____ of $1 \rightarrow 9 \rightarrow 8 \rightarrow 5 \rightarrow 1 \rightarrow 9 \rightarrow \ldots$.

26 Why don't you _____ _____ _____ _____? You have 30 seconds _____ _____!

27 Labyrinths and mazes _____ truly _____, but that's not _____ _____ of the story.

28 _____ _____ _____ closely, you may find the beauty of _____ and _____.

29 They may also show you _____ _____ _____ _____ _____.

30 If _____ _____ a maze park on your next trip, why don't you _____ and _____ _____ _____ to enjoy it?

31 It will surely _____ _____ _____!

16 많은 사람들이 미로 공원에 기꺼이 방문하여 '계획된 혼란'을 즐깁니다.

17 그리고 그들 중 몇몇은 자기들만의 해결 방법을 찾아냈습니다.

18 가장 쉽고 믿을 만한 해결 방법은 시작 지점부터 한쪽 벽에 손을 대는 것입니다.

19 그러고는 여러분은 단지 그 벽을 계속 따라가면 됩니다.

20 이것은 마치 어두운 방을 걷는 것과 같습니다.

21 불행하게도, 이 간단한 방법은 어떤 종류의 미로에서는 특히 모든 벽이 이어져 있지는 않은 경우 효과가 없을지도 모릅니다.

22 미로는 벽과 방, 울타리, 벽돌, 거울, 심지어는 눈 등 많은 다양한 재료로 제작됩니다.

23 사실, 미로는 종이에 인쇄되거나 그려질 수도 있습니다.

24 여기 그 예가 하나 있습니다. 이것은 숫자 미로라고 불립니다.

25 여러분은 A 지점에서 출발하여 1. 9. 8. 5. 1. 9 …의 순서로 이동해야 합니다.

26 한번 시도해 보시죠? 빠져나가는 데 30초가 주어집니다!

27 미궁과 미로는 정말 재미있지만, 그것이 전부가 아닙니다.

28 자세히 들여다보면, 여러분은 질서와 규칙성이라는 아름다움을 발견할 수 있을지도 모릅니다.

29 그것들은 또한 인간이 얼마나 창조적인가를 보여줄지도 모릅니다.

30 다음 여행에 미로 공원이 있으면, 들러서 즐겨보는 것은 어떨까요?

31 분명히 들를 가치가 있을 것입니다!

● 우리말을 참고하여 본문을 영작하시오.

Enjoy the "Planned Confusion"

1 아래 두 그림을 비교하면 몇 가지 차이를 쉽게 알아차릴 수 있습니다.

➡ _____

2 예를 들면, 왼쪽 그림은 미궁이라 불리고 입구만 있습니다.

➡ _____

3 오른쪽 그림은 미로라 불리며 입구와 출구가 둘 다 있습니다.

➡ _____

4 미궁의 기원은 그리스 신화에서 찾을 수 있습니다.

➡ _____

5 그것은 여러분이 빠져나올 수 없는 감옥으로 알려져 있습니다.

➡ _____

6 하지만 여러분이 알아차릴 수 있듯, 미궁은 통로가 하나입니다.

➡ _____

7 막다른 길이 없습니다.

➡ _____

8 이것은 여러분이 거기에 들어갈 때 빠져나올 것을 걱정하지 않아도 된다는 것을 의미합니다.

➡ _____

9 통로를 따라 끝까지 가면, 여러분은 미궁의 중앙에 도착할 것입니다.

➡ _____

10 빠져나오기 위해서는, 여러분은 단지 돌아서 들어간 길대로 걸어 나오면 됩니다.

➡ _____

11 미로 안에 있을 때에는 완전히 상황이 다릅니다.

➡ _____

12 결정할 많은 선택지가 있고 여러분을 좌절하게 만들 막다른 길들이 있습니다.

➡ _____

13 어느 길로 갈지 계속 선택을 해야만 합니다.

➡ _____

14 조심하지 않으면 길을 잃기 쉽습니다.

➡ _____

15 오늘날, 미로는 흔히 좌뇌형 퍼즐로 간주됩니다.

➡ _____

16 많은 사람들이 미로 공원에 기꺼이 방문하여 '계획된 혼란'을 즐깁니다.

➡ _____

17 그리고 그들 중 몇몇은 자기들만의 해결 방법을 찾아냈습니다.

➡ _____

18 가장 쉽고 믿을 만한 해결 방법은 시작 지점부터 한쪽 벽에 손을 대는 것입니다.

➡ _____

19 그러고는 여러분은 단지 그 벽을 계속 따라가면 됩니다.

➡ _____

20 이것은 마치 어두운 방을 걷는 것과 같습니다.

➡ _____

21 불행하게도, 이 간단한 방법은 어떤 종류의 미로에서는 특히 모든 벽이 이어져 있지는 않은 경우 효과가 없을지도 모릅니다.

➡ _____

➡ _____

22 미로는 벽과 방, 울타리, 벽돌, 거울, 심지어는 눈 등 많은 다양한 재료로 제작됩니다.

➡ _____

➡ _____

23 사실, 미로는 종이에 인쇄되거나 그려질 수도 있습니다.

➡ _____

24 여기 그 예가 하나 있습니다. 이것은 숫자 미로라고 불립니다.

➡ _____

25 여러분은 A 지점에서 출발하여 1, 9, 8, 5, 1, 9 …의 순서로 이동해야 합니다.

➡ _____

26 한번 시도해 보시죠? 빠져나가는 데 30초가 주어집니다!

➡ _____

27 미궁과 미로는 정말 재미있지만, 그것이 전부가 아닙니다.

➡ _____

28 자세히 들여다보면, 여러분은 질서와 규칙성이라는 아름다움을 발견할 수 있을지도 모릅니다.

➡ _____

29 그것들은 또한 인간이 얼마나 창조적인가를 보여줄지도 모릅니다.

➡ _____

30 다음 여행에 미로 공원이 있으면, 들러서 즐겨보는 것은 어떨까요?

➡ _____

31 분명히 들를 가치가 있을 것입니다!

➡ _____

[01~04] 다음 글을 읽고 물음에 답하시오.

(A)_____ the two pictures below, you can easily notice some differences. For example, the picture on the left is called a labyrinth and only has an entrance. The picture on the right is called a maze and has both an entrance and an exit.

You can find the origin of the labyrinth in Greek mythology. It is said to be a prison that you cannot escape. But you may notice that the labyrinth has only a single path. There are no dead ends. This means you don't have to worry about getting out of it when you enter it. If you follow the path all the way to the end, you will reach the center. To get out, you simply have to turn around and walk back out (B)_____.

서답형
01 주어진 단어를 어법에 맞게 빈칸 (A)에 쓰시오.

compare

➡ _____

중요
02 다음 중 빈칸 (B)에 들어갈 말로 가장 적절한 것은?

① where you come from
② to the hall a guide leads you to
③ where many people are crowded
④ the way you came in
⑤ following other people

서답형
03 다음과 같이 풀이되는 말을 위 글에서 찾아 쓰시오.

to become aware of somebody or something

➡ _____

중요
04 다음 중 위 글의 내용과 일치하는 것은?

① A labyrinth is the same as a maze.
② There are an entrance and an exit in a labyrinth.
③ A labyrinth is a prison in Greek mythology.
④ A labyrinth has some dead ends.
⑤ A labyrinth has many paths.

[05~09] 다음 글을 읽고 물음에 답하시오.

When you are in a maze, it's a different story. There are many choices to make and dead ends to frustrate you. You have to keep making decisions about which way to go. If you are not careful, you can easily lose your way.

(A)These days, mazes are often considered left-brain puzzles. ① Many people willingly visit maze parks and enjoy (B)the "planned confusion." ② And some of them came up with their own solutions. ③ The easiest and most reliable one is to place a hand on one wall from the very beginning. ④ It's like walking in a dark room. ⑤ Unfortunately, this simple method may not be effective in certain types of mazes, especially when all of the walls are not connected.

중요
05 ①~⑤ 중 주어진 문장이 들어가기에 가장 적절한 곳은?

Then you just keep following that wall.

①   ②   ③   ④   ⑤

06 다음 중 밑줄 친 (A)를 대신하여 쓸 수 있는 것은?

① For a long time   ② Rarely
③ Nowadays   ④ At last
⑤ All of a sudden

07 다음 중 (B)와 같이 표현한 이유로 가장 적절한 것은?

① Because people like to plan mazes.

② Because mazes confuse people without any plans.

③ Because mazes are planned to be solved easily.

④ Because nobody wants to be confused by some plans.

⑤ Because mazes are deliberately planned to confuse people.

서답형

08 According to the passage, what makes us frustrated? Answer in English with six words.

➡ _____

서답형

09 다음은 미로에 들어가기 전 친구에게 한 말이다. 위 글의 내용에 맞게 빈칸에 알맞은 말을 쓰시오.

_____ _____, or you will lose your way.

[10~13] 다음 글을 읽고 물음에 답하시오.

Mazes are made with a variety of different materials, like walls and rooms, hedges, bricks, mirrors, and even snow. In fact, they can also be printed or drawn on paper. Here is one as an example. This is called a number maze. You start from point A and have to go in the order of 1 → 9 → 8 → 5 → 1 → 9 → .... (A)Why don't you give it a try? You have 30 seconds to escape!

Labyrinths and mazes are truly fun, but that's not the end of the story. Looking at them closely, you may find the beauty of order and regularity. They may also show you how creative human beings are.

If there is a maze park on your next trip, why don't you stop and take some time to enjoy it? It will surely be worth visiting!

중요

10 다음 중 밑줄 친 (A)의 의미로 가장 적절한 것은?

① Why do you want to solve this maze?

② Do not try to solve the maze.

③ Why don't you try harder?

④ How about solving the maze?

⑤ Let's make some time to try harder.

11 다음 중 위 글을 읽고 답할 수 있는 것은?

① Why do people enjoy mazes?

② What can be used to make mazes?

③ How many paths are there in a maze?

④ Who invented a maze first in the world?

⑤ How many mirror mazes are there in the world?

서답형

12 글의 내용에 맞게 빈칸에 알맞은 말을 쓰시오.

Q: What is presented as an example of a printed maze?

A: _____ _____ _____ _____ _____ as an example of a printed maze.

서답형

13 How much time is given to solve the number maze? Answer in English with a full sentence.

➡ _____

[14~18] 다음 글을 읽고 물음에 답하시오.

ⓐ[Comparing / Compared] the two pictures below, you can easily notice some differences. (A)_____, the picture on the left is called a labyrinth and only has an entrance. The picture on the right is called a maze and ⓑ[has / have] both an entrance and an exit.

You can find the origin of the labyrinth in Greek mythology. It is said to be a prison that you cannot escape. But you may notice that the labyrinth has only a single path. There are no (B)dead ends. This means you don't have to worry about getting out of it when you ⓒ [enter / enter into] it. If you follow the path all the way to the end, you will reach the center. To get out, you simply have to turn around and walk back out the way you came in.

14 다음 중 빈칸 (A)에 들어갈 말로 가장 적절한 것은?

① In other words ② For example
③ On the contrary ④ However
⑤ Therefore

15 위 글의 내용에 맞게 빈칸에 알맞은 말을 쓰시오.

> Unlike _____, a maze has not only _____ but also _____.

16 다음 중 밑줄 친 (B)의 의미로 가장 적절한 것은?

① a path which is not used any more
② an end that people pursue
③ a passage where many people die
④ an other end that people usually use
⑤ a road that is closed at one end

17 ⓐ~ⓒ 중 어법상 옳은 것끼리 바르게 짝지은 것은?

① Comparing – has – enter
② Compared – has – enter
③ Comparing – has – enter into
④ Compared – have – enter into
⑤ Comparing – have – enter into

18 다음 중 위 글을 읽고 답할 수 있는 것은?

① Where can we find the origin of a maze?
② Who made a labyrinth in the mythology?
③ How many paths does a labyrinth have?
④ How can we get out of a maze easily?
⑤ What is the similarity between a maze and a labyrinth?

[19~21] 다음 글을 읽고 물음에 답하시오.

When you are in a maze, it's a different story. There are many choices to make and dead ends to frustrate you. You have to keep making decisions about which way to go. If you are not careful, you can easily lose your way.

(A) And some of them came up with their own solutions. The easiest and most reliable one is to place a hand on one wall from the very beginning. Then you just keep following that wall.

(B) These days, mazes are often considered left-brain puzzles. Many people willingly visit maze parks and enjoy the "planned confusion."

(C) It's like walking in a dark room. Unfortunately, this simple method may not be effective in certain types of mazes, especially when all of the walls are not connected.

19 자연스러운 글이 되도록 (A)~(C)를 바르게 나열한 것은?

① (A)–(C)–(B)   ② (B)–(A)–(C)
③ (B)–(C)–(A)   ④ (C)–(A)–(B)
⑤ (C)–(B)–(A)

20 다음 중 maze를 제대로 이해한 학생은?

① Andrew: I think a maze is so easy because there is only one choice to make.
② Brian: There is no need to make decisions in a maze.
③ Cindy: I think I use my right brain a lot when I enjoy a maze.
④ Dennis: Whenever I am in a maze, I am so discouraged because of many dead ends.
⑤ Erica: It's okay not to concentrate in a maze because it's easy to find my way.

서답형
21 위 글의 내용에 맞게 빈칸에 알맞은 말을 쓰시오.

> Placing a hand on one wall and following the wall is effective if ＿＿＿＿＿＿＿＿＿ ＿＿＿＿＿＿＿＿.

[22~24] 다음 글을 읽고 물음에 답하시오.

Mazes are made with a variety of different materials, like walls and rooms, hedges, bricks, mirrors, and even snow. In fact, they can also be printed or drawn on paper. Here is one as an example. This is called a number maze. You start (A)＿＿＿＿ point A and have to go in the order of 1 → 9 → 8 → 5 → 1 → 9 → …. Why don't you give it a try? You have 30 seconds to escape!

Labyrinths and mazes are truly fun, but that's not the end of the story. Looking at (B)them closely, you may find the beauty of order and regularity. They may also show you how creative human beings are.

If there is a maze park on your next trip, why don't you stop and take some time to enjoy it? It will surely be worth visiting!

22 다음 중 빈칸 (A)에 들어가는 말과 같은 말이 들어가는 것은?

① These cups are filled ＿＿＿＿ milk and orange juice.
② Can you please pay attention ＿＿＿＿ my speech?
③ When did you graduate ＿＿＿＿ university?
④ They turned ＿＿＿＿ my proposal, so I'm depressed.
⑤ The grocery store is crowded ＿＿＿＿ many people.

서답형
23 밑줄 친 (B)가 지칭하는 것을 위 글에서 찾아 쓰시오.

➡ ＿＿＿＿＿＿＿＿＿＿＿＿＿＿＿＿

24 Which one is true about the passage?

① It is impossible to draw mazes on paper.
② There are few materials to make mazes.
③ The writer gives half an hour to solve the number maze.
④ We can find that the labyrinths and mazes are disorganized.
⑤ The writer thinks a maze park will be worthwhile to visit.

[01~02] 다음 글을 읽고 물음에 답하시오.

(A)If you compare the two pictures below, you can easily notice some differences. For example, the picture on the left is called a labyrinth and only has an entrance. The picture on the right is called a maze and has both an entrance and an exit.

01 밑줄 친 (A)를 대신할 수 있는 말을 쓰시오.

➡ _____

02 What do people call the thing which has only one entrance? Answer in English.

➡ _____

[03~07] 다음 글을 읽고 물음에 답하시오.

You can find the origin of the labyrinth in Greek mythology. It is said to be a prison that you cannot escape. But you may notice that the labyrinth has only a single path. There are no dead ends. This means you don't have to worry about getting out of it when you enter it. If you follow the path all the way to the end, you will reach the center. To get out, you simply have to turn around and walk back out the way you came in.

When you are in a maze, it's a different story. There are many choices to make and dead ends to frustrate you. You have to keep making decisions about which way to go. If you are not careful, you can easily lose your way.

03 Where can we find the origin of the labyrinth? Answer in English.

➡ _____
_____

04 What does it mean that the labyrinth has a single path without any dead ends? Answer in English with a full sentence.

➡ _____
_____

05 위 글의 내용에 맞게 빈칸에 알맞은 말을 쓰시오.

The labyrinth is _____ in Greek mythology, which is impossible _____. But actually it is easy to get out of it because it has only _____.

06 What can we find if we follow the path all the way to the end in a labyrinth? Answer in English with five words.

➡ _____

07 How is a maze different from a labyrinth? Fill the blank with appropriate words.

A maze is different from a labyrinth in that it has _____ and _____.

[08~11] 다음 글을 읽고 물음에 답하시오.

These days, (A)미로는 종종 좌뇌형 퍼즐로 간주됩니다. Many people willingly visit maze parks and enjoy the "planned confusion." And some of them came up with their own solutions. The easiest and most reliable (B) one is to place a hand on one wall from the very beginning. Then you just keep following that wall. It's like walking in a dark room. Unfortunately, this simple method may not be effective in certain types of mazes, especially when all of the walls are not connected.

08 주어진 단어를 활용하여 밑줄 친 우리말 (A)를 영어로 쓰시오.

consider / often / left-brain puzzles

➡ _____

09 밑줄 친 (B)가 의미하는 것을 위 글에서 찾아 쓰시오.

➡ _____

10 According to the passage, what is the easiest and most reliable way to get out of a maze? Answer in English.

➡ _____
_____
_____

11 다음과 같이 풀이되는 말을 위 글에서 찾아 쓰시오.

worthy of trust; worthy of being depended on

➡ _____

[12~14] 다음 글을 읽고 물음에 답하시오.

Mazes are made with a variety of different materials, like walls and rooms, hedges, bricks, mirrors, and even snow. In fact, they can also be printed or drawn on paper. Here is one as an example. This is called a number maze. You start from point A and have to go in the order of 1 → 9 → 8 → 5 → 1 → 9 → .... Why don't you give it a try? You have 30 seconds to escape!

Labyrinths and mazes are truly fun, but that's not the end of the story. Looking at them closely, you may find the beauty of order and regularity. They may also show you how creative human beings are.

If there is a maze park on your next trip, why don't you stop and take some time to enjoy it? (A)그곳은 분명히 들를 가치가 있을 것이다!

12 주어진 단어를 바르게 나열하여 밑줄 친 우리말 (A)를 영어로 쓰시오. 필요하다면 어형을 바꾸시오.

(visit / be / surely / it / worth / will)!

➡ _____

13 What materials are used to make mazes? Answer in English with a full sentence.

➡ _____
_____
_____

14 If there is a maze park on your next trip, what does the writer suggest doing?

➡ _____
_____

Real Life Communication – C Communication Task

A: Let me ask you the first question. How do you get there?

B: I can go there by train.
<small>교통수단 앞에 전치사 by를 쓴다.</small>

A: Then how long does it take to get there?

B: It takes about 2 hours to get there.

A: Is it possible to get there by airplane?
<small>=Is it likely to = Is it probably to</small>
⋮

A: Oh, the answer is Gyeongju. Right?

After You Read

Today, I went to the nearby maze park with my friends. The maze looked hard

to solve. There were many choices, and I had to keep making decisions about
<small>to부정사의 부사적 용법: 형용사 수식</small>   <small>keep+Ving: 계속 V하다</small>

which way to go. My friends said that I should just place my hand on one
<small>의문형용사+명사+to부정사</small>   <small>명사절 접속사</small>

wall from the beginning and keep following the same wall. That solution was
<small>동사 place와 병렬 관계</small>

simple but not very effective. I enjoyed myself very much at the park. Also, I
<small>재귀대명사(주어와 목적어가 같을 때 사용)</small>

found the beauty of order and regularity there and thought that human beings

are really creative.

구문해설 · nearby: 근처의 · place: ～을 두다 · effective: 효과적인 · order: 질서 · regularity: 규칙성

Let's Write

I took a short survey about our class's preference between mountains and oceans.
<small>take a survey = survey</small>   <small>between A and B: A와 B 사이에</small>

Looking at the results, it is clear that our class prefers mountains to oceans. You
<small>비인칭 독립분사구문(If we look ～) 가주어</small>   <small>접속사</small>   <small>prefer A to B</small>

may wonder why our class prefers mountains. Regarding the reasons why they
<small>의문부사(명사절)</small>   <small>분사전치사(= Concerning)</small>   <small>관계부사(형용사절)</small>

like mountains more, I found key words like "more beautiful", "more exciting",
<small>부사</small>   <small>전치사</small>

and "lovelier."

구문해설 · survey: (설문) 조사 · preference: 선호도 · prefer: 선호하다 · regarding: ～에 관해서는

영역별 핵심문제

01 다음 짝지어진 단어의 관계가 같도록 빈칸에 알맞은 말을 쓰시오.

> reasonable : _____ = reliable : unreliable

02 다음 영영풀이가 가리키는 것을 고르시오.

> ancient myths in general; the ancient myths of a particular culture, society, etc.

① maze　　② origin　　③ regularity
④ worth　　⑤ mythology

03 다음 주어진 문장의 밑줄 친 mean과 다른 의미로 쓰인 것은?

> What does this sentence mean?

① The red light means that you must stop.
② Do you understand what I mean?
③ Her children mean the world to her.
④ You mean we have to start all over again?
⑤ Don't be mean over money.

04 다음 중 밑줄 친 부분의 뜻풀이가 바르지 않은 것은?

① It's not actually raining now. (사실상)
② Can you suggest a good dictionary? (추천하다)
③ Jane is a reliable friend. (믿을 만한)
④ I'll meet you at the main entrance. (출구)
⑤ You may notice that the labyrinth has only a single path. (미궁)

05 다음 문장의 빈칸에 들어갈 말을 〈보기〉에서 골라 쓰시오.

> ┌ 보기 ┐
> frustrate / prison / worth / exit / reliable

(1) Oh, there's the _____! We can escape the maze.
(2) There are many choices to make and dead ends to _____ you.
(3) It is said to be a _____ that you cannot escape.
(4) It's more _____ than the bus.
(5) It will surely be _____ visiting!

06 다음 우리말에 맞게 주어진 단어를 사용하여 영작하시오.

(1) 미로를 통과했을 때, 나는 늑대 한 마리를 만났다. (when, wolf, through)
➡ _____

(2) 그들의 음식은 훌륭하고 가격이 적당하다. (good, prices)
➡ _____

[07~08] 다음 대화를 읽고 물음에 답하시오.

W: How may I help you?
B: Hi! I bought these shoes yesterday. Is it possible to exchange them __(A)__ the red shoes?
W: Oh, actually white is really popular these days.
B: I know, and that's why I spent a long time making the decision yesterday. But I think that red will look better __(B)__ me.
W: Okay, no problem.

07 위 대화의 빈칸 (A)와 (B)에 들어갈 말로 알맞게 짝지어진 것은?

① to – for
② to – with
③ for – on
④ at – from
⑤ for – with

08 위 대화를 읽고 대답할 수 없는 것은?

① What color shoes did the boy buy?
② When did the boy buy the shoes?
③ What color is popular these days?
④ How much did the boy pay for the shoes?
⑤ Why isn't the boy satisfied with the white shoes?

[09~11] 다음 대화를 읽고 물음에 답하시오.

Gina: Mom, did you decide where to visit ⓐ during our family trip to Jeju?
Mom: Almost. Come here and see the plan I made.
Gina: It looks ⓑgood. Hmm... Mom, is it possible to visit Mirror Maze Park on our second day?
Mom: It sounds ⓒexciting, but I remember you said you wanted to go horseback riding.
Gina: I know, but I heard the park is a lot more fun. Please ….
Mom: All right. Let's change our schedule for the second day.
Gina: Thank you! I'm very ⓓexciting about the trip.
Mom: It's great to hear that you're looking ⓔforward to the trip.

09 위 대화의 밑줄 친 ⓐ~ⓔ 중 어법상 틀린 것을 찾아 바르게 고치시오.

➡ _____

10 위 대화에서 다음 영영풀이가 나타내는 말을 찾아 쓰시오.

a system of paths separated by walls or hedges built in a park or garden that is designed so that it is difficult to find your way through

➡ _____

11 위 대화의 내용과 일치하지 않는 것은?

① 엄마는 제주도 여행 계획을 세웠다.
② 지나는 둘째 날 거울 미로 공원 방문이 가능할지 물었다.
③ 지나는 말을 타러 가고 싶다고 엄마에게 이야기 했었다.
④ 엄마는 둘째 날 계획을 변경하였다.
⑤ 지나는 둘째 날 거울 미로 공원과 말을 타는 것을 모두 할 것이다.

12 다음 짝지어진 대화가 어색한 것을 고르시오.

① A: Is it possible to survive under the sea?
   B: Why not? All I need is a swimming mask.
② A: How do I get to the city hall?
   B: Go straight for two blocks and turn left. You can see it on your right.
③ A: Could you tell me the way to the post office?
   B: Okay! That's a great idea!
④ A: How do you get to school from your place?
   B: From my place, walk two blocks and turn right. It takes about 10 minutes.
⑤ A: How do we get to the city museum?
   B: How about taking the subway? I think it will be convenient.

[13~14] 다음 문장의 밑줄 친 부사절을 분사구문으로 바르게 바꾼 것은?

13

> If there comes a time when we can't be <u>together</u>, keep me in your heart. I'll stay there forever.

① Coming a time when we can't be together,

② We coming a time when we can't be together

③ If there coming a time when we can't be together,

④ There coming a time when we can't be together,

⑤ A time coming there when we can't be together,

14

> <u>Though Ms. Kim meets a lot of people these days,</u> she feels more lonely than before.

① Meeting a lot of people these days,

② Ms. Kim meeting a lot of people these days,

③ Ms. Kim met a lot of people these days,

④ Though Ms. Kim meeting a lot of people these days,

⑤ Meeting Ms. Kim a lot of people these days,

15 다음 중 어법상 어색한 문장을 모두 고르시오.

① Mom bought some cookies on her way home.

② Every athletes practices so hard to win a gold medal.

③ All the runners have to spend many hours at the track.

④ Tracy wondered if she could receive another when she dropped her spoon.

⑤ Dave has five big luxury cars, but I have only two small one.

16 다음 문장의 밑줄 친 부사절을 분사구문으로 알맞게 바꾼 것을 고르시오.

> <u>As she didn't get enough scores to enter the college,</u> Suji decided to study once more.

① As she getting not enough scores to enter the college,

② There not getting enough scores to enter the college,

③ Getting not enough scores to enter the college,

④ As getting not enough scores to enter the college,

⑤ Not getting enough scores to enter the college,

17 다음 괄호 안에서 어법상 알맞은 것을 고르시오.

(1) Either of the engineers (is / are) going to record the song today.

(2) Both of the dance teams (is / are) performing one of their best skills.

(3) (Every / Each) of the college students should complete their assignment by Friday next week.

(4) Neither of the two boys (like / likes) the soup made by Olga.

(5) This plate is dirty. Is there anyone to bring me (other / another)?

(6) Some of my apple (is / are) going to be cut for the chemical experiment.

(7) Julie can play two instruments, (neither / both) of which is a stringed one.

18 다음 밑줄 친 부분 중 어법상 어색한 것을 고르시오.

① Being tired, Chris lay down on the bed and took a rest.

② Strictly speaking, the prime minster of Japan can't make right decisions.

③ Raining all day, my friends and I stayed at home, watching movies.

④ Finding the necklace she had lost, I called Suji to come to my place.

⑤ Not having enough money, Ted couldn't buy the present for his daughter.

Reading

[19~22] 다음 글을 읽고 물음에 답하시오.

Comparing the two pictures below, you can easily notice some differences. For example, the picture on the left is called a labyrinth and only has an entrance. The picture on the right is called a maze and has both an entrance and an exit.

You can find the origin of the labyrinth in Greek mythology. It is said to be a prison that you cannot escape. But you may notice that the labyrinth has only a single path. There are no dead ends. This means you don't have to worry about getting out of it when you enter it. If you follow the path all the way to the end, you will reach the center. (A)_____, you simply have to turn around and walk back out the way you came in.

When you are in a maze, it's a different story. There are many choices (B)to make and dead ends to frustrate you. You have to keep making decisions about which way to go. If you are not careful, you can easily lose your way.

19 다음 중 빈칸 (A)에 들어갈 말로 가장 적절한 것은?

① To make out

② To find the center

③ To get out

④ To notice where you are

⑤ To know where the center is

20 다음 중 위 글을 읽고 답할 수 있는 것은?

① How many people can use a maze?

② When was the labyrinth made in Greek mythology?

③ Why does the maze have both an entrance and an exit?

④ Why does a maze make us frustrated?

⑤ What is the easy way to get out of a maze?

21 다음과 같이 풀이되는 말을 위 글에서 찾아 쓰시오.

> a road, passage, etc. that is closed at one end

➡ _____

22 다음 중 밑줄 친 (B)와 쓰임이 같은 것은?

① He went out to get some fresh air.
② June had the chance to apologize.
③ It is my job to please her.
④ She came in to find her book.
⑤ I was sad to see the news about virus.

[23~25] 다음 글을 읽고 물음에 답하시오.

Today, I went to the nearby maze park with my friends. ① The maze looked hard to solve. ② There were many choices, and I had to keep making decisions about which way to go. ③ My friends said that I should just place my hand on one wall from the beginning and keep following the same wall. ④ I enjoyed myself very much at the park. ⑤ Also, I found the beauty of order and regularity there and thought that human beings are really creative.

23 다음 중 위 글의 내용과 일치하는 것은?

① The writer went to the maze park alone.
② The maze wasn't difficult to solve.
③ The writer couldn't get out of the maze.
④ The maze made the writer ignorant of the creativeness of human beings.
⑤ The writer had the pleasure of experiencing the maze.

24 ①~⑤ 중 주어진 문장이 들어가기에 가장 적절한 곳은?

> That solution was simple but not very effective.

①　　　②　　　③　　　④　　　⑤

25 How did the maze look to the writer? Answer in English with a full sentence.

➡ _____

[26~27] 다음 글을 읽고 물음에 답하시오.

USA – Pineapple Garden Maze
If you visit Oahu, Hawaii, the Pineapple Garden Maze is a must see. It is the world's longest maze, and it attracts visitors from around the world. The maze has 11,400 native plants and covers about 5 kilometers.
England – Hampton Court Maze
The oldest hedge maze in Britain is the Hampton Court Maze. It was built in 1689. Hundreds of thousands of people visit this maze that was created during the time of William of Orange.

26 다음 중 위 글의 제목으로 가장 적절한 것은?

① Maze: an Infamous Prison
② World's Well Known Attractions
③ Famous Mazes Around the World
④ Things You Never Know about Mazes
⑤ The Origin of Mazes

27 How long is the Pineapple Garden Maze? Answer in English.

➡ _____

출제율 90%

01 다음 영영풀이가 가리키는 것을 〈보기〉에서 고르시오.

(1) to give things of a particular kind to each other at the same time

(2) to make somebody feel annoyed or impatient because they cannot do or achieve what they want

┌─── 보기 ───┐
confuse, frustrate, exit, exchange
└───────────┘

➡ (1) _____, (2) _____

출제율 95%

02 다음 우리말과 일치하도록 주어진 어구를 배열하여 완성하시오.

(1) 그는 오늘 아침 감옥에서 탈출했다.
(this / he / from / morning / the / escaped / prison)

➡ _____

(2) 그들은 그 문제를 해결하기 위해 효과적인 방법들을 생각해 내려고 노력했다.
(come / ways / the problem / with / they / up / tried to / effective / to solve)

➡ _____
_____

(3) 화성에서 생존하는 것이 가능한가?
(it / on / is / to / Mars / possible / survive)

➡ _____

(4) 그 3층으로 된 건물은 어린이를 위한 만 여권의 책을 보유하고 있다.
(three-story / building / kids / books / has / the / 10,000 / about / for)

➡ _____
_____

[03~05] 다음 대화를 읽고 물음에 답하시오.

W: How may I help you?
B: Hi! I ⓐbought these shoes yesterday. Is it possible ⓑto exchange them for the red shoes?
W: Oh, actually white is really popular ⓒthese days.
B: I know, and that's why I spent a long time ⓓmake the decision yesterday. But I think ⓔthat red will look better on me.
W: Okay, no problem.

출제율 90%

03 위 대화의 밑줄 친 ⓐ~ⓔ 중 어법상 어색한 것을 골라 바르게 고치시오.

➡ _____

출제율 100%

04 위 대화의 여자와 남자의 관계로 적절한 것은?

① clerk – customer
② teacher – student
③ doctor – nurse
④ tourist – guide
⑤ post officer – visitor

출제율 100%

05 위 대화의 내용과 일치하지 <u>않는</u> 것은?

① The boy bought the shoes yesterday.
② The boy wants to exchange the shoes for the red ones.
③ The white shoes are really popular these days.
④ It took a long time for the boy to make the decision about the color.
⑤ The woman suggested the red shoes because they looked better on him.

[06~07] 다음 대화를 읽고 물음에 답하시오.

Andrew: Hey, Minju, where are you?

Minju: Oh, Andrew, I'm coming. I'm coming.

Andrew: Good. I was worried that you were lost.

Minju: I think I'm okay. What about Mason and Jian?

Andrew: They are already here at my house.

Minju: Good! Oh, I see the post office. (A)여기서부터 너희 집까지 어떻게 가니?

Andrew: You are almost here. Go straight for one more block. Then you will see Kim's Bakery.

Minju: Kim's Bakery? Okay ....

Andrew: Then turn right and go straight for about 100 meters.

Minju: Turn right and go straight .... Okay, thanks! I'll see you soon.

✏️ 출제율 90%

06 밑줄 친 (A)의 우리말을 〈보기〉에 주어진 단어들을 배열하여 영작하시오.

┌─ 보기 ┤
place / here / how / to / from / I / do / get / your
└───────

➡ _____

✏️ 출제율 100%

07 위 대화의 내용과 일치하지 <u>않는</u> 것은?

① 민주는 Andrew네 집에 가고 있다.

② Andrew는 민주가 길을 잃었을까봐 걱정했다.

③ Mason과 지나는 이미 Andrew네 집에 도착했다.

④ 민주는 우체국에서 한 블록 더 직진하면 킴스 빵집이 보일 것이다.

⑤ 민주는 킴스 빵집에서 왼쪽으로 돌아 100미터 정도 직진하면 Andrew네 집을 찾을 수 있다.

[08~10] 다음 대화를 읽고 물음에 답하시오.

Mina: (A)너희 모두 이번 주말에 여행갈 준비됐니? (set, all, for, are)

Jinho, Claire, & Henry: Yes!

Mina: Good! Don't be late! We're meeting at 11 a.m. in front of the clock tower.

Jinho: You got it! How do we get to the airport? I don't think we've decided yet.

Henry: Jinho is right. We have two choices, bus or subway.

Claire: What about the subway? It's more reliable than the bus.

Henry: Is it possible to get to Terminal 2 by subway?

Claire: Yes, I already checked.

Mina: Good. Okay, then let's take the subway.

✏️ 출제율 90%

08 위 대화의 밑줄 친 (A)의 우리말을 주어진 단어들을 사용하여 영작하시오.

➡ _____

✏️ 출제율 95%

09 When and where are Mina, Jiho, Claire and Henry going to meet?

➡ _____

✏️ 출제율 95%

10 How will Mina, Jiho, Claire and Henry get to Terminal 2?

➡ _____

✏️ 출제율 90%

11 다음 중 빈칸에 들어갈 알맞은 말을 고르시오.

> Would you like to have _____ chocolate cookies and hot tea?

① some ② another ③ one
④ that ⑤ others

✏️ 출제율 100%

12 다음 중 어법상 올바른 문장을 모두 고르면?

① The director winning the big awards, her fans in France felt proud of her.
② Writing too quickly, the letter had many mistakes.
③ Worked hard to review the final experiment, Sean was not able to sleep.
④ There being no pickup service, we had to walk all the way to the hotel.
⑤ Being looked a lot more elegant than before, the flowers are in bloom.

✏️ 출제율 90%

13 다음 각 문장의 부사절을 알맞은 분사구문으로 전환하여, 빈칸을 채우시오.

(1) When I went to the nearby maze park with my parents, I found the maze there looked too hard to solve.

➡ _____

I found the maze there looked too hard to solve.

(2) After they looked at the labyrinths closely, they found the beauty of order and regularity.

➡ _____

they found the beauty of order and regularity.

(3) Since Katherine had not been invited to the wedding, she stayed at home all day long.

➡ _____

Katherine stayed at home all day long.

✏️ 출제율 100%

14 다음 중 우리말과 그 영작이 어법상 바르게 짝지어지지 <u>않</u>은 것은?

① Ben은 두 언어 모두에 흥미를 느꼈다.
  → Ben felt interested in both of the languages.
② 그 배우 두 사람 중 어느 누구도 영화에 출연한 적이 없다.
  → Neither of the actors has ever appeared in a movie.
③ 나는 장난감이 없어서 하나 갖고 싶다.
  → I have no toys, so I want to have one.
④ 우리 둘 다 클래식 음악을 좋아한다.
  → Both of us like classical music.
⑤ 나는 거리에서 세 마리의 개를 봤는데, 그것들 각각은 다른 종류였다.
  → I saw three dogs on the street, each of which were a different kind.

[15~18] 다음 글을 읽고 물음에 답하시오.

These days, mazes are often considered left-brain puzzles. Many people ①<u>willingly</u> visit maze parks and enjoy the "planned confusion." And some of (A)<u>them</u> ②<u>came down with</u> their own solutions. The easiest and most reliable one is to place a hand on one wall from the very beginning. Then you just keep following that wall. It's like walking ③<u>in a dark room</u>. Unfortunately, this simple method may not be ④<u>effective</u> in certain types of mazes, especially when all of the walls are not connected.

Mazes are made with a variety of different materials, like walls and rooms, hedges, bricks, mirrors, and even snow. In fact, they can also be ⑤printed or drawn on paper. Here is one as an example. This is called a number maze. You start from point A and have to go in the order of 1 → 9 → 8 → 5 → 1 → 9 → .... Why don't you give it a try? You have 30 seconds to escape!

15 ①~⑤ 중 글의 흐름상 적절하지 않은 것은?
①   ②   ③   ④   ⑤

16 다음 중 밑줄 친 (A)가 가리키는 것으로 가장 적절한 것은?
① left-brain puzzles   ② mazes
③ many people   ④ maze parks
⑤ solutions

17 다음 중 위 글의 내용과 일치하는 것은?
① There are few people who enjoy maze parks.
② It is impossible to find an easy solution to get out of a maze.
③ We can't enjoy mazes on paper.
④ People can make mazes with snow.
⑤ The number maze has no regularity.

18 What is one example of a printed maze? Answer in English.

➡ _____

[19~21] 다음 글을 읽고 물음에 답하시오.

USA – Pineapple Garden Maze
If you visit Oahu, Hawaii, the Pineapple Garden Maze is a ①must see. It is the world's longest maze, and it attracts visitors from around the world. The maze has 11,400 native plants and ②covers about 5 kilometers.

England – Hampton Court Maze
The oldest hedge maze in Britain is the Hampton Court Maze. It was built ③in 1689. Hundreds of thousands of people visit this maze that ④created during the time of William of Orange.

Italy – Labirinto di Villa Pasani
It was created in 1720 and is known as the most difficult ⑤one to solve. Part of the problem is the height of the hedges. (A)산울타리가 너무 높아서 사람들은 그 너머를 볼 수가 없다. You get a perfect view only once you've got to the center and climbed the stairs to the top of the tower.

19 다음 중 위 글을 읽고 답할 수 없는 것은?
① Where is the Pineapple Garden Maze located?
② What is the longest maze in the world?
③ When was the Hampton Court Maze built?
④ Who built the Hampton Court Maze?
⑤ What is the Labirinto di Villa Pasani known as?

20 ①~⑤ 중 어법상 바르지 않은 것은?
①   ②   ③   ④   ⑤

21 주어진 단어를 활용하여 밑줄 친 (A)의 우리말을 영어로 쓰시오.

they / so / that / over

➡ _____

[01~03] 다음 대화를 읽고 물음에 답하시오.

Gina: Mom, did you decide where to visit during our family trip to Jeju?

Mom: Almost. Come here and see the plan I made.

Gina: It looks good. Hmm... Mom, is it possible to visit Mirror Maze Park on our second day?

Mom: It sounds exciting, but I remember you said you wanted to go horseback riding.

Gina: I know, but I heard the park is a lot more fun. Please ....

Mom: All right. Let's change our schedule for the second day.

Gina: Thank you! I'm very excited about the trip.

Mom: It's great to hear that you're looking forward to the trip.

01 Where does Gina want to visit on the second day?

➡ _____

_____

02 What was the original plan on the second day?

➡ _____

03 Why does Gina want to change the schedule?

➡ _____

_____

04 다음 우리말에 맞도록 괄호 안에 주어진 어휘를 알맞게 배열하시오.

(1) 아래의 두 그림을 비교할 때, 당신은 몇 가지 차이점을 쉽게 알아차릴 수 있다. (pictures, the, below, two, comparing)

➡ _____

you can easily notice some differences.

(2) Jane은 Tom의 미로 탈출 방식을 이해하지 못했기 때문에, 그가 말한 대로 하지 않기로 결심했다. (Tom's, getting, not, the maze, out of, understanding, method of)

➡ _____

_____ Jane decided not to do as he said.

(3) 통로를 따라 끝까지 가면, 당신은 중앙에 도착할 것이다. (the path, to, through, the end, following)

➡ _____

you will reach the center.

05 다음 중에서 어법상 옳지 않은 표현이 들어간 문장을 찾아, 번호를 쓰고, 바르게 고쳐 문장을 다시 쓰시오.

① Someone having touched the doorlock of her apartment, Sam couldn't get into her place that night.

② Finding the puppy her brother had lost, Emily cried out with tears of joy.

③ Having just completed the final essay, Sam went to bed.

④ Talking with so many people for so long hours, the author got exhausted.

⑤ Anne having been infected with the virus before, she is well aware of the fear of the disease.

➡ _____

_____

06 다음 그림을 보고, 그림과 내용상 일치하는 문장을 고르시오.

① One of the animals doesn't seem to like the green food on the table.

② All are putting their hands out on the table which is full of food.

③ None of the animals is likely to pick up the carrot.

④ Every animal invited to the party seems to love eating vegetables.

⑤ Both of the rabbits have some whiskers.

*whisker: 수염

[07~10] 다음 글을 읽고 물음에 답하시오.

Comparing the two pictures below, you can easily notice some differences. For example, the picture on the left is called a labyrinth and only has an entrance. The picture on the right is called a maze and has both an entrance and an exit.

You can find the origin of the labyrinth in Greek mythology. It is said to be a prison that you cannot escape. But you may notice that the labyrinth has only a single path. There are no dead ends. This means you don't have to worry about getting out of it when you enter it. If you follow the path all the way to the end, you will reach the center. To get out, you simply have to turn around and (A)들어간 길대로 걸어 나오면 됩니다.

When you are in a maze, it's a different story. There are many choices to make and dead ends to frustrate you. You have to keep making decisions about which way to go. If you are not careful, you can easily lose your way.

07 Write the reason why you don't need to worry about getting out of the labyrinth when you enter it. Use the phrase 'It's because.'

➡ _____

_____

08 위 글의 내용에 맞게 미궁과 미로의 특징을 바르게 분류하시오.

ⓐ It has both an entrance and an exit.
ⓑ It has only a single path.
ⓒ You can find its origin in Greek mythology.
ⓓ It has many dead ends.

➡ 미궁: _____, 미로: _____

09 What happens if you are not careful in a maze? Answer in English.

➡ _____

10 주어진 단어를 바르게 나열하여 밑줄 친 우리말 (A)를 영어로 쓰시오.

in / out / the way / walk / came / back / you

➡ _____

01 다음 대화의 내용과 일치하도록 빈칸을 완성하시오.

> Andrew: Hey, Minju, where are you?
>
> Minju: Oh, Andrew, I'm coming. I'm coming.
>
> Andrew: Good. I was worried that you were lost.
>
> Minju: I think I'm okay. What about Mason and Jian?
>
> Andrew: They are already here at my house.
>
> Minju: Good! Oh, I see the post office. How do I get to your place from here?
>
> Andrew: You are almost here. Go straight for one more block. Then you will see Kim's Bakery.
>
> Minju: Kim's Bakery? Okay … .
>
> Andrew: Then turn right and go straight for about 100 meters.
>
> Minju: Turn right and go straight … . Okay, thanks! I'll see you soon.

> Minju was supposed to get together at (A)_____ with Mason and Jian. When Minju was late, Andrew was worried if (B)_____. When he called her, she was near (C)_____. Andrew explained to Minju how to get to his place. He said that she should go straight for one more block and then could see (D)_____. After that, she should (E)_____.

02 다음 그림에서 자신이 원하는 휴대전화 케이스를 선택하고, 〈보기〉의 대화문 문장을 응용하여, 자신의 답변을 2개 이상 만드시오.

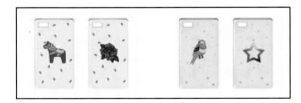

> ┤ 보기 ├
>
> A: What type of cell phone case would you choose?
>
> B: I'll choose a pink one. I also like the one with a horse on it.

(1) _____

(2) _____

(3) _____

단원별 모의고사

01 다음 짝지어진 단어의 관계가 같도록 빈칸에 알맞은 말을 쓰시오.

> act : activity = suggest : _____

02 다음 영영풀이가 가리키는 것을 고르시오.

> a door, gate, passage, etc. used for entering a room, building or place

① entrance
② exit
③ confusion
④ choice
⑤ labyrinth

03 다음 우리말을 주어진 단어를 이용하여 영작하시오.

(1) 우리는 미로에서 길을 잃었다. (get, in)

➡ _____

(2) 오늘의 실패에 좌절하지 마라. (failure, be)

➡ _____

(3) 우리는 믿을 만하고 열심히 일하는 사람을 찾고 있다. (look, reliable, hard-working, someone, who)

➡ _____

_____

04 다음 우리말에 맞게 빈칸에 알맞은 말을 쓰시오. (철자가 주어진 것도 있음.)

(1) 미로는 흔히 좌뇌형 퍼즐로 여겨진다.

➡ Mazes are often c_____ left-brain puzzles.

(2) 미궁은 입구만 있다.

➡ A labyrinth only has an _____.

(3) 자세히 들여다보면, 당신은 질서와 규칙성이라는 아름다움을 발견할 수 있을지도 모른다.

➡ Looking at them c_____, you may find the beauty of order and _____.

(4) 이것을 빨간색 신발로 교환하는 것이 가능한가요?

➡ Is it possible to _____ them for the red shoes?

05 다음 문장의 빈칸에 들어갈 말을 〈보기〉에서 골라 쓰시오.

> ┤ 보기 ├
> making decisions / a variety of / lose your way / dead ends / in the order of

(1) Mazes are made with _____ different materials.
(2) There are no _____.
(3) You start from point A and have to go _____ 1 → 2 → 3 → 4.
(4) If you are not careful, you can easily _____.
(5) You have to keep _____ about which way to go.

[06~07] 다음 대화를 읽고 물음에 답하시오.

Juwon: What are you reading, Alice?

Alice: It's about the origin of the labyrinth.

Juwon: Labyrinth? Wasn't that an old mythological prison to keep the half-man, half-bull monster?

Alice: Oh, Juwon, you know about the story.

Juwon: Not really. I forgot the name of the monster.

Alice: The Minotaur. The king of Crete was angry at it and put it in a labyrinth.

Juwon: Interesting! Alice, is it possible to borrow the book after you're finished with it?

Alice: Sure, no problem. Maybe this Friday.

06 위 대화의 내용과 일치하도록 빈칸을 완성하시오.

> A labyrinth was an (A)_____
> _____ to keep the half-man, half-
> bull monster, named (B)_____.
> It was built by (C)_____
> because he was upset at it and he wanted
> to lock it up in the (D)_____.

07 When can Juwon borrow the book from Alice?

➡ _____

[08~09] 다음 대화를 읽고 물음에 답하시오.

> Mike: Hi, do you need any help?
> Sora: (A) Yes, please. Could you suggest a good Chinese restaurant in this building? I can't decide between the two.
> Mike: (B) Hmm.... What about Pappa Chen's? Their food is good and the prices are reasonable.
> Sora: (C) Sounds great! How do I get to the restaurant?
> Mike: (D) Pappa Chen's is next to the elevator.
> Sora: (E) Great! Thank you very much for your help.
> Mike: My pleasure. Enjoy your dinner.

08 위 대화의 (A)~(E) 중 주어진 문장이 들어가기에 적절한 곳은?

> It's on the fourth floor. You can use the elevator over there.

① (A) ② (B) ③ (C) ④ (D) ⑤ (E)

09 위 대화를 읽고 대답할 수 <u>없는</u> 것은?

① What does Sora ask Mike to do?
② What does Mike recommend?
③ Where is Pappa Chen's in this building?
④ How can Sora get to Pappa Chen's?
⑤ With whom will Sora go to a good Chinese restaurant?

[10~12] 다음 대화를 읽고 물음에 답하시오.

> Andrew: Hey, Minju, where are you?
> Minju: Oh, Andrew, I'm coming. I'm coming.
> Andrew: Good. I was worried that you were lost.
> Minju: I think I'm okay. What about Mason and Jian?
> Andrew: They are already here at my house.
> Minju: Good! Oh, I see the post office. How do I get to your place from here?
> Andrew: You are almost here. Go straight for one more block. Then you will see Kim's Bakery.
> Minju: Kim's Bakery? Okay ....
> Andrew: Then turn right and go straight for about 100 meters.
> Minju: Turn right and go straight .... Okay, thanks! I'll see you soon.

10 Why was Andrew worried about Minju?

➡ _____

11 With whom is Minju supposed to get together at Andrew's place?

➡ _____
_____

12 How does Minju get to Andrew's place from Kim's Bakery?

➡ _____
_____

13 다음 각 문장의 밑줄 친 분사구문을 부사절로 바꿀 때 어법상 어색한 것은?

① <u>Completing the important project</u>, all of his team members were rewarded.

→ After they completed the important project,

② <u>It being cloudy and chilly</u>, she went outside to see the blossoms.

→ Though it was cloudy and chilly,

③ <u>Seen from far away</u>, the high building will look like a devil's tower in the movie.

→ If it is seen from far away,

④ <u>Learning the computer language</u>, she couldn't understand the program.

→ When she learned the computer language,

⑤ <u>There being nothing to listen to</u>, I turned off the radio.

→ Since there was nothing to listen to,

[14~16] 다음 문장의 밑줄 친 부분 중 어법상 어색한 것을 고르시오.

14 ① Ben bought a big boat and his sister bought a small <u>one</u>.

② Franklin has three shirts. One is black, <u>another</u> navy, and the other sky-blue.

③ My daughter doesn't need this. Show her <u>another</u>, please.

④ Helen had two dreams. One was to see her mom, and <u>other</u> was to marry Jack.

⑤ There were a lot of stars in the sky. Some were bright, while <u>others</u> were dim.

15 ① We have no boxes to put things in, so if you have any, please lend us <u>one</u>.

② The officers required that we finish reviewing <u>all</u> of the reports.

③ He made a lot of mistakes, <u>none</u> of which is completely wrong.

④ <u>Anyone</u> interested in joining the club should contact Ms. Baker.

⑤ If you're looking for a Korean restaurant, I will let you know <u>it</u>.

16 ① <u>Being nervous</u>, the kids searched for a way to get out of the maze.

② <u>Having written quickly</u>, the book has a lot of mistakes.

③ <u>Wanting to praise him</u>, his father gave James a big hug.

④ <u>Having nothing to do</u>, the dogs sat quietly in the corner of the living room.

⑤ <u>It being stormy</u>, a ship went fishing early that morning.

17 다음 각 그림과 우리말에 맞게 주어진 단어들과 필요한 부정대명사를 추가하여, 영작하시오. (동사 변형 가능, 단어 수 조건 맞출 것)

(1) 어떤 사람들은 피자를 먹고, 또 다른 사람들은 집으로 가져간다. (it, eat, home, take, and, pizza 총 8 단어)

➡ _____

(2) 둘 다 물고기를 잡는 것에 관심이 있다. (interested, fish, be, in, catching 총 6 단어)

➡ _____

18 다음 각 문장의 밑줄 친 부사절을 분사구문으로 바꾼 것 중 옳은 것은?

① If the hero had cut off the wrong wire, the building would have exploded.
  → Having cut off the wrong wire,
② Since Sharon went to bed earlier, she woke up at dawn.
  → Sharon going to bed earlier,
③ When it is seen from one side, the grass in the other side always looks greener.
  → Seen from one side,
④ While mom was reading a story book, the baby fell asleep.
  → Reading a story book,
⑤ As there was no umbrella, I came home without it.
  → Being no umbrella,

[19~21] 다음 글을 읽고 물음에 답하시오.

You can find the origin of the labyrinth in Greek mythology. ① It is said to be a prison that you cannot escape. ② But you may notice that the labyrinth has only a single path. ③ There are no dead ends. ④ If you follow the path all the way to the end, you will reach the center. ⑤ To get out, you simply have to turn around and walk back out the way you came in.

When you are in a maze, it's a different story. There are many choices to make and dead ends to frustrate you. You have to keep making decisions about which way to go. If you are not careful, you can easily lose your way.

19 ①~⑤ 중 주어진 문장이 들어가기에 가장 적절한 곳은?

> This means you don't have to worry about getting out of it when you enter it.

①   ②   ③   ④   ⑤

20 다음 중 위 글을 읽고 답할 수 있는 것은?

① Who is the first person that made a maze?
② How many solutions are there to get out of a maze?
③ Why do we need to be careful in a maze?
④ How many dead ends are there in a maze?
⑤ Why does a labyrinth have only one path?

21 다음은 labyrinth에 들어온 친구들의 대화이다. 글의 내용에 맞게 빈칸에 알맞은 말을 쓰시오.

> A: Do you know how we can reach the center?
> B: Sure. Just _____
> _____, and you will reach the center.

[22~25] 다음 글을 읽고 물음에 답하시오.

Mazes are made with ①a variety of different materials, ②like walls and rooms, hedges, bricks, mirrors, and even snow. In fact, ③they can also be printed or drawn on paper. Here is one as an example. This is called a number maze. You start from point A and have to go in the order of 1 → 9 → 8 → 5 → 1 → 9 → ... . Why don't you give it a try? You have 30 seconds to escape!

Labyrinths and mazes are truly fun, but (A) that's not the end of the story. (B)If you look at them closely, you may find the beauty of order and regularity. They may also show you ④how creative human beings are.

⑤If there is a maze park on your next trip, why don't you stop and take some time to enjoy it? It will surely be worth visiting!

22 ①~⑤에 관한 설명으로 바르지 <u>않은</u> 것은?

① various로 바꾸어 쓸 수 있다.

② such as로 바꾸어 쓸 수 있다.

③ mazes를 지칭하는 말이다.

④ 간접의문문이므로 'how human beings are creative'로 고쳐 써야 한다.

⑤ 조건절을 이끄는 접속사이다.

23 다음 중 밑줄 친 (A)의 의미로 가장 적절한 것은?

① There is nothing in labyrinths and mazes except being fun.

② Labyrinths and mazes have something good other than being fun.

③ There are many stories related to labyrinths and mazes.

④ It is the end of the story of labyrinths and mazes.

⑤ It is hard to say that labyrinths and mazes have their own stories.

24 밑줄 친 (B)를 분사구문으로 바꿔 쓰시오.

➡ _____

25 What may you find when you look at labyrinths and mazes closely? Answer in English with a full sentence.

➡ _____

_____

26 다음 중 Labirinto di Villa Pasani에 관한 내용과 일치하지 <u>않는</u> 것은?

Italy – Labirinto di Villa Pasani
It was created in 1720 and is known as the most difficult one to solve. Part of the problem is the height of the hedges. They are so high that people can't see over them. You get a perfect view only once you've got to the center and climbed the stairs to the top of the tower.

① It is located in Italy.

② It was built in 1720.

③ People think it is the most difficult to solve.

④ There are stairs leading to the top of the tower.

⑤ The height of the hedges enables people to see over them with ease.

MEMO

INSIGHT
on the textbook

교과서 파헤치기

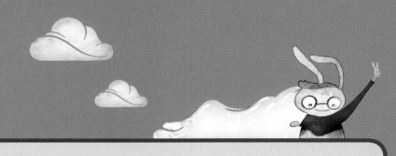

※ 다음 영어를 우리말로 쓰시오.

01 high-speed	
02 burr	
03 explain	
04 imitate	
05 absorb	
06 all-purpose	
07 fascinate	
08 holder	
09 fastener	
10 article	
11 beak	
12 contact	
13 bite	
14 pressure	
15 redesign	
16 apply	
17 explore	
18 genius	
19 hairy	
20 increase	
21 notice	

22 solution	
23 painful	
24 inspire	
25 successful	
26 cause	
27 gracefully	
28 sudden	
29 surface	
30 reduce	
31 reflect	
32 survivor	
33 length	
34 necessity	
35 glide over	
36 make contact with	
37 float away	
38 keep A from -ing	
39 on one's way to	
40 be stuck to	
41 not only A but also B	
42 as a result	
43 That's why ~.	

※ 다음 우리말을 영어로 쓰시오.

01	흡수하다	22	생존자
02	곤충, 벌레	23	발명
03	창의적인	24	자세히
04	적용하다	25	접촉
05	길이	26	필요성
06	(새의) 부리	27	매혹하다
07	물린 상처	28	천재
08	만능의, 다용도의	29	주목하다
09	탐색하다	30	압력
10	우아하게	31	다시 디자인하다
11	관찰하다	32	표면
12	고통스러운	33	줄이다
13	성공적인	34	갑작스러운
14	모방하다	35	~을 찾고 있는
15	증가; 증가하다	36	~와 연락하다, 접촉하다
16	가시 식물	37	~에 붙다
17	기사, 논문	38	~로 덮여 있다
18	초래하다	39	A가 ~하지 못하게 하다
19	무게	40	떠다니다
20	영감을 불러일으키다	41	결과적으로
21	고속의	42	~로 가는 길에
		43	A뿐만 아니라 B도 역시

※ 다음 영영풀이에 알맞은 단어를 <보기>에서 골라 쓴 후, 우리말 뜻을 쓰시오.

1 _____ : pain in your head: _____

2 _____ : long and not wide: _____

3 _____ : suitable for many uses: _____

4 _____ : the act of inventing something: _____

5 _____ : a natural ability to do something well: _____

6 _____ : covered with a lot of hair: _____

7 _____ : to see or notice somebody/something: _____

8 _____ : a passage that goes under the ground: _____

9 _____ : a very smart or talented person: _____

10 _____ : the hard usually pointed parts that over a bird's mouth: _____

11 _____ : to move down through the air at a steep angle: _____

12 _____ : to make or do something the same way as something else: _____

13 _____ : to change the design of something: _____

14 _____ : a part of an animal's body that is used for flying or gliding: _____

15 _____ : a device used to close a piece of clothing, a window, suitcase, etc. tightly: _____

16 _____ : a person who continues to live, especially despite being nearly killed or experiencing great danger or difficulty: _____

보기			
talent	hairy	dive	wing
narrow	headache	fastener	imitate
tunnel	observe	genius	redesign
invention	all-purpose	survivor	beak

※ 다음 우리말과 일치하도록 빈칸에 알맞은 말을 쓰시오.

Listen & Speak 1 A

G: You _____ that Leonardo da Vinci _____ the *Mona Lisa*, _____ you?

B: Sure. I _____ he was a really _____ _____.

G: He was _____ a _____ _____.

B: _____ did he _____?

G: He _____ _____ _____ _____ a bird. So, he _____ a _____ machine that _____ _____ a bird.

B: _____ he _____ that _____?

G: No, but his _____ _____ _____ many _____ _____.

G: 레오나르도 다빈치가 모나리자를 그린 것을 알지, 그렇지 않니?
B: 물론. 그는 정말로 위대한 미술가라고 생각해.
G: 그는 또한 위대한 발명가였어.
B: 그가 무엇을 발명했니?
G: 그는 새처럼 나는 것을 꿈꿨어. 그래서 그는 새처럼 보이는 나는 기계를 그렸어.
B: 그가 그 기계도 만들었니?
G: 아니, 하지만 그의 창의적인 생각은 많은 발명가들에게 영감을 주었어.

Listen & Speak 1 B

B: _____ _____ _____ _____ of a mosquito _____, Jian?

G: A mosquito needle? _____ you _____ to me?

B: Some scientists _____ _____ new needle by _____ a _____ _____.

G: That's interesting. So _____ _____ that help?

B: You _____ mosquito _____ are not _____ _____, _____ _____? The new _____ will also _____ _____ _____.

G: That's great. _____ _____ it's _____ _____?

B: _____ a mosquito's mouth, it makes _____ _____ _____ our skin.

G: Wow, I _____ that there's _____ _____ in the world!

B: Jian, mosquito needle을 들어본 적이 있니?
G: mosquito needle이라고? 그것 좀 설명해 줄 수 있니?
B: 몇몇 과학자들이 모기의 입을 모방하여 이 새로운 바늘을 만들었어.
G: 흥미롭군. 그럼 그것이 어떻게 도움이 될까?
B: 모기가 무는 것은 별로 고통스럽지 않다는 건 알지? 이 새로운 주사바늘도 역시 통증을 줄여 줄 거야.
G: 대단한데. 어째서 덜 고통스럽지?
B: 모기의 입처럼 그것은 우리의 피부에 덜 닿아.
G: 와, 세상에 쓸모없는 것은 아무것도 없는 것 같아!

Listen & Speak 2 A-2

G: This candle _____ can make _____ _____ _____ as long.

B: Really? How's that _____?

G: _____ a candle _____, it _____ _____ the _____ _____ the holder to _____ a new candle.

B: Wow, I am so _____ by the idea! Now we can _____ candles _____.

G: 이 양초 받침이 양초를 두 배나 오래 지속되도록 만들 수 있어.
B: 정말? 어떻게 그것이 가능해?
G: 양초가 탈 때 그것은 받침 아래에 있는 관으로 녹아들어 새로운 양초를 만들어.
B: 와, 나는 그 아이디어에 매료되었어! 이제 우리는 양초를 더 오래 사용할 수 있어.

Listen & Speak 2 A-3

B: You know _____? I'm really _____ _____ the _____ door in Juwon's room.

G: _____ _____ the door so _____?

B: Juwon and I _____ _____ _____ on it.

G: _____ could you play table tennis on a _____?

B: The door can _____ _____ _____ a _____.

G: That's _____!

Listen & Speak 2 B

W: Today, we _____ a special _____, Thomas Thwaites, the Goat Man. Hello, Thomas.

M: Hello, Anna. _____ to _____ here.

W: Thomas, I'm so _____ by the _____ that you _____ _____ a _____ in the Alps _____ _____ _____. _____ did you _____ that?

M: One day, I _____ _____ _____ on the mountain. They _____ so _____ that I wanted to _____ _____ them.

W: _____ you _____ any _____ being a goat?

M: _____ all four legs _____ very _____ for me.

W: Do you have _____ plans _____ _____ _____ a goat again?

M: Sure. I'm _____ my second _____ to the Alps.

W: I _____ _____ _____ hear about your next _____. Thank you, Thomas, for your time.

Real Life Communication

Henry: _____ are you _____, Mina?

Mina: I'm _____ _____ _____ about a bug robot.

Henry: A bug robot? Is it _____?

Mina: Yes. I'm _____ _____ _____ this thing.

Henry: _____ you tell me _____ about it?

Mina: You _____ that some _____ can _____ _____ _____ _____, don't you?

Henry: Yeah. That's _____ it's _____ to catch them.

Mina: A bug robot can do the same. It can _____ to find _____ after _____ or _____ _____.

Henry: That's really _____!

B: 너 그거 알아? 나는 주원이네 방의 특별한 문에 매료되었어.
G: 왜 그 문이 그리 특별하니?
B: 주원이와 내가 그 위에서 탁구를 쳤어.
G: 어떻게 문 위에서 탁구를 칠 수 있어?
B: 문이 탁구대로 바뀔 수 있어.
G: 멋있는데!

W: 오늘 우리는 특별 손님인 염소 인간 Thomas Thwaites를 모시게 되었습니다. 안녕하세요, Thomas.
M: 안녕하세요, Anna. 여기 오게 되어 기쁩니다.
W: Thomas, 나는 당신이 3일 동안 알프스에서 염소처럼 살았다는 사실에 매료되었습니다. 왜 그렇게 했나요?
M: 어느 날, 나는 염소들이 산에서 노는 것을 보았어요. 그들이 너무 평화로워 보여서 나는 그들처럼 살고 싶었습니다.
W: 염소가 되는 데 아무 문제가 없었나요?
M: 네 발로 걷는 것이 나에게는 매우 어려웠어요.
W: 당신은 다시 염소처럼 살 계획이 있나요?
M: 물론이죠. 나는 알프스를 다시 방문할 계획을 하고 있어요.
W: 당신의 다음 모험에 대해 빨리 듣고 싶어요. 시간 내주셔서 감사합니다, Thomas.

Henry: 미나야, 뭐 하고 있니?
Mina: 나는 bug robot에 관한 기사를 읽고 있어.
Henry: "bug robot"라고? 재미있니?
Mina: 응, 나는 이것에 정말로 매료되었어.
Henry: 그것에 대해 좀 더 말해줄 수 있니?
Mina: 너는 몇몇 곤충이 좁은 공간에 미끄러져 들어갈 수 있는 것을 알지?
Henry: 알아. 그것이 그들을 잡기 어려운 이유이지.
Mina: bug robot이 똑같이 할 수 있어. 그것은 지진이나 대형 화재 이후에 생존자들을 찾는 것을 도와줄 수 있어.
Henry: 그거 정말 흥미롭다!

※ 다음 우리말에 맞도록 대화를 영어로 쓰시오.

Listen & Speak 1 A

G: _____

B: _____

G: _____

B: _____

G: _____

B: _____

G: _____

G: 레오나르도 다빈치가 모나리자를 그린 것을 알지, 그렇지 않니?
B: 물론. 그는 정말로 위대한 미술가라고 생각해.
G: 그는 또한 위대한 발명가였어.
B: 그가 무엇을 발명했니?
G: 그는 새처럼 나는 것을 꿈꿨어. 그래서 그는 새처럼 보이는 나는 기계를 그렸어.
B: 그가 그 기계도 만들었니?
G: 아니, 하지만 그의 창의적인 생각은 많은 발명가들에게 영감을 주었어.

Listen & Speak 1 B

B: _____

G: _____

B: _____

G: _____

B: _____

G: _____

B: _____

G: _____

B: Jian, mosquito needle을 들어본 적이 있니?
G: mosquito needle이라고? 그것 좀 설명해 줄 수 있니?
B: 몇몇 과학자들이 모기의 입을 모방하여 이 새로운 바늘을 만들었어.
G: 흥미롭군. 그럼 그것이 어떻게 도움이 될까?
B: 모기가 무는 것은 별로 고통스럽지 않다는 건 알지? 이 새로운 주사바늘도 역시 통증을 줄여 줄 거야.
G: 대단한대. 어째서 덜 고통스럽지?
B: 모기의 입처럼 그것은 우리의 피부에 덜 닿아.
G: 와, 세상에 쓸모없는 것은 아무것도 없는 것 같아!

Listen & Speak 2 A-2

G: _____

B: _____

G: _____

B: _____

G: 이 양초 받침이 양초를 두 배나 오래 지속되도록 만들 수 있어.
B: 정말? 어떻게 그것이 가능해?
G: 양초가 탈 때 그것은 받침 아래에 있는 관으로 녹아들어 새로운 양초를 만들어.
B: 와, 나는 그 아이디어에 매료되었어! 이제 우리는 양초를 더 오래 사용할 수 있어.

Listen & Speak 2 A-3

B: _____

G: _____

B: _____

G: _____

B: _____

G: _____

B: 너 그거 알아? 나는 주원이네 방의 특별한 문에 매료되었어.
G: 왜 그 문이 그리 특별하니?
B: 주원이와 내가 그 위에서 탁구를 쳤어.
G: 어떻게 문 위에서 탁구를 칠 수 있어?
B: 문이 탁구대로 바뀔 수 있어.
G: 멋있는데!

Listen & Speak 2 B

W: _____

M: _____

W: _____

_____

M: _____

_____

W: _____

M: _____

W: _____

M: _____

W: _____

W: 오늘 우리는 특별 손님인 염소 인간 Thomas Thwaites를 모시게 되었습니다. 안녕하세요, Thomas.
M: 안녕하세요, Anna. 여기 오게 되어 기쁩니다.
W: Thomas, 나는 당신이 3일 동안 알프스에서 염소처럼 살았다는 사실에 매료되었습니다. 왜 그렇게 했나요?
M: 어느 날, 나는 염소들이 산에서 노는 것을 보았어요. 그들이 너무 평화로워 보여서 나는 그들처럼 살고 싶었습니다.
W: 염소가 되는 데 아무 문제가 없었나요?
M: 네 발로 걷는 것이 나에게는 매우 어려웠어요.
W: 당신은 다시 염소처럼 살 계획이 있나요?
M: 물론이죠. 나는 알프스를 다시 방문할 계획을 하고 있어요.
W: 당신의 다음 모험에 대해 빨리 듣고 싶어요. 시간 내주셔서 감사합니다, Thomas.

Real Life Communication

Henry: _____

Mina: _____

Henry: _____

Mina: _____

Henry: _____

Mina: _____

Henry: _____

Mina: _____

_____

Henry: _____

Henry: 미나야, 뭐 하고 있니?
Mina: 나는 bug robot에 관한 기사를 읽고 있어.
Henry: "bug robot"라고? 재미있니?
Mina: 응, 나는 이것에 정말로 매료되었어.
Henry: 그것에 대해 좀 더 말해줄 수 있니?
Mina: 너는 몇몇 곤충이 좁은 공간에 미끄러져 들어갈 수 있는 것을 알지?
Henry: 알아. 그것이 그들을 잡기 어려운 이유이지.
Mina: bug robot이 똑같이 할 수 있어. 그것은 지진이나 대형 화재 이후에 생존자들을 찾는 것을 도와줄 수 있어.
Henry: 그거 정말 흥미롭다!

※ 다음 우리말과 일치하도록 빈칸에 알맞은 것을 골라 쓰시오.

Nature's Inspiration

1 From _____ birds to _____ plants, the _____ nature works _____ us.

    A. fascinates   B. self-cleaning   C. flying   D. way

2 Some people not _____ use nature but _____ imitate _____ to find _____ to their problems.

    A. also   B. solutions   C. only   D. it

3 Leonardo da Vinci (1452-1519) was _____ _____ _____ _____.

    A. such   B. one   C. person

4 He wondered _____ _____ _____ _____.

    A. could   B. how   C. fly   D. birds

5 He _____ watched birds, _____ notes, and _____ pictures _____ them.

    A. drew   B. closely   C. made   D. of

6 Even _____ his invention was not _____, he _____ a bird's wings to _____ to make a flying machine.

    A. imitated   B. try   C. though   D. successful

7 _____ then, more and more people _____ successfully _____ the surprising _____ of nature's genius.

    A. abilities   B. since   C. imitated   D. have

8 _____ some _____ them.

    A. explore   B. let's   C. of

Learning from a Bird: Moving Fast and Quietly

9 The _____ _____ was first _____ in Japan. But it _____ one problem.

    A. train   B. had   C. high-speed   D. made

10 When the train _____ a tunnel, the _____ _____ in air pressure created a very _____ sound.

    A. loud   B. sudden   C. entered   D. increase

11 It often _____ _____ _____ and _____ headaches.

    A. caused   B. people   C. up   D. woke

12 A team of engineers tried to _____ the problem, but they didn't know _____ they _____ _____ the noise.

    A. reduce   B. solve   C. how   D. could

---

1 나는 새에서 자정 작용을 하는 식물까지, 자연이 기능하는 방식은 우리를 매료시킵니다.

2 몇몇 사람들은 그들의 문제에 대한 해결책을 찾기 위해 자연을 이용할 뿐만 아니라 자연을 모방하기까지 합니다.

3 레오나르도 다빈치(1452-1519)가 이러한 사람들 중 한 사람이었습니다.

4 그는 새들이 어떻게 날 수 있는지 궁금했습니다.

5 그는 새를 자세히 관찰했고, 기록했으며, 그림으로 그렸습니다.

6 그의 발명은 비록 성공하지 못했지만, 그는 나는 기계를 만들어 보려고 새의 날개를 모방했습니다.

7 그 후로, 점점 더 많은 사람들이 자연 속 천재의 놀라운 능력을 성공적으로 모방해 오고 있습니다.

8 그들 중 몇 가지를 알아봅시다.

새에게서 배우기: 빠르고 조용하게 움직이기

9 고속 열차는 일본에서 처음 만들어졌습니다. 하지만 그것은 한 가지 문제점이 있었습니다.

10 열차가 터널에 들어갔을 때, 갑작스러운 기압의 상승은 매우 시끄러운 소리를 발생시켰습니다.

11 그것은 종종 사람들의 잠을 깨웠고 두통을 일으켰습니다.

12 한 공학자 팀이 그 문제를 해결하려 했지만, 그들은 어떻게 소음을 줄일 수 있을지 몰랐습니다.

13 One day, one of the _____ was watching a bird _____ _____ _____ a meal.

    A. search   B. engineers   C. of   D. in

14 He _____ the bird quickly and _____ _____ _____ the water.

    A. diving   B. saw   C. quietly   D. into

15 He wondered _____ the _____ _____ the water so _____.

    A. entered   B. gracefully   C. bird   D. how

16 So, he studied _____ about the bird and _____ its long, _____ _____.

    A. discovered   B. more   C. beak   D. narrow

17 He _____ the _____ of the train _____ _____ the bird's beak.

    A. front   B. imitating   C. redesigned   D. by

18 It was successful. Now the new train travels _____ only more quietly _____ also 10% faster _____ 15% _____ electricity.

    A. with   B. but   C. less   D. not

Learning from Burrs: Inventing an All-Purpose Fastener

19 _____ day, a Swiss engineer, George de Mestral, _____ _____ in the woods _____ his dog.

    A. was   B. with   C. one   D. hiking

20 _____ his way _____, he saw that _____ were _____ to his clothes and his dog's hair.

    A. burrs   B. home   C. on   D. stuck

21 He wanted to _____ _____ _____ _____.

    A. how   B. happened   C. know   D. that

22 He _____ a _____ look at the burrs and _____ that the ends of the burr needles were not _____.

    A. noticed   B. straight   C. closer   D. took

23 He wondered _____ he could _____ that to make _____.

    A. apply   B. useful   C. if   D. something

13 어느 날, 공학자들 중 한 사람이 먹이를 찾고 있는 새를 관찰하고 있었습니다.

14 그는 새가 빠르고 조용하게 물속으로 뛰어드는 것을 보았습니다.

15 그는 새가 어떻게 그렇게 우아하게 물속으로 들어가는지 궁금했습니다.

16 그래서 그는 그 새에 대해 더 연구했고, 새의 길고 좁은 부리를 발견했습니다.

17 그는 새의 부리를 모방하여 열차의 앞면을 다시 디자인했습니다.

18 그것은 성공이었습니다. 이제 새로운 열차는 더 조용할 뿐만 아니라 전기는 15% 덜 사용하면서 10% 더 빠르게 이동합니다.

가시 식물들에게서 배우기: 만능 고정 장치 발명하기

19 어느 날, 스위스 공학자 George de Mestral은 그의 개와 숲에서 하이킹하고 있었습니다.

20 집으로 돌아오는 길에, 그는 가시 식물이 자신의 옷과 개의 털에 붙어 있는 것을 보았습니다.

21 그는 어떻게 그런 일이 일어났는지 알고 싶었습니다.

22 그는 가시 식물들을 자세히 들여다보았고, 가시의 끝이 곧지 않다는 것을 알아챘습니다.

23 그는 유용한 뭔가를 만드는 데 그것을 적용할 수 있을지 궁금했습니다.

24 _____ a lot of _____, he finally _____ two new _____.

A. materials   B. after   C. invented   D. testing

25 One had many _____ needles like those of _____ and the _____ had a hairy _____.

A. other   B. tiny   C. surface   D. burrs

26 When they _____ _____ together, they _____ a very good _____.

A. pressed   B. became   C. were   D. fastener

27 It was not _____ _____ _____ also _____ to use.

A. strong   B. but   C. easy   D. only

28 _____ then, many people have _____ his invention in many _____ _____.

A. different   B. since   C. ways   D. used

29 It _____ _____ _____ clothing, shoes, and bags.

A. used   B. is   C. for   D. often

30 Some people _____ it to _____ a _____ of _____ games.

A. number   B. different   C. use   D. play

31 In space, it _____ things _____ _____ _____.

A. away   B. keeps   C. floating   D. from

32 There is _____ _____ in nature. We just have to become _____ and _____ questions.

A. curious   B. nothing   C. ask   D. useless

24 수많은 실험 후에, 그는 마침내 두 가지 새로운 소재를 발명했습니다.

25 하나는 가시 식물과 같은 조그만 가시들이 많이 있는 것이었고, 다른 하나는 털로 덮인 표면이 있는 것이었습니다.

26 두 소재를 함께 붙이면, 매우 훌륭한 고정 장치가 되었습니다.

27 그것은 튼튼할 뿐만 아니라 사용하기도 쉬웠습니다.

28 그 후로, 많은 사람들이 그의 발명품을 다양한 방법으로 사용해 오고 있습니다.

29 그것은 옷, 신발, 가방에 흔히 사용됩니다.

30 몇몇 사람들은 여러 가지 게임을 하기 위해 그것을 사용합니다.

31 우주에서, 그것은 물건들이 떠다니는 것을 막아줍니다.

32 자연에 쓸모없는 것은 하나도 없습니다. 우리는 그저 호기심을 갖고 질문을 던지면 됩니다.

※ 다음 우리말과 일치하도록 빈칸에 알맞은 말을 쓰시오.

Nature's Inspiration

1 _____ flying birds _____ _____ plants, the way nature _____ _____ _____.

2 Some people _____ _____ use nature _____ _____ _____ _____ to find _____ to their problems.

3 Leonardo da Vinci (1452-1519) was _____ _____.

4 He wondered _____ _____ _____ _____.

5 He _____ watched birds, _____ _____, and drew pictures of them.

6 _____ _____ his invention was not _____, he _____ a bird's wings _____ _____ _____ _____ _____ a _____ _____.

7 _____ then, more and more people _____ successfully _____ the _____ _____ of _____ _____.

8 _____ _____ some of them.

Learning from a Bird: Moving Fast and Quietly

9 The _____ _____ was first made in Japan. But it _____ one problem.

10 When the train _____ a tunnel, the _____ _____ in air pressure _____ a very _____ _____.

11 It often _____ _____ _____ and _____ headaches.

12 A team of engineers _____ _____ _____ the problem, but they didn't know _____ _____ _____ _____ _____ the noise.

13 One day, one of _____ _____ _____ watching a bird _____ _____ _____ a meal.

14 He _____ the bird _____ and _____ _____ _____ _____ the water.

15 He wondered _____ _____ _____ _____ _____ the water so _____.

1 나는 새에서 자정 작용을 하는 식물까지, 자연이 기능하는 방식은 우리를 매료시킵니다.

2 몇몇 사람들은 그들의 문제에 대한 해결책을 찾기 위해 자연을 이용할 뿐만 아니라 자연을 모방하기까지 합니다.

3 레오나르도 다빈치(1452-1519)가 이러한 사람들 중 한 사람이었습니다.

4 그는 새들이 어떻게 날 수 있는지 궁금했습니다.

5 그는 새를 자세히 관찰했고, 기록했으며, 그림으로 그렸습니다.

6 그의 발명은 비록 성공하지 못했지만, 그는 나는 기계를 만들어 보려고 새의 날개를 모방했습니다.

7 그 후로, 점점 더 많은 사람들이 자연 속 천재의 놀라운 능력을 성공적으로 모방해 오고 있습니다.

8 그들 중 몇 가지를 알아봅시다.

새에게서 배우기: 빠르고 조용하게 움직이기

9 고속 열차는 일본에서 처음 만들어졌습니다. 하지만 그것은 한 가지 문제점이 있었습니다.

10 열차가 터널에 들어갔을 때, 갑작스러운 기압의 상승은 매우 시끄러운 소리를 발생시켰습니다.

11 그것은 종종 사람들의 잠을 깨웠고 두통을 일으켰습니다.

12 한 공학자 팀이 그 문제를 해결하려 했지만, 그들은 어떻게 소음을 줄일 수 있을지 몰랐습니다.

13 어느 날, 공학자들 중 한 사람이 먹이를 찾고 있는 새를 관찰하고 있었습니다.

14 그는 새가 빠르고 조용하게 물속으로 뛰어드는 것을 보았습니다.

15 그는 새가 어떻게 그렇게 우아하게 물속으로 들어가는지 궁금했습니다.

16 So, he _____ _____ about the bird and _____ its long, _____ _____ .

17 He _____ the _____ of the train _____ _____ the bird's _____ .

18 It was successful. Now the new train travels _____ _____ more quietly _____ _____ 10% faster _____ 15% _____ _____ .

Learning from Burrs: Inventing an All-Purpose Fastener

19 _____ _____ , a Swiss engineer, George de Mestral, _____ in the woods _____ his dog.

20 _____ his _____ _____ , he saw that _____ _____ his clothes and his dog's _____ .

21 He wanted _____ .

22 He _____ the burrs and _____ the ends of the burr needles _____ not _____ .

23 He wondered _____ that to make _____ .

24 _____ a _____ of _____ , he finally _____ two new materials.

25 One had many _____ _____ like _____ _____ _____ and _____ _____ had a _____ _____ .

26 When they _____ , they became a very good _____ .

27 It was _____ to use.

28 _____ then, many people _____ _____ his invention in _____ .

29 It _____ clothing, shoes, and bags.

30 Some people use it _____ _____ _____ games.

31 In space, it _____ things _____ _____ .

32 There is _____ _____ in nature. We just have to become _____ and _____ questions.

16 그래서 그는 그 새에 대해 더 연구했고, 새의 길고 좁은 부리를 발견했습니다.

17 그는 새의 부리를 모방하여 열차의 앞면을 다시 디자인했습니다.

18 그것은 성공이었습니다. 이제 새로운 열차는 더 조용할 뿐만 아니라 전기는 15% 덜 사용하면서 10% 더 빠르게 이동합니다.

가시 식물들에게서 배우기: 만능 고정 장치 발명하기

19 어느 날, 스위스 공학자 George de Mestral은 그의 개와 숲에서 하이킹하고 있었습니다.

20 집으로 돌아오는 길에, 그는 가시 식물이 자신의 옷과 개의 털에 붙어 있는 것을 보았습니다.

21 그는 어떻게 그런 일이 일어났는지 알고 싶었습니다.

22 그는 가시 식물들을 자세히 들여다보았고, 가시의 끝이 곧지 않다는 것을 알아챘습니다.

23 그는 유용한 뭔가를 만드는 데 그것을 적용할 수 있을지 궁금했습니다.

24 수많은 실험 후에, 그는 마침내 두 가지 새로운 소재를 발명했습니다.

25 하나는 가시 식물과 같은 조그만 가시들이 많이 있는 것이었고, 다른 하나는 털로 덮인 표면이 있는 것이었습니다.

26 두 소재를 함께 붙이면, 매우 훌륭한 고정 장치가 되었습니다.

27 그것은 튼튼할 뿐만 아니라 사용하기도 쉬웠습니다.

28 그 후로, 많은 사람들이 그의 발명품을 다양한 방법으로 사용해 오고 있습니다.

29 그것은 옷, 신발, 가방에 흔히 사용됩니다.

30 몇몇 사람들은 여러 가지 게임을 하기 위해 그것을 사용합니다.

31 우주에서, 그것은 물건들이 떠다니는 것을 막아줍니다.

32 자연에 쓸모없는 것은 하나도 없습니다. 우리는 그저 호기심을 갖고 질문을 던지면 됩니다.

※ 다음 문장을 우리말로 쓰시오.

Nature's Inspiration

1 From flying birds to self-cleaning plants, the way nature works fascinates us.

➡ _____

2 Some people not only use nature but also imitate it to find solutions to their problems.

➡ _____

3 Leonardo da Vinci (1452-1519) was one such person.

➡ _____

4 He wondered how birds could fly.

➡ _____

5 He closely watched birds, made notes, and drew pictures of them.

➡ _____

6 Even though his invention was not successful, he imitated a bird's wings to try to make a flying machine.

➡ _____

7 Since then, more and more people have successfully imitated the surprising abilities of nature's genius.

➡ _____

8 Let's explore some of them.

➡ _____

Learning from a bird: Moving Fast and Quietly

9 The high-speed train was first made in Japan. But it had one problem.

➡ _____

10 When the train entered a tunnel, the sudden increase in air pressure created a very loud sound.

➡ _____

11 It often woke people up and caused headaches.

➡ _____

12 A team of engineers tried to solve the problem, but they didn't know how they could reduce the noise.

➡ _____

13 One day, one of the engineers was watching a bird in search of a meal.

➡ _____

14 He saw the bird quickly and quietly diving into the water.

➡ _____

15 He wondered how the bird entered the water so gracefully.
➡ _____

16 So, he studied more about the bird and discovered its long, narrow beak.
➡ _____

17 He redesigned the front of the train by imitating the bird's beak.
➡ _____

18 It was successful. Now the new train travels not only more quietly but also 10% faster with 15% less electricity.
➡ _____

Learning from Burrs: Inventing an All-Purpose Fastener

19 One day, a Swiss engineer, George de Mestral, was hiking in the woods with his dog.
➡ _____

20 On his way home, he saw that burrs were stuck to his clothes and his dog's hair.
➡ _____

21 He wanted to know how that happened.
➡ _____

22 He took a closer look at the burrs and noticed that the ends of the burr needles were not straight.
➡ _____

23 He wondered if he could apply that to make something useful.
➡ _____

24 After a lot of testing, he finally invented two new materials.
➡ _____

25 One had many tiny needles like those of burrs and the other had a hairy surface.
➡ _____

26 When they were pressed together, they became a very good fastener.
➡ _____

27 It was not only strong but also easy to use.
➡ _____

28 Since then, many people have used his invention in many different ways.
➡ _____

29 It is often used for clothing, shoes, and bags.
➡ _____

30 Some people use it to play a number of different games.
➡ _____

31 In space, it keeps things from floating away.
➡ _____

32 There is nothing useless in nature. We just have to become curious and ask questions.
➡ _____

※ 다음 괄호 안의 단어들을 우리말에 맞도록 바르게 배열하시오.

Nature's Inspiration

1 (flying / from / to / birds / plants, / self-cleaning / way / the / works / nature / us. / fascinates)

➡ _____

_____

2 (people / some / only / not / nature / use / also / but / it / imitate / find / to / solutions / their / to / problems.)

➡ _____

_____

3 (da / Leonardo / Vinci / (1452-1519) / one / was / person. / such)

➡ _____

4 (wondered / he / birds / how / fly. / could)

➡ _____

5 (closely / he / birds, / watched / notes, / made / drew / and / of / them. / pictures)

➡ _____

6 (though / even / invention / his / not / was / successful, / imitated / he / birds's / a / wings / try / to / make / to / flying / a / machine.)

➡ _____

_____

7 (then, / since / more / more / and / people / have / successfully / the / imitated / abilities / surprising / nature's / of / genius.)

➡ _____

_____

8 (explore / let's / of / some / them.)

➡ _____

Learning from a bird: Moving Fast and Quietly

9 (high-speed / the / was / train / made / first / Japan. / in // but / had / it / one / problem.)

➡ _____

10 (the / when / entered / train / tunnel, / a / sudden / the / in / increase / pressure / air / created / very / a / sound. / loud)

➡ _____

_____

11 (often / it / people / woke / up / and / headaches. / caused)

➡ _____

1 나는 새에서 자정 작용을 하는 식물까지, 자연이 기능하는 방식은 우리를 매료시킵니다.

2 몇몇 사람들은 그들의 문제에 대한 해결책을 찾기 위해 자연을 이용할 뿐만 아니라 자연을 모방하기까지 합니다.

3 레오나르도 다빈치(1452-1519)가 이러한 사람들 중 한 사람이었습니다.

4 그는 새들이 어떻게 날 수 있는지 궁금했습니다.

5 그는 새를 자세히 관찰했고, 기록했으며, 그림으로 그렸습니다.

6 그의 발명은 비록 성공하지 못했지만, 그는 나는 기계를 만들어 보려고 새의 날개를 모방했습니다.

7 그 후로, 점점 더 많은 사람들이 자연 속 천재의 놀라운 능력을 성공적으로 모방해 오고 있습니다.

8 그들 중 몇 가지를 알아봅시다.

새에게서 배우기: 빠르고 조용하게 움직이기

9 고속 열차는 일본에서 처음 만들어졌습니다. 하지만 그것은 한 가지 문제점이 있었습니다.

10 열차가 터널에 들어갔을 때, 갑작스러운 기압의 상승은 매우 시끄러운 소리를 발생시켰습니다.

11 그것은 종종 사람들의 잠을 깨웠고 두통을 일으켰습니다.

12 (team / a / engineers / of / to / tried / the / solve / problem, / they / but / know / didn't / they / how / reduce / could / noise. / the)

➡ _____

_____

13 (day, / one / of / one / engineers / the / was / a / watching / bird / search / in / a / of / meal.)

➡ _____

14 (saw / he / the / quickly / bird / and / diving / quietly / into / water. / the)

➡ _____

15 (wondered / he / the / how / bird / the / entered / water / gracefully. / so)

➡ _____

16 (he / so, / studied / about / more / bird / the / and / its / discovered / long, / beak. / narrow)

➡ _____

17 (redesigned / he / the / of / front / the / by / train / imitating / bird's / the / beak.)

➡ _____

18 (was / it / successful. // the / now / train / new / not / travels / more / only / quietly / also / but / 10% / with / faster / 15% / electricity. / less)

➡ _____

_____

Learning from Burrs: Inventing an All-Purpose Fastener

19 (day, / one / Swiss / a / engineer, / de / George / Mestral, / hiking / was / the / in / woods / his / dog. / with)

➡ _____

_____

20 (his / way / on / home, / saw / he / burrs / that / stuck / were / his / to / clothes / and / dog's / his / hair.)

➡ _____

_____

21 (wanted / he / know / to / how / happened. / that)

➡ _____

22 (took / he / closer / a / at / look / burrs / the / and / that / noticed / ends / the / of / burr / the / were / needles / straight. / not)

➡ _____

_____

12 한 공학자 팀이 그 문제를 해결하려 했지만, 그들은 어떻게 소음을 줄일 수 있을지 몰랐습니다.

13 어느 날, 공학자들 중 한 사람이 먹이를 찾고 있는 새를 관찰하고 있었습니다.

14 그는 새가 빠르고 조용하게 물속으로 뛰어드는 것을 보았습니다.

15 그는 새가 어떻게 그렇게 우아하게 물속으로 들어가는지 궁금했습니다.

16 그래서 그는 그 새에 대해 더 연구했고, 새의 길고 좁은 부리를 발견했습니다.

17 그는 새의 부리를 모방하여 열차의 앞면을 다시 디자인했습니다.

18 그것은 성공이었습니다. 이제 새로운 열차는 더 조용할 뿐만 아니라 전기는 15% 덜 사용하면서 10% 더 빠르게 이동합니다.

가시 식물들에게서 배우기: 만능 고정 장치 발명하기

19 어느 날, 스위스 공학자 George de Mestral은 그의 개와 숲에서 하이킹하고 있었습니다.

20 집으로 돌아오는 길에, 그는 가시 식물이 자신의 옷과 개의 털에 붙어 있는 것을 보았습니다.

21 그는 어떻게 그런 일이 일어났는지 알고 싶었습니다.

22 그는 가시 식물들을 자세히 들여다보았고, 가시의 끝이 곧지 않다는 것을 알아챘습니다.

23 (wondered / he / if / could / he / that / apply / to / something / make / useful.)

➡ _____

24 (a / after / of / lot / testing, / finally / he / two / invented / materials. / new)

➡ _____

25 (had / one / tiny / many / needles / those / like / burrs / of / the / and / had / other / a / surface. / hairy)

➡ _____
_____

26 (they / when / pressed / were / together, / became / they / very / a / fastener. / good)

➡ _____

27 (was / it / only / not / strong / also / but / to / easy / use.)

➡ _____

28 (then, / since / people / many / have / his / used / invention / many / in / ways. / different)

➡ _____
_____

29 (it / it / often / for / used / clothing, / and / shoes, / bags.)

➡ _____

30 (people / some / it / use / play / to / a / of / number / games. / different)

➡ _____

31 (space, / in / keeps / it / from / things / away. / floating)

➡ _____

32 (is / there / useless / nothing / nature. / in // just / we / to / have / curious / become / and / questions. / ask)

➡ _____
_____

23 그는 유용한 뭔가를 만드는 데 그것을 적용할 수 있을지 궁금했습니다.

24 수많은 실험 후에, 그는 마침내 두 가지 새로운 소재를 발명했습니다.

25 하나는 가시 식물과 같은 조그만 가시들이 많이 있는 것이었고, 다른 하나는 털로 덮인 표면이 있는 것이었습니다.

26 두 소재를 함께 붙이면, 매우 훌륭한 고정 장치가 되었습니다.

27 그것은 튼튼할 뿐만 아니라 사용하기도 쉬웠습니다.

28 그 후로, 많은 사람들이 그의 발명품을 다양한 방법으로 사용해 오고 있습니다.

29 그것은 옷, 신발, 가방에 흔히 사용됩니다.

30 몇몇 사람들은 여러 가지 게임을 하기 위해 그것을 사용합니다.

31 우주에서, 그것은 물건들이 떠다니는 것을 막아줍니다.

32 자연에 쓸모없는 것은 하나도 없습니다. 우리는 그저 호기심을 갖고 질문을 던지면 됩니다.

※ 다음 우리말을 영어로 쓰시오.

Nature's Inspiration

1 나는 새에서 자정 작용을 하는 식물까지, 자연이 기능하는 방식은 우리를 매료시킵니다.

➡ _____

2 몇몇 사람들은 그들의 문제에 대한 해결책을 찾기 위해 자연을 이용할 뿐만 아니라 자연을 모방하기까지 합니다.

➡ _____

3 레오나르도 다빈치(1452–1519)가 이러한 사람들 중 한 사람이었습니다.

➡ _____

4 그는 새들이 어떻게 날 수 있는지 궁금했습니다.

➡ _____

5 그는 새를 자세히 관찰했고, 기록했으며, 그림으로 그렸습니다.

➡ _____

6 그의 발명은 비록 성공하지 못했지만, 그는 나는 기계를 만들어 보려고 새의 날개를 모방했습니다.

➡ _____

7 그 후로, 점점 더 많은 사람들이 자연 속 천재의 놀라운 능력을 성공적으로 모방해 오고 있습니다.

➡ _____

8 그들 중 몇 가지를 알아봅시다.

➡ _____

Learning from a bird: Moving Fast and Quietly

9 고속 열차는 일본에서 처음 만들어졌습니다. 하지만 그것은 한 가지 문제점이 있었습니다.

➡ _____

10 열차가 터널에 들어갔을 때, 갑작스러운 기압의 상승은 매우 시끄러운 소리를 발생시켰습니다.

➡ _____

11 그것은 종종 사람들의 잠을 깨웠고 두통을 일으켰습니다.

➡ _____

12 한 공학자 팀이 그 문제를 해결하려 했지만, 그들은 어떻게 소음을 줄일 수 있을지 몰랐습니다.

➡ _____

13 어느 날, 공학자들 중 한 사람이 먹이를 찾고 있는 새를 관찰하고 있었습니다.

➡ _____

14 그는 새가 빠르고 조용하게 물속으로 뛰어드는 것을 보았습니다.

➡ _____

15 그는 새가 어떻게 그렇게 우아하게 물속으로 들어가는지 궁금했습니다.
➡ _____

16 그래서 그는 그 새에 대해 더 연구했고, 새의 길고 좁은 부리를 발견했습니다.
➡ _____

17 그는 새의 부리를 모방하여 열차의 앞면을 다시 디자인했습니다.
➡ _____

18 그것은 성공적이었습니다. 이제 새로운 열차는 더 조용할 뿐만 아니라 전기는 15% 덜 사용하면서 10% 더 빠르게 이동합니다.
➡ _____
_____

Learning from Burrs: Inventing an All-Purpose Fastener
19 어느 날, 스위스 공학자 George de Mestral은 그의 개와 숲에서 하이킹하고 있었습니다.
➡ _____

20 집으로 돌아오는 길에, 그는 가시 식물이 자신의 옷과 개의 털에 붙어 있는 것을 보았습니다.
➡ _____

21 그는 어떻게 그런 일이 일어났는지 알고 싶었습니다.
➡ _____

22 그는 가시 식물들을 자세히 들여다보았고, 가시의 끝이 곧지 않다는 것을 알아챘습니다.
➡ _____

23 그는 유용한 뭔가를 만드는 데 그것을 적용할 수 있을지 궁금했습니다.
➡ _____

24 수많은 실험 후에, 그는 마침내 두 가지 새로운 소재를 발명했습니다.
➡ _____

25 하나는 가시 식물과 같은 조그만 가시들이 많이 있는 것이었고, 다른 하나는 털로 덮인 표면이 있는 것이었습니다.
➡ _____

26 두 소재를 함께 붙이면, 매우 훌륭한 고정 장치가 되었습니다.
➡ _____

27 그것은 튼튼할 뿐만 아니라 사용하기도 쉬웠습니다.
➡ _____

28 그 후로, 많은 사람들이 그의 발명품을 다양한 방법으로 사용해 오고 있습니다.
➡ _____

29 그것은 옷, 신발, 가방에 흔히 사용됩니다.
➡ _____

30 몇몇 사람들은 여러 가지 게임을 하기 위해 그것을 사용합니다.
➡ _____

31 우주에서, 그것은 물건들이 떠다니는 것을 막아줍니다.
➡ _____

32 자연에 쓸모없는 것은 하나도 없습니다. 우리는 그저 호기심을 갖고 질문을 던지면 됩니다.
➡ _____

※ 다음 우리말과 일치하도록 빈칸에 알맞은 말을 쓰시오.

Culture & Life

1. Polar Bears, _____ _____

2. Polar bears _____ _____ _____ because they have _____ _____ _____ _____ the heat from the sun.

3. _____ _____ their hairs _____ an _____ _____ .

4. This also _____ them _____ _____ .

1. 북극곰, 북극
2. 북극곰은 태양열을 쉽게 흡수할 수 있는 검은 피부를 가지고 있기 때문에 추위에서 생존한다.
3. 북극곰 털 하나하나에는 공기층이 있다.
4. 이것 또한 따뜻함을 유지하는 데 도움이 된다.

Culture & Life

1. Sahara Desert _____ , _____ _____

2. The Sahara Desert is _____ _____ the driest but also the _____ _____ _____ _____ _____ .

3. But even at _____ _____ _____ _____ of day, Sahara Desert ants _____ _____ .

4. Do you know _____ _____ _____ _____ _____ _____ ?

5. Their bodies _____ _____ _____ unique hairs _____ _____ _____ _____ the sun.

1. 사하라 사막 개미들, 북아프리카
2. 사하라 사막은 지구상에서 가장 건조할 뿐만 아니라 가장 뜨거운 곳이다.
3. 하지만 하루 중 가장 뜨거운 시간에도 사하라 사막 개미들은 사냥을 간다.
4. 그들이 어떻게 그 열기에서 살아남는지 아는가?
5. 개미들의 몸은 태양으로부터의 열기를 반사해내는 독특한 털로 덮여 있다.

Culture & Life Project

1. You know horses _____ _____ _____ , _____ _____ ?

2. _____ _____ _____ _____ is that they have _____ _____ .

3. Our group designed shoes _____ _____ a _____ _____ .

4. _____ you _____ them, you will _____ _____ run faster _____ _____ _____ .

1. 여러분은 말이 빨리 달리는 것을 알고 있습니다, 그렇죠?
2. 그 이유 중의 하나는 그들이 튼튼한 발을 가지고 있다는 겁니다.
3. 우리 모둠은 말의 발을 모방해서 신발을 만들었습니다.
4. 여러분이 그것을 신으면, 여러분은 빨리 달릴 뿐만 아니라 키가 더 커 보일 겁니다.

※ 다음 우리말을 영어로 쓰시오.

> **Culture & Life**

1. 북극곰, 북극

   ➡ _____

2. 북극곰은 태양열을 쉽게 흡수할 수 있는 검은 피부를 가지고 있기 때문에 추위에서 생존한다.

   ➡ _____

3. 북극곰 털 하나하나에는 공기층이 있다.

   ➡ _____

4. 이것 또한 따뜻함을 유지하는 데 도움이 된다.

   ➡ _____

> **Culture & Life**

1. 사하라 사막 개미들, 북아프리카

   ➡ _____

2. 사하라 사막은 지구상에서 가장 건조할 뿐만 아니라 가장 뜨거운 곳이다.

   ➡ _____

3. 하지만 하루 중 가장 뜨거운 시간에도 사하라 사막 개미들은 사냥을 간다.

   ➡ _____

4. 그들이 어떻게 그 열기에서 살아남는지 아는가?

   ➡ _____

5. 개미들의 몸은 태양으로부터의 열기를 반사해내는 독특한 털로 덮여 있다.

   ➡ _____

> **Culture & Life Project**

1. 여러분은 말이 빨리 달리는 것을 알고 있습니다, 그렇죠?

   ➡ _____

2. 그 이유 중의 하나는 그들이 튼튼한 발을 가지고 있다는 겁니다.

   ➡ _____

3. 우리 모둠은 말의 발을 모방해서 신발을 만들었습니다.

   ➡ _____

4. 여러분이 그것을 신으면, 여러분은 빨리 달릴 뿐만 아니라 키가 더 커 보일 겁니다.

   ➡ _____

※ 다음 영어를 우리말로 쓰시오.

01 apologize _____

02 trouble _____

03 unique _____

04 response _____

05 creative _____

06 responsible _____

07 beak _____

08 sneeze _____

09 compare _____

10 actually _____

11 crime _____

12 retelling _____

13 unfortunately _____

14 steadily _____

15 advantage _____

16 straw _____

17 deserve _____

18 stepmother _____

19 borrow _____

20 stork _____

21 complain _____

22 frame _____

23 bother _____

24 support _____

25 grab _____

26 hairy _____

27 impolite _____

28 independent _____

29 skinny _____

30 peacefully _____

31 shocked _____

32 completely _____

33 artwork _____

34 rude _____

35 break into _____

36 be made of _____

37 instead of _____

38 point of view _____

39 be taken to _____

40 run out of _____

41 fall in love with _____

42 on one's own _____

43 make sense _____

※ 다음 우리말을 영어로 쓰시오.

01	부리	
02	등장인물	
03	범죄	
04	꾸준히	
05	계모	
06	벽돌	
07	붙잡다	
08	불행하게도, 안타깝게도	
09	털이 많은	
10	무례한	
11	완전하게	
12	무례한	
13	짚, 지푸라기	
14	예술 작품	
15	누명을 씌우다	
16	자립심이 강한, 독립적인	
17	사과	
18	부양하다, 지지하다	
19	땀; 땀을 흘리다	
20	비교하다	
21	비슷한, 유사한	

22	실제로	
23	불평하다	
24	반응, 응답	
25	~을 받을 만하다	
26	궁전	
27	장점	
28	사과하다	
29	책임이 있는	
30	마른	
31	선호하다	
32	괴롭히다	
33	재채기하다	
34	귀찮게 하다	
35	침입하다	
36	스스로	
37	관점, 견해	
38	~ 대신에	
39	~로 만들어지다	
40	~이 다 떨어지다	
41	끌려가다	
42	적어도	
43	~와 사랑에 빠지다	

※ 다음 영영풀이에 알맞은 단어를 <보기>에서 골라 쓴 후, 우리말 뜻을 쓰시오.

1 _____ : not polite: _____

2 _____ : covered with a lot of hair: _____

3 _____ : by bad luck: _____

4 _____ : very thin or too thin: _____

5 _____ : be worthy: _____

6 _____ : to disturb or bother someone: _____

7 _____ : the hard usually pointed parts that cover a bird's mouth: _____

8 _____ : a large bird that has long legs and a long bill and neck: _____

9 _____ : having features that are the same: _____

10 _____ : a statement saying that you are sorry about something: _____

11 _____ : the dry stems of wheat and other grain plants: _____

12 _____ : an illegal action or activity for which a person can be punished by law:
_____

13 _____ : to produce a clear liquid from your skin when you are hot or nervous:
_____

14 _____ : to have air come suddenly and noisily out through your nose and mouth in
a way that you cannot control: _____

15 _____ : confident and free to do things without needing help from other people:
_____

16 _____ : to say or write that you are unhappy, sick, uncomfortable, etc., or that
you do not like something: _____

보기

skinny	hairy	apology	straw
trouble	stork	sneeze	independent
unfortunately	rude	similar	crime
deserve	beak	complain	sweat

※ 다음 우리말과 일치하도록 빈칸에 알맞은 말을 쓰시오.

Listen & Speak 1 A

G: _____ you _____ the book, Taeho?

B: Yes. I finished it yesterday, Anna.

G: _____ _____ _____ _____ it?

B: It was _____.

G: _____ is the book _____?

B: You know the story of Heungbu, _____? In the book, Nolbu tells the story from his _____ _____ _____.

G: What does he _____?

B: Well, he says he didn't help Heungbu for a _____. He wanted Heungbu to _____ _____ on his own and be _____.

G: Wow, it's a _____ story! I _____ _____ _____ the book. Thanks, Taeho.

Listen & Speak 1 B

B: _____ did you _____ the movie *Good Friends*, Yura?

G: I liked it. It was fun to _____ the movie _____ the original book.

B: _____ did you like _____, the movie or the book?

G: Well, I liked the movie, but I think I _____ the book _____. The book _____ _____ _____ the _____ better.

B: That's interesting. To me, the movie was _____ because it was _____ _____ _____ the story.

G: That's true. I guess they _____ have their own _____.

B: You're _____.

Listen & Speak 2 A

W: You look _____, Juwon.

B: I think we will _____ _____ _____ _____ tomorrow, Ms. Kim.

W: Why do _____ _____ _____?

B: We will have a _____ _____ Class 3. They have _____ _____ in the school.

W: Look on the _____ _____. They might have strong players, but your class has _____ _____.

B: You're right. I didn't think about it _____. I'll go and practice!

G: 그 책 다 읽었니, 태호야?
B: 응. 어제 다 읽었어, Anna.
G: 어땠니?
B: 재미있었어.
G: 그 책은 무슨 내용이니?
B: 너 흥부 이야기 알지, 그렇지? 책에서는 놀부가 자신의 관점에서 이야기해.
G: 놀부가 뭐라고 하는데?
B: 음, 놀부는 이유가 있어서 흥부를 도와주지 않았다고 말하고 있어. 그는 흥부가 스스로 돈을 벌고 자립할 수 있기를 바랐거든.
G: 와, 독특한 이야기구나! 그 책을 빨리 읽고 싶어. 고마워, 태호야.

B: 'Good Friends' 영화 어땠니, 유라야?
G: 좋았어. 영화를 원작과 비교하는 게 재미있었어.
B: 너는 영화와 책 중 어떤 것이 더 좋았니?
G: 글쎄, 영화가 좋았지만 책이 더 재미있었던 것 같아. 책이 등장인물을 더 잘 이해하게 해줬거든.
B: 그거 흥미롭구나. 나는 이야기를 이해하기 더 쉬워서 영화가 더 좋았어.
G: 그건 맞아. 책과 영화 둘 다 각각의 장점들이 있는 것 같아.
B: 맞아.

W: 걱정스러워 보이는구나, 주원아.
B: 내일 축구 경기에서 질 것 같아요, 김 선생님.
W: 왜 그렇게 생각하니?
B: 저희는 3반과 경기가 있거든요. 3반에는 학교에서 가장 잘하는 선수들이 있잖아요.
W: 긍정적으로 생각하렴. 3반에 잘하는 선수들이 있을지 모르지만, 너희 반은 팀워크가 가장 좋잖아.
B: 선생님 말씀이 맞아요. 저는 그렇게 생각하지 못했어요. 가서 연습할게요!

Listen & Speak 2 B

M: _____ do you _____ about my drawing, Prince?

B: Wow, this picture is very _____!

M: _____ do you _____ _____?

B: I mean the picture shows a _____ that _____ an elephant.

M: You're right. Actually, many people thought it was a picture of a _____.

B: Really? That's _____.

M: I know. That's _____ I _____ to become a _____ _____ a painter.

B: Haha. _____ _____ I can understand _____ _____ _____ _____.

M: Thank you, Prince.

M: 왕자님, 제 그림에 대해 어떻게 생각하세요?

B: 우와, 이 그림은 너무 무섭군요!

M: 왜 그렇게 생각하죠?

B: 그림이 코끼리를 먹은 뱀을 보여주잖아요.

M: 왕자님 말이 맞아요. 사실 많은 사람들이 모자 그림이라고 생각했어요.

B: 정말요? 그거 재미있군요.

M: 맞아요. 그래서 제가 화가 대신에 비행사가 되기로 결심했던 거예요.

B: 하하. 적어도 나는 당신이 무엇을 의도한 건지 이해할 수 있어요.

M: 고마워요, 왕자님.

Real Life Communication

Ms. Parker: Now, _____ _____ _____ _____ this work of art. _____ _____ you _____ it?

Jinho: Well, is it even art?

Henry: _____ _____, it isn't _____ _____ a _____.

Ms. Parker: It is not just art. I think it is the _____ _____ _____ of the 20th century.

Mina: _____ do you _____ _____?

Ms. Parker: It is a perfect example of a _____ _____ _____ _____. The artist used _____ _____ to create art.

Claire: So, he didn't create _____ _____?

Ms. Parker: That's _____. He simply wanted people to look at the _____ _____ _____ _____ _____.

Mina: Thank you so much, Ms. Parker. I _____ today!

Ms. Parker: 자, 이 예술 작품을 보세요. 어떤가요?

Jinho: 글쎄요, 이것도 예술인가요?

Henry: 저한테는 변기 그 이상은 아닌데요.

Ms. Parker: 이건 그냥 예술이 아니에요. 나는 20세기의 가장 위대한 예술 작품이라고 생각해요.

Mina: 왜 그렇게 생각하세요?

Ms. Parker: 이것은 다른 관점에 대한 완벽한 예시예요. 작가는 작품을 만들기 위해 실생활 물건을 사용했어요.

Claire: 그러면 작가가 새로운 것을 만들지 않았다는 건가요?

Ms. Parker: 맞아요. 그는 그저 사람들이 다른 방식으로 사물을 보기를 원했어요.

Mina: 정말 감사합니다. Parker 선생님. 오늘 많은 걸 배웠어요!

Let's Check

B: Do you know the story *The Rabbit and the Turtle*?

G: Of _____, I do.

B: I think the _____ in the story is _____.

G: _____ do you _____ _____?

B: The turtle sees the rabbit _____ but doesn't _____ _____ _____. It is not _____.

G: I don't see it _____ _____. Why should the turtle _____ _____ _____ the rabbit? I don't think he _____ be.

B: That's _____.

B: 너는 '토끼와 거북이' 이야기를 아니?

G: 물론 알지.

B: 난 그 이야기 속의 거북이가 못됐다고 생각해.

G: 왜 그렇게 생각하니?

B: 거북이는 토끼가 자고 있는 것을 보지만 그를 깨우지 않잖아. 그건 공정하지 않아.

G: 나는 그렇게 보지 않아. 왜 거북이가 토끼에 대해 책임을 져야 해? 그가 그래야 한다고 생각하지 않아.

B: 흥미로운데.

※ 다음 우리말에 맞도록 대화를 영어로 쓰시오.

Listen & Speak 1 A

G: _____

B: _____

G: _____

B: _____

G: _____

B: _____

G: _____

B: _____

G: _____

G: 그 책 다 읽었니, 태호야?
B: 응. 어제 다 읽었어, Anna.
G: 어땠니?
B: 재미있었어.
G: 그 책은 무슨 내용이니?
B: 너 흥부 이야기 알지, 그렇지? 책에서는 놀부가 자신의 관점에서 이야기해.
G: 놀부가 뭐라고 하는데?
B: 음, 놀부는 이유가 있어서 흥부를 도와주지 않았다고 말하고 있어. 그는 흥부가 스스로 돈을 벌고 자립할 수 있기를 바랐거든.
G: 와, 독특한 이야기구나! 그 책을 빨리 읽고 싶어. 고마워, 태호야.

Listen & Speak 1 B

B: _____

G: _____

B: _____

G: _____

B: _____

G: _____

B: _____

B: 'Good Friends' 영화 어땠니, 유라야?
G: 좋았어. 영화를 원작과 비교하는 게 재미있었어.
B: 너는 영화와 책 중 어떤 것이 더 좋았니?
G: 글쎄, 영화가 좋았지만 책이 더 재미있었던 것 같아. 책이 등장인물을 더 잘 이해하게 해줬거든.
B: 그거 흥미롭구나. 나는 이야기를 이해하기 더 쉬워서 영화가 더 좋았어.
G: 그건 맞아. 책과 영화 둘 다 각각의 장점들이 있는 것 같아.
B: 맞아.

Listen & Speak 2 A

W: _____

B: _____

W: _____

B: _____

W: _____

B: _____

W: 걱정스러워 보이는구나, 주원아.
B: 내일 축구 경기에서 질 것 같아요, 김 선생님.
W: 왜 그렇게 생각하니?
B: 저희는 3반과 경기가 있거든요. 3반에는 학교에서 가장 잘하는 선수들이 있잖아요.
W: 긍정적으로 생각하렴. 3반에 잘하는 선수들이 있을지 모르지만, 너희 반은 팀워크가 가장 좋잖아.
B: 선생님 말씀이 맞아요. 저는 그렇게는 생각하지 못했어요. 가서 연습할게요!

Listen & Speak 2 B

M: _____

B: _____

M: _____

B: _____

M: _____

B: _____

M: _____

B: _____

M: _____

M: 왕자님, 제 그림에 대해 어떻게 생각하세요?

B: 우와, 이 그림은 너무 무섭군요!

M: 왜 그렇게 생각하죠?

B: 그림이 코끼리를 먹은 뱀을 보여주잖아요.

M: 왕자님 말이 맞아요. 사실 많은 사람들이 모자 그림이라고 생각했어요.

B: 정말요? 그거 재미있군요.

M: 맞아요. 그래서 제가 화가 대신에 비행사가 되기로 결심했던 거예요.

B: 하하. 적어도 나는 당신이 무엇을 의도한 건지 이해할 수 있어요.

M: 고마워요, 왕자님.

Real Life Communication

Ms. Parker: _____

Jinho: _____

Henry: _____

Ms. Parker: _____

Mina: _____

Ms. Parker: _____

_____

Claire: _____

Ms. Parker: _____

_____

Mina: _____

Ms. Parker: 자, 이 예술 작품을 보세요. 어떤가요?

Jinho: 글쎄요, 이것도 예술인가요?

Henry: 저한테는 변기 그 이상은 아닌데요.

Ms. Parker: 이건 그냥 예술이 아니에요. 나는 20세기의 가장 위대한 예술 작품이라고 생각해요.

Mina: 왜 그렇게 생각하세요?

Ms. Parker: 이것은 다른 관점에 대한 완벽한 예시예요. 작가는 작품을 만들기 위해 실생활 물건을 사용했어요.

Claire: 그러면 작가가 새로운 것을 만들지 않았다는 건가요?

Ms. Parker: 맞아요. 그는 그저 사람들이 다른 방식으로 사물을 보기를 원했어요.

Mina: 정말 감사합니다. Parker 선생님. 오늘 많은 걸 배웠어요!

Let's Check

B: _____

G: _____

B: _____

G: _____

B: _____

G: _____

B: _____

B: 너는 '토끼와 거북이' 이야기를 아니?

G: 물론 알지.

B: 난 그 이야기 속의 거북이가 못됐다고 생각해.

G: 왜 그렇게 생각하니?

B: 거북이는 토끼가 자고 있는 것을 보지만 그를 깨우지 않잖아. 그건 공정하지 않아.

G: 나는 그렇게 보지 않아. 왜 거북이가 토끼에 대해 책임을 져야 해? 그가 그래야 한다고 생각하지 않아.

B: 흥미로운데.

※ 다음 우리말과 일치하도록 빈칸에 알맞은 것을 골라 쓰시오.

The Three Little Pigs: Its True Story

1 Reporter: _____ to Animal World News. Last Sunday, a wolf was _____ to the police station for _____ _____ pigs' houses.

   A. blowing   B. taken   C. down   D. welcome

2 Today, we have the _____ _____ _____ and the wolf _____ us.

   A. little   B. with   C. third   D. pig

3 Mr. Pig, could you _____ _____ _____ _____ you and your brothers?

   A. what   B. to   C. explain   D. happened

4 Pig: Yes. My brothers and I thought it was time to _____ our own houses, so we _____ houses with _____, sticks, and _____.

   A. build   B. bricks   C. built   D. straw

5 _____ day, the wolf came and _____ _____ _____ my brothers' houses.

   A. blew   B. completely   C. down   D. one

6 He almost _____ _____ my house, but it was _____ _____ bricks, so he couldn't.

   A. of   B. blew   C. made   D. down

7 Reporter: _____ are your brothers _____ _____?

   A. doing   B. how   C. now

8 Pig: They are _____ _____ _____ their houses. They are _____ in my house.

   A. resting   B. to   C. shocked   D. lose

9 Reporter: Thank you, Mr. Pig. Now, _____ meet our second _____, the wolf. Mr. Wolf, could you tell us _____ _____?

   A. happened   B. guest   C. what   D. let's

10 Wolf: This _____ "Big Bad Wolf" _____ is _____.

   A. wrong   B. whole   C. thing

11 The _____ story is about a _____ from a _____ _____ and a cup of sugar.

   A. terrible   B. sneeze   C. cold   D. real

12 Reporter: _____ _____ you _____?

   A. mean   B. do   C. what

13 Wolf: _____ then, I _____ _____ a birthday cake _____ my dear old grandmother.

   A. for   B. was   C. back   D. making

14 I _____ _____ of sugar. I _____ the street to ask my neighbor for a cup of sugar.

   A. out   B. down   C. ran   D. walked

아기 돼지 삼 형제: 그것의 진짜 이야기

1 리포터: 'Animal World News' 에 오신 것을 환영합니다. 지난 일요일, 돼지들의 집들을 바람을 불어 넘어뜨린 늑대가 경찰서로 연행되었습니다.

2 오늘, 우리는 셋째 아기 돼지와 늑대를 모셨습니다.

3 Pig씨, 당신과 당신 형제들에게 무슨 일이 일어났는지 설명해 주시겠어요?

4 돼지: 네. 제 형제들과 저는 각자의 집들을 지을 때라고 생각했어요. 그래서 우리는 짚, 나무 막대기, 그리고 벽돌로 집을 지었어요.

5 어느 날, 늑대가 와서 제 형들의 집들을 바람을 불어 완전히 날려 버렸어요.

6 그는 제 집도 거의 날려 버릴 뻔했는데, 벽돌로 만들어져서 그럴 수가 없었죠.

7 리포터: 당신의 형제들은 지금 어떻게 지내고 있나요?

8 돼지: 그들은 집을 잃어서 충격을 받았어요. 그들은 제 집에서 쉬고 있어요.

9 리포터: 감사합니다, Pig씨. 이제 두 번째 손님인 늑대를 만나 보시죠. Wolf씨, 무슨 일이 있었는지 말씀해 주시겠어요?

10 늑대: 이 모든 '덩치 크고 못된 늑대' 사건은 잘못된 거예요.

11 진짜 이야기는 지독한 감기로 인한 재채기와 설탕 한 컵에 관한 거예요.

12 리포터: 무슨 말씀인가요?

13 늑대: 그때, 저는 사랑하는 할머니를 위해 생일 케이크를 만들고 있었어요.

14 설탕이 다 떨어졌더라고요. 저는 이웃에게 설탕 한 컵을 달라고 부탁하기 위해 길을 걸어갔어요.

15 When I _____ the door, it _____ _____ .
A. on   B. down   C. fell   D. knocked

16 Then I _____, "_____ pig, are you _____?"
A. little   B. in   C. called

17 I _____ just _____ the broken door when I felt a sneeze _____ _____ .
A. coming   B. grabbed   C. on   D. had

18 I _____ a great _____ and you know what? The whole straw house _____ _____ .
A. fell   B. sneeze   C. down   D. sneezed

19 I was very surprised _____ _____ _____ _____ .
A. had   B. by   C. happened   D. what

20 _____, the _____ thing _____ the second little pig's house.
A. to   B. unfortunately   C. happened   D. same

21 Reporter: Then _____ _____ _____ _____ to the third little pig's house?
A. you   B. why   C. go   D. did

22 Wolf: I still _____ that _____ of _____, so I went to the _____ house.
A. next   B. needed   C. sugar   D. cup

23 The _____ little pig _____ _____ his house _____ bricks.
A. of   B. had   C. third   D. built

24 I _____ _____, "I'm sorry to _____ you, but are you _____?"
A. trouble   B. in   C. out   D. called

25 And do you know _____ he _____? "Go _____. Don't _____ me again!"
A. bother   B. answered   C. what   D. away

26 How _____! I thought I _____ an _____, so I kept _____.
A. apology   B. knocking   C. deserved   D. impolite

27 When the police _____, of _____ they thought I was _____ this pig's house.
A. into   B. came   C. breaking   D. course

28 Reporter: Do you _____ you _____ _____?
A. were   B. think   C. framed

29 Wolf: Yes. The news reporters of the town thought a sick wolf _____ _____ _____ a cup of sugar didn't sound very _____.
A. exciting   B. to   C. going   D. borrow

30 So, they _____ me the "Big Bad Wolf." _____ you maybe _____ me a _____ of sugar?
A. could   B. lend   C. made   D. cup

31 Reporter: Thank you for your time. Everyone, _____ _____ _____ is the true story, the pig's or the wolf's?
A. think   B. do   C. which   D. you

15 제가 이웃집 문을 두드렸을 때, 문이 떨어졌어요.

16 그다음에 저는 "아기 돼지 씨, 안에 계신가요?"라고 불렀어요.

17 제가 부서진 문을 막 움켜잡았을 때 재채기가 나오는 걸 느꼈어요.

18 저는 재채기를 아주 크게 했고, 그거 아세요? 짚으로 만든 집 전체가 무너졌어요.

19 저는 일어난 일에 매우 놀랐어요.

20 안타깝게도, 둘째 아기 돼지의 집에서도 같은 일이 일어나고 말았어요.

21 리포터: 그렇다면 셋째 아기 돼지의 집에 왜 갔죠?

22 늑대: 저는 여전히 설탕 한 컵이 필요했어요. 그래서 옆집으로 갔어요.

23 셋째 아기 돼지는 벽돌로 집을 지었더라고요.

24 제가 소리쳤어요, "귀찮게 해 드려 죄송하지만, 안에 계신가요?"

25 그리고 그가 뭐라고 대답했는지 아세요? "가버려, 다신 귀찮게 하지 마!"

26 얼마나 무례한가요! 저는 사과를 받아 마땅하다고 생각했기 때문에 계속 문을 두드렸어요.

27 경찰이 왔을 때, 물론 그들은 제가 이 돼지의 집에 침입하고 있다고 생각했죠.

28 리포터: 당신은 당신이 누명을 썼다고 생각하나요?

29 늑대: 네. 마을의 신문 기자들은 설탕 한 컵을 빌리러 간 아픈 늑대가 별로 흥미롭지 않다고 생각했겠죠.

30 그래서 그들은 저를 '덩치 크고 못된 늑대'로 만든 거예요. 당신은 아마 제게 설탕 한 컵쯤은 빌려 줄 수 있으시겠죠?

31 리포터: 시간 내 주셔서 감사합니다. 여러분, 어떤 이야기가 진짜 이야기라고 생각하시나요, 돼지의 이야기일까요, 아니면 늑대의 이야기일까요?

※ 다음 우리말과 일치하도록 빈칸에 알맞은 것을 골라 쓰시오.

The Three Little Pigs: Its True Story

1 Reporter: _____ _____ Animal World News. Last Sunday, a wolf _____ _____ _____ the police station _____ _____ _____ _____ _____ .

2 Today, we have _____ _____ _____ _____ and the wolf _____ us.

3 Mr. Pig, could you _____ _____ _____ _____ _____ you and your brothers?

4 Pig: Yes. My brothers and I thought it was _____ _____ _____ _____ own houses, _____ we built houses _____ _____ , _____ , and _____ .

5 One day, the wolf came and _____ _____ my _____ .

6 He _____ _____ _____ my house, but it was _____ _____ bricks, _____ he _____ .

7 Reporter: _____ are your brothers _____ _____ ?

8 Pig: They are _____ _____ _____ their houses. They are _____ _____ my house.

9 Reporter: Thank you, Mr. Pig. Now, _____ _____ our second guest, the wolf. Mr. Wolf, could you _____ _____ _____ ?

10 Wolf: This _____ "Big Bad Wolf" thing _____ _____ .

11 The _____ _____ is _____ _____ from _____ _____ and a cup of sugar.

12 Reporter: _____ do you _____ ?

13 Wolf: Back then, I _____ _____ a birthday cake _____ my dear old grandmother.

14 I _____ _____ _____ sugar. I _____ _____ the street _____ _____ my neighbor _____ a cup of sugar.

아기 돼지 삼 형제: 그것의 진짜 이야기

1 리포터: 'Animal World News' 에 오신 것을 환영합니다. 지난 일요일, 돼지들의 집들을 바람을 불어 넘어뜨린 늑대가 경찰서로 연행되었습니다.

2 오늘, 우리는 셋째 아기 돼지와 늑대를 모셨습니다.

3 Pig씨, 당신과 당신 형제들에게 무슨 일이 일어났는지 설명해 주시겠어요?

4 돼지: 네. 제 형제들과 저는 각자의 집들을 지을 때라고 생각했어요. 그래서 우리는 짚, 나무 막대기, 그리고 벽돌로 집을 지었어요.

5 어느 날, 늑대가 와서 제 형들의 집들을 바람을 불어 완전히 날려 버렸어요.

6 그는 제 집도 거의 날려 버릴 뻔했는데, 벽돌로 만들어져서 그럴 수가 없었죠.

7 리포터: 당신의 형제들은 지금 어떻게 지내고 있나요?

8 돼지: 그들은 집을 잃어서 충격을 받았어요. 그들은 제 집에서 쉬고 있어요.

9 리포터: 감사합니다, Pig씨. 이제 두 번째 손님인 늑대를 만나 보시죠. Wolf씨, 무슨 일이 있었는지 말씀해 주시겠어요?

10 늑대: 이 모든 '덩치 크고 못된 늑대' 사건은 잘못된 거예요.

11 진짜 이야기는 지독한 감기로 인한 재채기와 설탕 한 컵에 관한 거예요.

12 리포터: 무슨 말씀인가요?

13 늑대: 그때, 저는 사랑하는 할머니를 위해 생일 케이크를 만들고 있었어요.

14 설탕이 다 떨어졌더라고요. 저는 이웃에게 설탕 한 컵을 달라고 부탁하기 위해 길을 걸어갔어요.

15 When I _____ _____ the door, it _____ _____.

16 Then I _____, "Little pig, are you _____?"

17 I _____ _____ _____ the broken door when I felt a _____ _____ _____.

18 I _____ a great _____ and you know what? The whole _____ house _____ _____.

19 I was very surprised _____ _____ _____ _____.

20 _____, the same thing _____ _____ the second little pig's house.

21 Reporter: Then _____ _____ _____ _____ _____ _____ the third little pig's house?

22 Wolf: I still needed _____ _____ _____ _____, so I went to the next house.

23 The third little pig _____ _____ his house _____ bricks.

24 I _____ _____, "I'm sorry _____ _____ _____, but are you _____?"

25 And do you know _____ _____ _____? " _____. Don't _____ _____ again!"

26 _____ _____! I thought I _____ an _____, _____ I _____ _____.

27 _____ the police _____, _____ _____ they thought I was _____ _____ this pig's house.

28 Reporter: Do you think you _____ _____?

29 Wolf: Yes. The news reporters of the town _____ a sick wolf _____ _____ a cup of sugar didn't sound very _____.

30 So, they made me the "Big Bad Wolf." _____ you maybe _____ _____ a cup of sugar?

31 Reporter: Thank you for your time. Everyone, _____ _____ _____ _____ the true story, the pig's or the wolf's?

15 제가 이웃집 문을 두드렸을 때, 문이 떨어졌어요.

16 그다음에 저는 "아기 돼지 씨, 안에 계신가요?"라고 불렀어요.

17 제가 부서진 문을 막 움켜잡았을 때 재채기가 나오는 걸 느꼈어요.

18 저는 재채기를 아주 크게 했고, 그거 아세요? 짚으로 만든 집 전체가 무너졌어요.

19 저는 일어난 일에 매우 놀랐어요.

20 안타깝게도, 둘째 아기 돼지의 집에서도 같은 일이 일어나고 말았어요.

21 리포터: 그렇다면 셋째 아기 돼지의 집에 왜 갔죠?

22 늑대: 저는 여전히 설탕 한 컵이 필요했어요. 그래서 옆집으로 갔어요.

23 셋째 아기 돼지는 벽돌로 집을 지었더라고요.

24 제가 소리쳤어요, "귀찮게 해 드려 죄송하지만, 안에 계신가요?"

25 그리고 그가 뭐라고 대답했는지 아세요? "가버려, 다신 귀찮게 하지 마!"

26 얼마나 무례한가요! 저는 사과를 받아 마땅하다고 생각했기 때문에 계속 문을 두드렸어요.

27 경찰이 왔을 때, 물론 그들은 제가 이 돼지의 집에 침입하고 있다고 생각했죠.

28 리포터: 당신은 당신이 누명을 썼다고 생각하나요?

29 늑대: 네. 마을의 신문 기자들은 설탕 한 컵을 빌리러 간 아픈 늑대가 별로 흥미롭지 않다고 생각했겠죠.

30 그래서 그들은 저를 '덩치 크고 못된 늑대'로 만든 거예요. 당신은 아마 제게 설탕 한 컵쯤은 빌려 줄 수 있으시겠죠?

31 리포터: 시간 내 주셔서 감사합니다. 여러분, 어떤 이야기가 진짜 이야기라고 생각하시나요, 돼지의 이야기일까요, 아니면 늑대의 이야기일까요?

※ 다음 문장을 우리말로 쓰시오.

The Three Little Pigs: Its True Story

1 Reporter: Welcome to Animal World News. Last Sunday, a wolf was taken to the police station for blowing down pigs' houses.

➡ _____

_____

2 Today, we have the third little pig and the wolf with us.

➡ _____

3 Mr. Pig, could you explain what happened to you and your brothers?

➡ _____

4 Pig: Yes. My brothers and I thought it was time to build our own houses, so we built houses with straw, sticks, and bricks.

➡ _____

_____

5 One day, the wolf came and completely blew down my brothers' houses.

➡ _____

6 He almost blew down my house, but it was made of bricks, so he couldn't.

➡ _____

7 Reporter: How are your brothers doing now?

➡ _____

8 Pig: They are shocked to lose their houses. They are resting in my house.

➡ _____

9 Reporter: Thank you, Mr. Pig. Now, let's meet our second guest, the wolf. Mr. Wolf, could you tell us what happened?

➡ _____

10 Wolf: This whole "Big Bad Wolf" thing is wrong.

➡ _____

11 The real story is about a sneeze from a terrible cold and a cup of sugar.

➡ _____

12 Reporter: What do you mean?

➡ _____

13 Wolf: Back then, I was making a birthday cake for my dear old grandmother.

➡ _____

14 I ran out of sugar. I walked down the street to ask my neighbor for a cup of sugar.

➡ _____

15 When I knocked on the door, it fell down.

➡ _____

16 Then I called, "Little pig, are you in?"

➡ _____

17 I had just grabbed the broken door when I felt a sneeze coming on.

➡ _____

18 I sneezed a great sneeze and you know what? The whole straw house fell down.

➡ _____

19 I was very surprised by what had happened.

➡ _____

20 Unfortunately, the same thing happened to the second little pig's house.

➡ _____

21 Reporter: Then why did you go to the third little pig's house?

➡ _____

22 Wolf: I still needed that cup of sugar, so I went to the next house.

➡ _____

23 The third little pig had built his house of bricks.

➡ _____

24 I called out, "I'm sorry to trouble you, but are you in?"

➡ _____

25 And do you know what he answered? "Go away. Don't bother me again!"

➡ _____

26 How impolite! I thought I deserved an apology, so I kept knocking.

➡ _____

27 When the police came, of course they thought I was breaking into this pig's house.

➡ _____

28 Reporter: Do you think you were framed?

➡ _____

29 Wolf: Yes. The news reporters of the town thought a sick wolf going to borrow a cup of sugar didn't sound very exciting.

➡ _____

30 So, they made me the "Big Bad Wolf." Could you maybe lend me a cup of sugar?

➡ _____

31 Reporter: Thank you for your time. Everyone, which do you think is the true story, the pig's or the wolf's?

➡ _____

_____

※ 다음 괄호 안의 단어들을 우리말에 맞도록 바르게 배열하시오.

The Three Little Pigs: Its True Story

1 (Reporter: / to / welcome / World / Animal / News. // Sunday, / last / wolf / a / was / to / taken / the / station / police / blowing / for / pigs' / down / houses.)
➡ _____

2 (we / today, / the / have / third / pig / little / and / wolf / the / us. / with)
➡ _____

3 (Pig, / Mr. / you / could / what / explain / to / happened / you / your / and / brothers?)
➡ _____

4 (Pig: / yes. // brothers / my / and / thought / I / was / it / to / time / build / own / our / houses, / we / so / houses / built / straw, / with / sticks, / bricks. / and)
➡ _____

5 (day, / one / wolf / the / came / and / blew / completely / down / brothers' / my / houses.)
➡ _____

6 (almost / he / down / blew / house, / my / it / but / was / of / made / bricks, / he / so / couldn't.)
➡ _____

7 (Reporter: / are / how / brothers / your / now? / doing)
➡ _____

8 (Pig: / are / they / to / shocked / lose / houses. / their // are / they / in / resting / house. / my)
➡ _____

9 (Reporter: / you, / thank / Pig. / Mr. // now, / meet / let's / second / our / guest, / wolf. / the // Wolf, / Mr. / you / could / us / tell / happened? / what)
➡ _____

10 (Wolf: / whole / this / Bad / "Big / thing / Wolf" / wrong. / is)
➡ _____

11 (real / the / is / story / about / sneeze / a / from / a / cold / terrible / and / / cup / a / sugar. / of)
➡ _____

12 (Reporter: / do / what / mean? / you)
➡ _____

13 (Wolf: / then, / back / was / I / making / birthday / a / for / cake / dear / my / grandmother. / old)
➡ _____

14 (ran / I / of / out / sugar. // walked / I / down / street / the / ask / to / neighbor / my / a / for / of / cup / sugar.)
➡ _____

아기 돼지 삼 형제: 그것의 진짜 이야기

1 리포터: 'Animal World News'에 오신 것을 환영합니다. 지난 일요일, 돼지들의 집들을 바람을 불어 넘어뜨린 늑대가 경찰서로 연행되었습니다.

2 오늘, 우리는 셋째 아기 돼지와 늑대를 모셨습니다.

3 Pig씨, 당신과 당신 형제들에게 무슨 일이 일어났는지 설명해 주시겠어요?

4 돼지: 네. 제 형제들과 저는 각자의 집들을 지을 때라고 생각했어요. 그래서 우리는 짚, 나무 막대기, 그리고 벽돌로 집을 지었어요.

5 어느 날, 늑대가 와서 제 형들의 집들을 바람을 불어 완전히 날려 버렸어요.

6 그는 제 집도 거의 날려 버릴 뻔했는데, 벽돌로 만들어져서 그럴 수가 없었죠.

7 리포터: 당신의 형제들은 지금 어떻게 지내고 있나요?

8 돼지: 그들은 집을 잃어서 충격을 받았어요. 그들은 제 집에서 쉬고 있어요.

9 리포터: 감사합니다, Pig씨. 이제 두 번째 손님인 늑대를 만나 보시죠. Wolf씨, 무슨 일이 있었는지 말씀해 주시겠어요?

10 늑대: 이 모든 '덩치 크고 못된 늑대' 사건은 잘못된 거예요.

11 진짜 이야기는 지독한 감기로 인한 재채기와 설탕 한 컵에 관한 거예요.

12 리포터: 무슨 말씀인가요?

13 늑대: 그때, 저는 사랑하는 할머니를 위해 생일 케이크를 만들고 있었어요.

14 설탕이 다 떨어졌더라고요. 저는 이웃에게 설탕 한 컵을 달라고 부탁하기 위해 길을 걸어갔어요.

15 (I / when / knocked / the / on / door, / fell / it / down.)
➡ _____

16 (I / then / called, / pig, / "little / are / in?" / you)
➡ _____

17 (had / I / just / the / grabbed / door / broken / when / felt / I / a / sneeze / on. / coming)
➡ _____

18 (sneezed / I / great / a / sneeze / you / and / what? / know // whole / the / straw / fell / house / down.)
➡ _____

19 (was / I / surprised / very / what / by / happened. / had)
➡ _____

20 (the / unfortunately, / same / happened / thing / the / to / little / second / house. / pig's)
➡ _____

21 (Reporter: / why / then / you / did / to / go / third / the / pig's / little / house?)
➡ _____

22 (Wolf: / still / I / that / needed / cup / sugar, / of / so / went / I / the / to / house. / next)
➡ _____

23 (third / the / pig / little / built / had / house / his / bricks. / of)
➡ _____

24 (called / I / out, / sorry / "I'm / to / you, / trouble / are / but / in?" / you)
➡ _____

25 (do / and / know / you / he / what / answered? // away. / "go // bother / don't / again!" / me)
➡ _____

26 (impolite! / how // thought / I / deserved / I / apology, / an / I / so / knocking. / kept)
➡ _____

27 (the / when / police / of / came, / course / thought / they / was / I / breaking / into / pig's / this / house.)
➡ _____
➡ _____

28 (Reporter: / you / do / you / think / framed? / were)
➡ _____

29 (Wolf: / yes. // news / the / of / reporters / town / the / thought / a / wolf / sick / to / going / borrow / cup / a / of / didn't / sugar / sound / exciting. / very)
➡ _____

30 (they / so, / me / made / the / Bad / "Big / Wolf." // you / could / lend / maybe / me / cup / a / sugar? / of)
➡ _____

31 (Reporter: / you / thank / for / time. / your // which / everyone, / you / do / think / the / is / story, / true / pig's / the / the / or / wolf's?)
➡ _____

15 제가 이웃집 문을 두드렸을 때, 문이 떨어졌어요.

16 그다음에 저는 "아기 돼지 씨, 안에 계신가요?"라고 불렀어요.

17 제가 부서진 문을 막 움켜잡았을 때 재채기가 나오는 걸 느꼈어요.

18 저는 재채기를 아주 크게 했고, 그거 아세요? 짚으로 만든 집 전체가 무너졌어요.

19 저는 일어난 일에 매우 놀랐어요.

20 안타깝게도, 둘째 아기 돼지의 집에서도 같은 일이 일어나고 말았어요.

21 리포터: 그렇다면 셋째 아기 돼지의 집에 왜 갔죠?

22 늑대: 저는 여전히 설탕 한 컵이 필요했어요. 그래서 옆집으로 갔어요.

23 셋째 아기 돼지는 벽돌로 집을 지었더라고요.

24 제가 소리쳤어요. "귀찮게 해 드려 죄송하지만, 안에 계신가요?"

25 그리고 그가 뭐라고 대답했는지 아세요? "가버려, 다신 귀찮게 하지 마!"

26 얼마나 무례한가요! 저는 사과를 받아 마땅하다고 생각했기 때문에 계속 문을 두드렸어요.

27 경찰이 왔을 때, 물론 그들은 제가 이 돼지의 집에 침입하고 있다고 생각했죠.

28 리포터: 당신은 당신이 누명을 썼다고 생각하나요?

29 늑대: 네. 마을의 신문 기자들은 설탕 한 컵을 빌리러 간 아픈 늑대가 별로 흥미롭지 않다고 생각했겠죠.

30 그래서 그들은 저를 '덩치 크고 못된 늑대'로 만든 거예요. 당신은 아마 제게 설탕 한 컵쯤은 빌려 줄 수 있으시겠죠?

31 리포터: 시간 내 주셔서 감사합니다. 여러분, 어떤 이야기가 진짜 이야기라고 생각하시나요. 돼지의 이야기일까요. 아니면 늑대의 이야기일까요?

※ 다음 우리말을 영어로 쓰시오.

The Three Little Pigs: Its True Story

1 리포터: 'Animal World News'에 오신 것을 환영합니다. 지난 일요일, 돼지들의 집들을 바람을 불어 넘어뜨린 늑대가 경찰서로 연행되었습니다.

➡ _____

_____

2 오늘, 우리는 셋째 아기 돼지와 늑대를 모셨습니다.

➡ _____

3 Pig씨, 당신과 당신 형제들에게 무슨 일이 일어났는지 설명해 주시겠어요?

➡ _____

4 돼지: 네. 제 형제들과 저는 각자의 집들을 지을 때라고 생각했어요. 그래서 우리는 짚, 나무 막대기, 그리고 벽돌로 집을 지었어요.

➡ _____

_____

5 어느 날, 늑대가 와서 제 형들의 집들을 바람을 불어 완전히 날려 버렸어요.

➡ _____

6 그는 제 집도 거의 날려 버릴 뻔했는데, 벽돌로 만들어져서 그럴 수가 없었죠.

➡ _____

7 리포터: 당신의 형제들은 지금 어떻게 지내고 있나요?

➡ _____

8 돼지: 그들은 집을 잃어서 충격을 받았어요. 그들은 제 집에서 쉬고 있어요.

➡ _____

9 리포터: 감사합니다, Pig씨. 이제 두 번째 손님인 늑대를 만나 보시죠. Wolf씨, 무슨 일이 있었는지 말씀해 주시겠어요?

➡ _____

10 늑대: 이 모든 '덩치 크고 못된 늑대' 사건은 잘못된 거예요.

➡ _____

11 진짜 이야기는 지독한 감기로 인한 재채기와 설탕 한 컵에 관한 거예요.

➡ _____

12 리포터: 무슨 말씀인가요?

➡ _____

13 늑대: 그때, 저는 사랑하는 할머니를 위해 생일 케이크를 만들고 있었어요.

➡ _____

14 설탕이 다 떨어졌더라고요. 저는 이웃에게 설탕 한 컵을 달라고 부탁하기 위해 길을 걸어갔어요.

➡ _____

15 제가 이웃집 문을 두드렸을 때, 문이 떨어졌어요.

➡ _____

16 그다음에 저는 "아기 돼지 씨, 안에 계신가요?"라고 불렀어요.

➡ _____

17 제가 부서진 문을 막 움켜잡았을 때 재채기가 나오는 걸 느꼈어요.

➡ _____

18 저는 재채기를 아주 크게 했고, 그거 아세요? 짚으로 만든 집 전체가 무너졌어요.

➡ _____

19 저는 일어난 일에 매우 놀랐어요.

➡ _____

20 안타깝게도, 둘째 아기 돼지의 집에서도 같은 일이 일어나고 말았어요.

➡ _____

21 리포터: 그렇다면 셋째 아기 돼지의 집에 왜 갔죠?

➡ _____

22 늑대: 저는 여전히 설탕 한 컵이 필요했어요. 그래서 옆집으로 갔어요.

➡ _____

23 셋째 아기 돼지는 벽돌로 집을 지었더라고요.

➡ _____

24 제가 소리쳤어요, "귀찮게 해 드려 죄송하지만, 안에 계신가요?"

➡ _____

25 그리고 그가 뭐라고 대답했는지 아세요? "가버려, 다신 귀찮게 하지 마!"

➡ _____

26 얼마나 무례한가요! 저는 사과를 받아 마땅하다고 생각했기 때문에 계속 문을 두드렸어요.

➡ _____

27 경찰이 왔을 때, 물론 그들은 제가 이 돼지의 집에 침입하고 있다고 생각했죠.

➡ _____

28 리포터: 당신은 당신이 누명을 썼다고 생각하나요?

➡ _____

29 늑대: 네. 마을의 신문 기자들은 설탕 한 컵을 빌리러 간 아픈 늑대가 별로 흥미롭지 않다고 생각했겠죠.

➡ _____
_____

30 그래서 그들은 저를 '덩치 크고 못된 늑대'로 만든 거예요. 당신은 아마 제게 설탕 한 컵쯤은 빌려 줄 수 있으시겠죠?

➡ _____

31 리포터: 시간 내 주셔서 감사합니다. 여러분, 어떤 이야기가 진짜 이야기라고 생각하시나요, 돼지의 이야기일까요, 아니면 늑대의 이야기일까요?

➡ _____
_____

※ 다음 우리말과 일치하도록 빈칸에 알맞은 말을 쓰시오.

Communication Task

1. A: Can anyone _____ the _____ _____ _____ _____?

2. B: _____ _____ it is *Sleeping Beauty*.

3. A: _____ do you _____ _____?

4. B: I think Semi is the princess _____ _____ _____ and Minsu is the _____ _____ _____ _____ _____ the princess.

5. A: Sorry, but that's _____ _____ _____.

1. A: 이야기의 제목을 추측해 볼 수 있나요?
2. B: 제 생각에 '잠자는 숲속의 공주' 같아요.
3. A: 왜 그렇게 생각하니?
4. B: 세미는 평화롭게 잠을 자고 있는 공주이고 민수는 공주를 찾고 있는 왕자예요.
5. A: 미안하지만 정답이 아니에요.

Before You Read

1. _____ _____ a fun story _____ this. - *Book Weekly*

2. I think I should _____ _____ _____ to the wolf. I'd _____ _____ about _____ _____ _____ _____. - *The Book Times*

3. I still don't know _____ _____ _____ _____, but I learned _____ everyone _____ _____ _____ _____ a crime. - *Library & Paper*

1. 모든 사람이 이와 같은 재미있는 이야기를 읽을 자격이 있다. – Book Weekly
2. 내 생각에 나는 늑대에게 사과해야 할 것 같다. 나는 그의 관점에 대해 생각해 본 적이 없었다. – The Book Times
3. 나는 여전히 누구의 이야기가 진실인지 모르겠지만, 누구든지 범죄에 누명을 쓸 수 있다는 것을 알게 되었다. – Library & Paper

After You Read

1. The _____ _____

2. The _____ _____ _____ _____ decided _____ _____ _____ _____ _____.

3. So, they _____ houses _____ _____ _____.

4. _____ _____, the wolf _____ _____ _____ _____ _____ the first and the _____ _____ _____ _____ _____.

5. But the wolf _____ _____ the third pig's house _____ it _____ _____ bricks.

1. 돼지 이야기
2. 세 마리의 아기 돼지들은 자신들의 집을 짓기로 결정했다.
3. 그래서 그들은 다른 재료들로 집을 지었다.
4. 어느 날, 늑대가 와서 첫째와 둘째 아기 돼지의 집을 바람을 불어 완전히 무너뜨렸다.
5. 하지만 늑대는 셋째 돼지의 집은 무너뜨릴 수 없었는데, 왜냐하면 그것은 벽돌로 만들어졌기 때문이었다.

※ 다음 우리말을 영어로 쓰시오.

Communication Task

1. A: 이야기의 제목을 추측해 볼 수 있나요?

   ➡ _____

2. B: 제 생각에 '잠자는 숲속의 공주' 같아요.

   ➡ _____

3. A: 왜 그렇게 생각하니?

   ➡ _____

4. B: 세미는 평화롭게 잠을 자고 있는 공주이고 민수는 공주를 찾고 있는 왕자예요.

   ➡ _____

   _____

5. A: 미안하지만 정답이 아니에요.

   ➡ _____

Before You Read

1. 모든 사람이 이와 같은 재미있는 이야기를 읽을 자격이 있다. – *Book Weekly*

   ➡ _____

2. 내 생각에 나는 늑대에게 사과해야 할 것 같다. 나는 그의 관점에 대해 생각해 본 적이 없었다. – *The Book Times*

   ➡ _____

3. 나는 여전히 누구의 이야기가 진실인지 모르겠지만, 누구든지 범죄에 누명을 쓸 수 있다는 것을 알게 되었다. –
   Library & Paper

   ➡ _____

After You Read

1. 돼지 이야기

   ➡ _____

2. 세 마리의 아기 돼지들은 자신들의 집을 짓기로 결정했다.

   ➡ _____

3. 그래서 그들은 다른 재료들로 집을 지었다.

   ➡ _____

4. 어느 날, 늑대가 와서 첫째와 둘째 아기 돼지의 집을 바람을 불어 완전히 무너뜨렸다.

   ➡ _____

5. 하지만 늑대는 셋째 돼지의 집은 무너뜨릴 수 없었는데, 왜냐하면 그것은 벽돌로 만들어졌기 때문이었다.

   ➡ _____

※ 다음 영어를 우리말로 쓰시오.

01 decision	22 consider	
02 difference	23 suggest	
03 especially	24 exchange	
04 convenient	25 prison	
05 dead end	26 reasonable	
06 frustrate	27 effective	
07 hedge	28 mythology	
08 beauty	29 escape	
09 origin	30 regularity	
10 solution	31 entrance	
11 confusion	32 reliable	
12 compare	33 choice	
13 unfortunately	34 exit	
14 maze	35 get out of	
15 labyrinth	36 look forward to	
16 actually	37 give it a try	
17 willingly	38 make a decision	
18 connect	39 turn around	
19 worth	40 lose one's way	
20 monster	41 a variety of	
21 closely	42 come up with	
	43 make a choice	

※ 다음 우리말을 영어로 쓰시오.

01 혼란, 혼동	
02 미, 아름다움	
03 믿을 만한	
04 결정하다	
05 제안하다	
06 자세히	
07 괴물	
08 탈출하다	
09 층, 바닥	
10 조심스러운	
11 방해하다, 좌절시키다	
12 출구	
13 신화	
14 선택	
15 편리한	
16 산울타리	
17 여기다	
18 미궁	
19 미로	
20 차이	
21 입구	

22 주목하다, 알아차리다	
23 출구	
24 감옥	
25 연결하다, 이어지다	
26 순서, 질서	
27 (가격이) 적당한	
28 결정, 결심	
29 규칙성	
30 불행하게도	
31 해결책	
32 기꺼이	
33 비교하다	
34 효과적인	
35 다양한	
36 ~에서 나오다, 도망치다	
37 선택하다	
38 돌다, 돌아서다	
39 ~을 기대하다	
40 시도하다, 한번 해보다	
41 ~을 생각해 내다	
42 결정하다	
43 길을 잃다	

※ 다음 영영풀이에 알맞은 단어를 <보기>에서 골라 쓴 후, 우리말 뜻을 쓰시오.

1 _____ : a way out of a public building or vehicle: _____

2 _____ : having a specified value: _____

3 _____ : to become joined or united or linked: _____

4 _____ : the point or place where something begins or is created: _____

5 _____ : the act of picking or deciding between two or more possibilities: _____

6 _____ : a door, gate, passage, etc. used for entering a room, building or place: _____

7 _____ : the quality that makes one person or thing unlike another: _____

8 _____ : to give things of a particular kind to each other at the same time: _____

9 _____ : a complicated series of paths, which it is difficult to find your way through: _____

10 _____ : ancient myths in general; the ancient myths of a particular culture, society, etc.: _____

11 _____ : to get away from a place where you have been kept as a prisoner or not allowed to leave: _____

12 _____ : a building where criminals are kept as punishment or where people accused of a crime are kept before their trial: _____

13 _____ : a situation in which people are uncertain about what to do or are unable to understand something clearly: _____

14 _____ : to make somebody feel annoyed or impatient because they cannot do or achieve what they want: _____

15 _____ : a row of bushes or small trees planted close together, usually along the edge of a field, garden, yard or road: _____

16 _____ : a system of paths separated by walls or hedges built in a park or garden that is designed so that it is difficult to find your way through: _____

보기			
frustrate	maze	connect	mythology
labyrinth	confusion	difference	choice
hedge	escape	exit	origin
prison	worth	exchange	entrance

※ 다음 우리말과 일치하도록 빈칸에 알맞은 말을 쓰시오.

Listen & Speak 1 A

W: How may I help you?

B: Hi! I _____ these shoes yesterday. Is it _____ to _____ them for the red shoes?

W: Oh, actually white is really _____ _____ _____.

B: I know, and that's _____ I spent a long time _____ _____ _____ yesterday. But I think that red will _____ _____ me.

W: Okay, no _____.

해석

W: 무엇을 도와드릴까요?
B: 안녕하세요! 제가 어제 이 신발을 샀는데요. 이것을 빨간색 신발로 교환하는 것이 가능한가요?
W: 오, 사실은 하얀색이 요즘 정말 인기 있어요.
B: 저도 알아요. 그래서 제가 어제 결정하는 데 오랜 시간을 보냈어요. 하지만 빨간색이 제게 더 잘 어울릴 것 같아요.
W: 알았어요, 문제없어요.

Listen & Speak 1 B

G: Mom, did you _____ where _____ _____ _____ our family trip to Jeju?

W: Almost. Come here and see the _____ _____ _____.

G: It looks good. Hmm... Mom, _____ _____ _____ to visit Mirror Maze Park _____ our second day?

W: It sounds _____, but I remember you said you wanted to go _____ _____.

G: I know, but I heard the park is _____ _____ more fun. Please ....

W: All right. _____ _____ our _____ for the second day.

G: Thank you! I'm very _____ about the trip.

W: It's great to hear that you're _____ _____ _____ the trip.

G: 엄마, 제주도 가족 여행 동안 어디 방문할지 정하셨어요?
W: 거의. 이리 와서 내가 만든 일정표를 보렴.
G: 좋아 보여요. 흠. 엄마, 우리 두 번째 날에 거울 미로 공원에 가는 것이 가능할까요?
W: 재미있을 거 같지만, 네가 말 타러 가고 싶다고 말한 것으로 기억하는데.
G: 저도 알아요, 근데 공원이 훨씬 더 재미있다고 들었어요. 제발요....
W: 알았다. 두 번째 날 우리의 일정을 변경하자.
G: 감사합니다! 전 이번 여행에 대해 너무 신이 나요.
W: 네가 이번 여행을 고대한다니 아주 좋구나.

Listen & Speak 2 A

M: Hi, do you _____ any _____?

G: Yes, please. Could you _____ a good Chinese restaurant in this building? I can't _____ _____ the two.

M: Hmm.... What _____ Pappa Chen's? Their food is good and the prices are _____.

G: Sounds great! How do I _____ _____ the restaurant?

M: It's on the _____ _____. You can use the elevator _____ _____. Pappa Chen's is _____ _____ the elevator.

G: Great! Thank you very much _____ your _____.

M: My _____. Enjoy your dinner.

M: 안녕하세요, 도움이 필요하신가요?
G: 네, 부탁드려요. 이 건물에서 좋은 중국 음식점을 추천해 주실 수 있나요? 두 개 중에 결정할 수가 없네요.
M: 음… 파파첸스는 어떠세요? 그곳 음식은 훌륭하고 가격이 합리적이에요.
G: 좋을 것 같은데요! 그 음식점에 어떻게 가나요?
M: 그것은 4층에 있습니다. 당신은 저기 있는 승강기를 탈 수 있고요. 파파첸스는 승강기 옆에 있습니다.
G: 아주 좋아요! 도와주셔서 정말 감사합니다.
M: 천만에요. 저녁 맛있게 드세요.

Listen & Speak 2 B

B: Hey, Minju, where are you?

G: Oh, Andrew, I'm _____. I'm _____.

B: Good. I was _____ that you were _____.

G: I think I'm okay. _____ _____ Mason and Jian?

B: They are already here at my house.

G: Good! Oh, I see the _____ _____. _____ _____ _____ _____ _____ your place from here?

B: You are almost here. _____ _____ _____ one more block. Then you will see Kim's Bakery.

G: Kim's Bakery? Okay ….

B: Then _____ _____ and _____ _____ for about 100 meters.

G: _____ _____ and _____ _____ …. Okay, thanks! I'll see you soon.

Real Life Communication

Mina: _____ _____ _____ _____ _____ the trip this weekend?

Jinho, Claire, & Henry: Yes!

Mina: Good! Don't _____ _____! We're meeting at 11 a.m. _____ _____ _____ the clock tower.

Jinho: You _____ _____! How do we _____ _____ the airport? I don't think we've _____ yet.

Henry: Jinho is right. We have two_____, bus or _____.

Claire: What about the subway? It's more _____ than the bus.

Henry: Is it _____ _____ get to Terminal 2 _____ _____?

Claire: Yes, I _____ _____.

Mina: Good. Okay, then let's _____ _____ _____.

Let's Check 1

B: What are you _____, Alice?

G: It's about the _____ of the _____.

B: _____? Wasn't that an old _____ _____ to keep the half-man, half-bull _____?

G: Oh, Juwon, you know about the story.

B: Not really. I _____ the name of the monster.

G: The Minotaur. The king of Crete was _____ at it and _____ it in a _____.

B: 민주야, 너 어디야?

G: 오, Andrew, 나 가고 있어. 가고 있어.

B: 좋아. 네가 길을 잃었을까봐 걱정했어.

G: 괜찮은 것 같아. Mason이랑 지안이는?

B: 그들은 우리 집에 벌써 왔지.

G: 좋아! 오, 우체국이 보여. 여기서부터 너희 집까지 어떻게 가니?

B: 거의 다 왔네. 한 블록 더 직진해. 그럼 너는 킴스 빵집이 보일 거야.

G: 킴스 빵집? 알았어… .

B: 그럼 오른쪽으로 돌아서 100m 정도 직진해.

G: 오른쪽으로 돌아서 직진이라… . 알았어, 고마워! 곧 보자.

Mina: 너희 모두 이번 주말에 여행갈 준비 됐니?

Jinho, Claire, & Henry: 응!

Mina: 좋아! 늦지 마! 우리는 시계탑 앞에서 오전 11시에 만날 거야.

Jinho: 알았어! 우리 공항까지 어떻게 가지? 우리가 아직 결정하지 않은 것 같은데.

Henry: 진호 말이 맞아. 우리는 버스랑 지하철, 두 가지 선택이 있어.

Claire: 지하철은 어때? 그것은 버스보다 더 믿을 만하잖아.

Henry: 2터미널까지 지하철로 가는 것이 가능하니?

Claire: 응, 내가 이미 확인해 봤어.

Mina: 좋아. 그래, 그럼 지하철을 타자.

B: 무엇을 읽고 있니, Alice?

G: 미궁의 기원에 관한 거야.

B: 미궁? 그건 반인반수 괴물을 가두기 위한 옛 신화 속 감옥 아니니?

G: 와, 주원아, 너 그 이야기에 대해 아는구나.

B: 그다지 잘 아는 건 아니야. 그 괴물의 이름을 잊어버렸어.

G: 미노타우루스야. 크레타의 왕이 그 괴물에 화가 나서 그것을 미궁에 가두었지.

※ 다음 우리말에 맞도록 대화를 영어로 쓰시오.

Listen & Speak 1 A

W: _____

B: _____

_____

W: _____

B: _____

_____

W: _____

Listen & Speak 1 B

G: _____

W: _____

G: _____

_____

W: _____

G: _____

W: _____

G: _____

W: _____

Listen & Speak 2 A

M: _____

G: _____

M: _____

_____

G: _____

M: _____

_____

G: _____

M: _____

해석

W: 무엇을 도와드릴까요?
B: 안녕하세요! 제가 어제 이 신발을 샀는데요. 이것을 빨간색 신발로 교환하는 것이 가능한가요?
W: 오, 사실은 하얀색이 요즘 정말 인기 있어요.
B: 저도 알아요. 그래서 제가 어제 결정하는 데 오랜 시간을 보냈어요. 하지만 빨간색이 제게 더 잘 어울릴 것 같아요.
W: 알았어요. 문제없어요.

G: 엄마, 제주도 가족 여행 동안 어디 방문할지 정하셨어요?
W: 거의. 이리 와서 내가 만든 일정표를 보렴.
G: 좋아 보여요. 흠. 엄마, 우리 두 번째 날에 거울 미로 공원에 가는 것이 가능할까요?
W: 재미있을 거 같지만, 네가 말 타러 가고 싶다고 말한 것으로 기억하는데.
G: 저도 알아요. 근데 공원이 훨씬 더 재미있다고 들었어요. 제발요....
W: 알았다. 두 번째 날 우리의 일정을 변경하자.
G: 감사합니다! 전 이번 여행에 대해 너무 신이 나요.
W: 네가 이번 여행을 고대한다니 아주 좋구나.

M: 안녕하세요, 도움이 필요하신가요?
G: 네, 부탁드려요. 이 건물에서 좋은 중국 음식점을 추천해 주실 수 있나요? 두 개 중에 결정할 수가 없네요.
M: 음… 파파첸스는 어떠세요? 그곳 음식은 훌륭하고 가격이 합리적이에요.
G: 좋을 것 같은데요! 그 음식점에 어떻게 가나요?
M: 그것은 4층에 있습니다. 당신은 저기 있는 승강기를 탈 수 있고요. 파파첸스는 승강기 옆에 있습니다.
G: 아주 좋아요! 도와주셔서 정말 감사합니다.
M: 천만에요. 저녁 맛있게 드세요.

Listen & Speak 2 B

B: _____

G: _____

B: _____

G: _____

B: _____

G: _____

B: _____

G: _____

B: _____

G: _____

B: 민주야, 너 어디야?

G: 오, Andrew, 나 가고 있어. 가고 있어.

B: 좋아. 네가 길을 잃었을까봐 걱정했어.

G: 괜찮은 것 같아. Mason이랑 지안이는?

B: 그들은 우리 집에 벌써 왔지.

G: 좋아! 오, 우체국이 보여. 여기서부터 너희 집까지 어떻게 가니?

B: 거의 다 왔네. 한 블록 더 직진해. 그럼 너는 킴스 빵집이 보일 거야.

G: 킴스 빵집? 알았어….

B: 그럼 오른쪽으로 돌아서 100m 정도 직진해.

G: 오른쪽으로 돌아서 직진이라…. 알았어, 고마워! 곧 보자.

Real Life Communication

Mina: _____

Jinho, Claire, & Henry: _____

Mina: _____

Jinho: _____

Henry: _____

Claire: _____

Henry: _____

Claire: _____

Mina: _____

Mina: 너희 모두 이번 주말에 여행갈 준비 됐니?

Jinho, Claire, & Henry: 응!

Mina: 좋아! 늦지 마! 우리는 시계탑 앞에서 오전 11시에 만날 거야.

Jinho: 알았어! 우리 공항까지 어떻게 가지? 우리가 아직 결정하지 않은 것 같은데.

Henry: 진호 말이 맞아. 우리는 버스랑 지하철, 두 가지 선택이 있어.

Claire: 지하철은 어때? 그것은 버스보다 더 믿을 만하잖아.

Henry: 2터미널까지 지하철로 가는 것이 가능하니?

Claire: 응, 내가 이미 확인해 봤어.

Mina: 좋아. 그래, 그럼 지하철을 타자.

Let's Check 1

B: _____

G: _____

B: _____

G: _____

B: _____

G: _____

B: 무엇을 읽고 있니, Alice?

G: 미궁의 기원에 관한 거야.

B: 미궁? 그건 반인반수 괴물을 가두기 위한 옛 신화 속 감옥 아니니?

G: 와, 주원아, 너 그 이야기에 대해 아는구나.

B: 그다지 잘 아는 건 아니야. 그 괴물의 이름을 잊어버렸어.

G: 미노타우루스야. 크레타의 왕이 그 괴물에 화가 나서 그것을 미궁에 가두었지.

※ 다음 우리말과 일치하도록 빈칸에 알맞은 것을 골라 쓰시오.

Enjoy the "Planned Confusion"

1 _____ the two pictures _____, you can easily _____ some
_____.
    A. notice   B. comparing   C. differences   D. below

2 For _____, the picture on the left is _____ a _____ and
only has an _____.
    A. entrance   B. example   C. labyrinth   D. called

3 The picture on the right is _____ a _____ and has _____
an entrance _____ an exit.
    A. both   B. and   C. called   D. maze

4 You can _____ the _____ of the _____ in Greek _____.
    A. labyrinth   B. mythology   C. origin   D. find

5 It is _____ to _____ a _____ that you cannot _____.
    A. escape   B. prison   C. be   D. said

6 But you may _____ _____ the labyrinth has only a _____
_____.
    A. single   B. notice   C. path   D. that

7 There are _____ _____ _____.
    A. dead   B. no   C. ends

8 This means you don't _____ to _____ about _____ out
of it when you _____ it.
    A. enter   B. have   C. getting   D. worry

9 If you _____ the path all the _____ to the _____, you will
_____ the center.
    A. end   B. follow   C. reach   D. way

10 To _____ out, you simply _____ to turn _____ and walk
back out the way you _____ in.
    A. around   B. get   C. came   D. have

11 _____ you are _____ a _____, it's a _____ story.
    A. different   B. maze   C. when   D. in

12 There are many _____ to _____ and dead _____ to
_____ you.
    A. frustrate   B. choices   C. ends   D. make

13 You have to _____ _____ decisions about _____ _____
to go.
    A. way   B. making   C. which   D. keep

14 _____ you are not _____, you can easily _____ your
_____.
    A. way   B. careful   C. lose   D. if

15 _____ days, _____ are often _____ puzzles.
    A. considered   B. these   C. left-brain   D. mazes

'계획된 혼란'을 즐겨라

1 아래 두 그림을 비교하면 몇 가지 차이를 쉽게 알아차릴 수 있습니다.

2 예를 들면, 왼쪽 그림은 미궁이라 불리고 입구만 있습니다.

3 오른쪽 그림은 미로라 불리며 입구와 출구가 둘 다 있습니다.

4 미궁의 기원은 그리스 신화에서 찾을 수 있습니다.

5 그것은 여러분이 빠져나올 수 없는 감옥으로 알려져 있습니다.

6 하지만 여러분이 알아차릴 수 있듯, 미궁은 통로가 하나입니다.

7 막다른 길이 없습니다.

8 이것은 여러분이 거기에 들어갈 때 빠져나올 것을 걱정하지 않아도 된다는 것을 의미합니다.

9 통로를 따라 끝까지 가면, 여러분은 미궁의 중앙에 도착할 것입니다.

10 빠져나오기 위해서는, 여러분은 단지 돌아서 들어간 길대로 걸어 나오면 됩니다.

11 미로 안에 있을 때에는 완전히 상황이 다릅니다.

12 결정할 많은 선택지가 있고 여러분을 좌절하게 만들 막다른 길들이 있습니다.

13 어느 길로 갈지 계속 선택을 해야만 합니다.

14 조심하지 않으면 길을 잃기 쉽습니다.

15 오늘날, 미로는 흔히 좌뇌형 퍼즐로 간주됩니다.

16 Many people _____ _____ maze parks and enjoy the "_____ _____."

A. confusion　　B. visit　　C. planned　　D. willingly

17 And some of them _____ _____ _____ their own _____.

A. solutions　　B. came　　C. with　　D. up

18 The easiest and most _____ one is to _____ a hand on one wall from the _____ _____.

A. beginning　　B. reliable　　C. place　　D. very

19 Then you just _____ _____ that _____.

A. following　　B. wall　　C. keep

20 It's _____ _____ in a _____ room.

A. walking　　B. dark　　C. like

21 _____, this simple method may not be _____ in _____ types of mazes, especially when all of the walls are not _____.

A. effective　　B. connected　　C. certain　　D. unfortunately

22 Mazes are _____ with a variety of _____ _____, like walls and rooms, _____, bricks, mirrors, and even snow.

A. hedges　　B. materials　　C. made　　D. different

23 _____ _____, they can also be _____ or _____ on paper.

A. printed　　B. fact　　C. drawn　　D. in

24 _____ is one _____ an example. This is _____ a number _____.

A. called　　B. as　　C. here　　D. maze

25 You start _____ _____ A and have to go _____ the _____ of 1 → 9 → 8 → 5 → 1 → 9 → … .

A. order　　B. point　　C. in　　D. from

26 Why don't you _____ it a _____? You have 30 _____ to _____!

A. seconds　　B. try　　C. escape　　D. give

27 _____ and mazes _____ truly _____, but that's not the _____ of the story.

A. fun　　B. end　　C. are　　D. labyrinths

28 _____ at them closely, you may find the _____ of _____ and _____.

A. order　　B. beauty　　C. regularity　　D. looking

29 They may also show you _____ _____ _____ are.

A. creative　　B. beings　　C. human　　D. how

30 If _____ is a maze park on your next trip, _____ don't you _____ and _____ some time to enjoy it?

A. stop　　B. take　　C. there　　D. why

31 It will surely _____ _____ _____!

A. worth　　B. visiting　　C. be

16 많은 사람들이 미로 공원에 기꺼이 방문하여 '계획된 혼란'을 즐깁니다.

17 그리고 그들 중 몇몇은 자기들만의 해결 방법을 찾아냈습니다.

18 가장 쉽고 믿을 만한 해결 방법은 시작 지점부터 한쪽 벽에 손을 대는 것입니다.

19 그리고는 여러분은 단지 그 벽을 계속 따라가면 됩니다.

20 이것은 마치 어두운 방을 걷는 것과 같습니다.

21 불행하게도, 이 간단한 방법은 어떤 종류의 미로에서는 특히 모든 벽이 이어져 있지는 않은 경우 효과가 없을지도 모릅니다.

22 미로는 벽과 방, 울타리, 벽돌, 거울, 심지어는 눈 등 많은 다양한 재료로 제작됩니다.

23 사실, 미로는 종이에 인쇄되거나 그려질 수도 있습니다.

24 여기 그 예가 하나 있습니다. 이것은 숫자 미로라고 불립니다.

25 여러분은 A 지점에서 출발하여 1. 9. 8. 5. 1. 9 …의 순서로 이동해야 합니다.

26 한번 시도해 보시죠? 빠져나가는 데 30초가 주어집니다!

27 미궁과 미로는 정말 재미있지만, 그것이 전부가 아닙니다.

28 자세히 들여다보면, 여러분은 질서와 규칙성이라는 아름다움을 발견할 수 있을지도 모릅니다.

29 그것들은 또한 인간이 얼마나 창조적인가를 보여줄지도 모릅니다.

30 다음 여행에 미로 공원이 있으면, 들러서 즐겨보는 것은 어떨까요?

31 분명히 들를 가치가 있을 것입니다!

※ 다음 우리말과 일치하도록 빈칸에 알맞은 것을 골라 쓰시오.

Enjoke the "Planned Confusion"

1 _____ the two pictures _____ , you can easily _____ some
   _____ .

2 _____ _____ , the picture _____ _____ _____ is
   _____ a _____ and only _____ an _____ .

3 The picture _____ _____ is _____ a maze and
   _____ _____ an entrance _____ an _____ .

4 You can find _____ _____ the labyrinth in Greek
   _____ .

5 It _____ _____ _____ a prison _____ you
   _____ _____ .

6 But you may _____ _____ the labyrinth has only _____
   _____ _____ .

7 There are _____ _____ _____ .

8 This means you _____ _____ _____ _____
   getting out of it when you _____ _____ .

9 If you follow the path _____ _____
   _____ _____ , you _____ _____ the center.

10 _____ _____ _____ , you simply _____ _____
    _____ and walk back out the way you _____
    _____ .

11 When you are _____ a _____ , it's a _____ story.

12 There are many choices _____ _____ and _____ _____
    _____ _____ you.

13 You have to _____ _____ decisions about _____ _____
    _____ _____ .

14 _____ you _____ _____ , you can easily _____
    your way.

15 These days, mazes _____ often _____ _____ puzzles.

'계획된 혼란'을 즐겨라

1 아래 두 그림을 비교하면 몇 가지 차이를 쉽게 알아차릴 수 있습니다.

2 예를 들면, 왼쪽 그림은 미궁이라 불리고 입구만 있습니다.

3 오른쪽 그림은 미로라 불리며 입구와 출구가 둘 다 있습니다.

4 미궁의 기원은 그리스 신화에서 찾을 수 있습니다.

5 그것은 여러분이 빠져나올 수 없는 감옥으로 알려져 있습니다.

6 하지만 여러분이 알아차릴 수 있듯, 미궁은 통로가 하나입니다.

7 막다른 길이 없습니다.

8 이것은 여러분이 거기에 들어갈 때 빠져나올 것을 걱정하지 않아도 된다는 것을 의미합니다.

9 통로를 따라 끝까지 가면, 여러분은 미궁의 중앙에 도착할 것입니다.

10 빠져나오기 위해서는, 여러분은 단지 돌아서 들어간 길대로 걸어 나오면 됩니다.

11 미로 안에 있을 때에는 완전히 상황이 다릅니다.

12 결정할 많은 선택지가 있고 여러분을 좌절하게 만들 막다른 길들이 있습니다.

13 어느 길로 갈지 계속 선택을 해야만 합니다.

14 조심하지 않으면 길을 잃기 쉽습니다.

15 오늘날, 미로는 흔히 좌뇌형 퍼즐로 간주됩니다.

16 Many people _____ _____ maze parks and _____ the "_____ _____."

17 And some of _____ _____ _____ _____ their own _____.

18 The easiest and _____ _____ _____ is _____ place a hand _____ one wall from _____ _____ _____.

19 Then you just keep _____ _____ _____.

20 It's _____ _____ in a dark room.

21 _____, this simple method may not be _____ in _____ _____ of mazes, especially when all of the walls _____ _____ _____.

22 Mazes _____ _____ _____ a variety of _____ _____, _____ walls and rooms, _____, _____, mirrors, _____ even snow.

23 _____ _____, they can also _____ _____ or _____ on paper.

24 _____ _____ one as an example. This is _____ a number _____.

25 You start _____ point A and have to go _____ _____ _____ of 1 → 9 → 8 → 5 → 1 → 9 → . . . .

26 _____ _____ you _____ _____ _____ _____ _____? You have 30 seconds _____ _____!

27 Labyrinths and mazes _____ truly _____, but that's not _____ _____ of the story.

28 _____ _____ _____ _____, you may find the _____ of _____ and _____.

29 They may also show you _____ _____ _____ _____.

30 If _____ _____ a maze park on your next trip, why don't you _____ and _____ _____ _____ to enjoy it?

31 It will _____ _____ _____ _____!

16 많은 사람들이 미로 공원에 기꺼이 방문하여 '계획된 혼란'을 즐깁니다.

17 그리고 그들 중 몇몇은 자기들만의 해결 방법을 찾아냈습니다.

18 가장 쉽고 믿을 만한 해결 방법은 시작 지점부터 한쪽 벽에 손을 대는 것입니다.

19 그리고는 여러분은 단지 그 벽을 계속 따라가면 됩니다.

20 이것은 마치 어두운 방을 걷는 것과 같습니다.

21 불행하게도, 이 간단한 방법은 어떤 종류의 미로에서는 특히 모든 벽이 이어져 있지는 않은 경우 효과가 없을지도 모릅니다.

22 미로는 벽과 방, 울타리, 벽돌, 거울, 심지어는 눈 등 많은 다양한 재료로 제작됩니다.

23 사실, 미로는 종이에 인쇄되거나 그려질 수도 있습니다.

24 여기 그 예가 하나 있습니다. 이것은 숫자 미로라고 불립니다.

25 여러분은 A 지점에서 출발하여 1. 9. 8. 5. 1. 9 …의 순서로 이동해야 합니다.

26 한번 시도해 보시죠? 빠져나가는 데 30초가 주어집니다!

27 미궁과 미로는 정말 재미있지만, 그것이 전부가 아닙니다.

28 자세히 들여다보면, 여러분은 질서와 규칙성이라는 아름다움을 발견할 수 있을지도 모릅니다.

29 그것들은 또한 인간이 얼마나 창조적인가를 보여줄지도 모릅니다.

30 다음 여행에 미로 공원이 있으면, 들러서 즐겨보는 것은 어떨까요?

31 분명히 들를 가치가 있을 것입니다!

※ 다음 문장을 우리말로 쓰시오.

Enjoy the "Planned Confusion"

1 Comparing the two pictures below, you can easily notice some differences.

➡ _____

2 For example, the picture on the left is called a labyrinth and only has an entrance.

➡ _____

3 The picture on the right is called a maze and has both an entrance and an exit.

➡ _____

4 You can find the origin of the labyrinth in Greek mythology.

➡ _____

5 It is said to be a prison that you cannot escape.

➡ _____

6 But you may notice that the labyrinth has only a single path.

➡ _____

7 There are no dead ends.

➡ _____

8 This means you don't have to worry about getting out of it when you enter it.

➡ _____

9 If you follow the path all the way to the end, you will reach the center.

➡ _____

10 To get out, you simply have to turn around and walk back out the way you came in.

➡ _____

11 When you are in a maze, it's a different story.

➡ _____

12 There are many choices to make and dead ends to frustrate you.

➡ _____

13 You have to keep making decisions about which way to go.

➡ _____

14 If you are not careful, you can easily lose your way.

➡ _____

15 These days, mazes are often considered left-brain puzzles.

➡ _____

16 Many people willingly visit maze parks and enjoy the "planned confusion."

➡ _____

17 And some of them came up with their own solutions.

➡ _____

18 The easiest and most reliable one is to place a hand on one wall from the very beginning.

➡ _____

19 Then you just keep following that wall.

➡ _____

20 It's like walking in a dark room.

➡ _____

21 Unfortunately, this simple method may not be effective in certain types of mazes, especially when all of the walls are not connected.

➡ _____

_____

22 Mazes are made with a variety of different materials, like walls and rooms, hedges, bricks, mirrors, and even snow.

➡ _____

23 In fact, they can also be printed or drawn on paper.

➡ _____

24 Here is one as an example. This is called a number maze.

➡ _____

25 You start from point A and have to go in the order of $1 \rightarrow 9 \rightarrow 8 \rightarrow 5 \rightarrow 1 \rightarrow 9 \rightarrow \dots$.

➡ _____

26 Why don't you give it a try? You have 30 seconds to escape!

➡ _____

27 Labyrinths and mazes are truly fun, but that's not the end of the story.

➡ _____

28 Looking at them closely, you may find the beauty of order and regularity.

➡ _____

29 They may also show you how creative human beings are.

➡ _____

30 If there is a maze park on your next trip, why don't you stop and take some time to enjoy it?

➡ _____

31 It will surely be worth visiting!

➡ _____

※ 다음 괄호 안의 단어들을 우리말에 맞도록 바르게 배열하시오.

Enjoy the "Planned Confusion"

1 (the / comparing / pictures / two / below, / can / you / notice / easily / difference. / some)
➡ _____

2 (example, / for / picture / the / the / on / left / called / is / labyrinth / a / only / and / has / entrance. / an)
➡ _____

3 (picture / the / the / on / is / right / called / maze / a / and / both / has / entrance / an / and / exit. / an)
➡ _____

4 (can / you / the / find / origin / the / of / labyrinth / in / mythology. / Greek)
➡ _____

5 (is / it / said / be / to / prison / a / you / that / escape. / cannot)
➡ _____

6 (you / but / notice / may / the / that / has / labyrinth / only / single / a / path.)
➡ _____

7 (are / there / dead / no / ends.)
➡ _____

8 (means / this / don't / you / to / have / about / worry / out / getting / of / when / it / enter / you / it.)
➡ _____

9 (you / follow / if / path / the / the / all / way / the / to / end, / will / you / the / reach / center.)
➡ _____

10 (get / to / out, / simply / you / to / have / turn / and / around / walk / out / back / way / the / came / you / in.)
➡ _____

11 (you / when / in / are / maze, / a / it's / different / a / story.)
➡ _____

12 (are / there / choices / many / make / to / and / ends / dead / to / you. / frustrate)
➡ _____

13 (have / you / keep / to / decisions / making / which / about / way / go. / to)
➡ _____

14 (you / if / not / are / careful, / can / you / lose / easily / way. / your)
➡ _____

15 (days, / these / are / mazes / considered / often / puzzles. / left-brain)
➡ _____

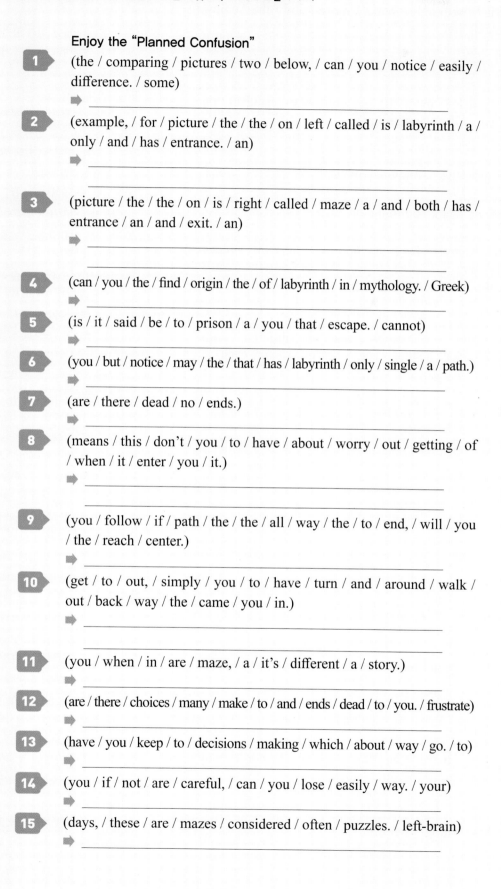

'계획된 혼란'을 즐겨라

1 아래 두 그림을 비교하면 몇 가지 차이를 쉽게 알아차릴 수 있습니다.

2 예를 들면, 왼쪽 그림은 미궁이라 불리고 입구만 있습니다.

3 오른쪽 그림은 미로라 불리며 입구와 출구가 둘 다 있습니다.

4 미궁의 기원은 그리스 신화에서 찾을 수 있습니다.

5 그것은 여러분이 빠져나올 수 없는 감옥으로 알려져 있습니다.

6 하지만 여러분이 알아차릴 수 있듯, 미궁은 통로가 하나입니다.

7 막다른 길이 없습니다.

8 이것은 여러분이 거기에 들어갈 때 빠져나올 것을 걱정하지 않아도 된다는 것을 의미합니다.

9 통로를 따라 끝까지 가면, 여러분은 미궁의 중앙에 도착할 것입니다.

10 빠져나오기 위해서는, 여러분은 단지 돌아서 들어간 길대로 걸어 나오면 됩니다.

11 미로 안에 있을 때에는 완전히 상황이 다릅니다.

12 결정할 많은 선택지가 있고 여러분을 좌절하게 만들 막다른 길들이 있습니다.

13 어느 길로 갈지 계속 선택을 해야만 합니다.

14 조심하지 않으면 길을 잃기 쉽습니다.

15 오늘날, 미로는 흔히 좌뇌형 퍼즐로 간주됩니다.

16 (people / many / visit / willingly / parks / maze / and / the / enjoy / confusion." / "planned)

➡ _____

17 (some / and / them / of / up / came / their / with / solutions. / own)

➡ _____

18 (easiest / the / and / reliable / most / is / one / place / to / hand / a / one / on / from / wall / very / the / beginning.)

➡ _____

19 (you / then / keep / just / that / following / wall.)

➡ _____

20 (like / it's / in / walking / dark / a / room.)

➡ _____

21 (this / unfortunately, / simple / may / method / be / not / in / effective / types / of / certain / mazes, / when / especially / of / all / the / walls / not / are / connected.)

➡ _____

22 (are / mazes / with / made / a / of / variety / materials, / different / walls / like / rooms, / and / bricks, / hedges, / and / mirrors, / snow. / even)

➡ _____

23 (fact, / in / can / they / be / also / printed / drawn / or / paper. / on)

➡ _____

24 (is / here / as / one / example. / an // is / this / a / called / maze. / number)

➡ _____

25 (start / you / point / from / A / have / and / go / to / the / in / order / 1 → / 8 → / 9 → / 1 → / 5 → / 9 → / ....)

➡ _____

26 (don't / why / give / you / a / it / try? // have / you / seconds / 30 / escape! / to)

➡ _____

27 (mazes / and / labyrinths / truly / are / fun, / that's / but / the / not / end / of / story. / the)

➡ _____

28 (at / looking / closely, / them / may / you / the / find / beauty / order / of / regularity. / and)

➡ _____

29 (may / they / show / also / how / you / human / creative / are. / beings)

➡ _____

30 (there / if / a / is / park / maze / your / on / trip, / next / don't / why / stop / you / and / some / take / to / time / it? / enjoy)

➡ _____

31 (will / it / be / surely / visiting! / worth)

➡ _____

---

16 많은 사람들이 미로 공원에 기꺼이 방문하여 '계획된 혼란'을 즐깁니다.

17 그리고 그들 중 몇몇은 자기들만의 해결 방법을 찾아냈습니다.

18 가장 쉽고 믿을 만한 해결 방법은 시작 지점부터 한쪽 벽에 손을 대는 것입니다.

19 그러고는 여러분은 단지 그 벽을 계속 따라가면 됩니다.

20 이것은 마치 어두운 방을 걷는 것과 같습니다.

21 불행하게도, 이 간단한 방법은 어떤 종류의 미로에서는 특히 모든 벽이 이어져 있지는 않은 경우 효과가 없을지도 모릅니다.

22 미로는 벽과 방, 울타리, 벽돌, 거울, 심지어는 눈 등 많은 다양한 재료로 제작됩니다.

23 사실, 미로는 종이에 인쇄되거나 그려질 수도 있습니다.

24 여기 그 예가 하나 있습니다. 이것은 숫자 미로라고 불립니다.

25 여러분은 A 지점에서 출발하여 1. 9. 8. 5. 1. 9 …의 순서로 이동해야 합니다.

26 한번 시도해 보시죠? 빠져나가는 데 **30**초가 주어집니다!

27 미궁과 미로는 정말 재미있지만, 그것이 전부가 아닙니다.

28 자세히 들여다보면, 여러분은 질서와 규칙성이라는 아름다움을 발견할 수 있을지도 모릅니다.

29 그것들은 또한 인간이 얼마나 창조적인가를 보여줄지도 모릅니다.

30 다음 여행에 미로 공원이 있으면, 들러서 즐겨보는 것은 어떨까요?

31 분명히 들를 가치가 있을 것입니다!

※ 다음 우리말을 영어로 쓰시오.

Enjoy the "Planned Confusion"

1 아래 두 그림을 비교하면 몇 가지 차이를 쉽게 알아차릴 수 있습니다.

➡ _____

2 예를 들면, 왼쪽 그림은 미궁이라 불리고 입구만 있습니다.

➡ _____

3 오른쪽 그림은 미로라 불리며 입구와 출구가 둘 다 있습니다.

➡ _____

4 미궁의 기원은 그리스 신화에서 찾을 수 있습니다.

➡ _____

5 그것은 여러분이 빠져나올 수 없는 감옥으로 알려져 있습니다.

➡ _____

6 하지만 여러분이 알아차릴 수 있듯, 미궁은 통로가 하나입니다.

➡ _____

7 막다른 길이 없습니다.

➡ _____

8 이것은 여러분이 거기에 들어갈 때 빠져나올 것을 걱정하지 않아도 된다는 것을 의미합니다.

➡ _____

9 통로를 따라 끝까지 가면, 여러분은 미궁의 중앙에 도착할 것입니다.

➡ _____

10 빠져나오기 위해서는, 여러분은 단지 돌아서 들어간 길대로 걸어 나오면 됩니다.

➡ _____

11 미로 안에 있을 때에는 완전히 상황이 다릅니다.

➡ _____

12 결정할 많은 선택지가 있고 여러분을 좌절하게 만들 막다른 길들이 있습니다.

➡ _____

13 어느 길로 갈지 계속 선택을 해야만 합니다.

➡ _____

14 조심하지 않으면 길을 잃기 쉽습니다.

➡ _____

15 오늘날, 미로는 흔히 좌뇌형 퍼즐로 간주됩니다.

➡ _____

16 많은 사람들이 미로 공원에 기꺼이 방문하여 '계획된 혼란'을 즐깁니다.

➡ _____

17 그리고 그들 중 몇몇은 자기들만의 해결 방법을 찾아냈습니다.

➡ _____

18 가장 쉽고 믿을 만한 해결 방법은 시작 지점부터 한쪽 벽에 손을 대는 것입니다.

➡ _____

19 그러고는 여러분은 단지 그 벽을 계속 따라가면 됩니다.

➡ _____

20 이것은 마치 어두운 방을 걷는 것과 같습니다.

➡ _____

21 불행하게도, 이 간단한 방법은 어떤 종류의 미로에서는 특히 모든 벽이 이어져 있지는 않은 경우 효과가 없을지도 모릅니다.

➡ _____

    _____

22 미로는 벽과 방, 울타리, 벽돌, 거울, 심지어는 눈 등 많은 다양한 재료로 제작됩니다.

➡ _____

    _____

23 사실, 미로는 종이에 인쇄되거나 그려질 수도 있습니다.

➡ _____

24 여기 그 예가 하나 있습니다. 이것은 숫자 미로라고 불립니다.

➡ _____

25 여러분은 A 지점에서 출발하여 1, 9, 8, 5, 1, 9 …의 순서로 이동해야 합니다.

➡ _____

26 한번 시도해 보시죠? 빠져나가는 데 30초가 주어집니다!

➡ _____

27 미궁과 미로는 정말 재미있지만, 그것이 전부가 아닙니다.

➡ _____

28 자세히 들여다보면, 여러분은 질서와 규칙성이라는 아름다움을 발견할 수 있을지도 모릅니다.

➡ _____

29 그것들은 또한 인간이 얼마나 창조적인가를 보여줄지도 모릅니다.

➡ _____

30 다음 여행에 미로 공원이 있으면, 들러서 즐겨보는 것은 어떨까요?

➡ _____

31 분명히 들를 가치가 있을 것입니다!

➡ _____

※ 다음 우리말과 일치하도록 빈칸에 알맞은 말을 쓰시오.

Real Life Communication – C Communication Task

1. A: _____ _____ _____ you the first question. _____ do you _____ _____?

2. B: I _____ _____ there _____ _____.

3. A: Then _____ _____ does it _____ _____ _____ there?

4. B: It _____ _____ 2 hours _____ _____ there.

5. A: Is _____ _____ _____ _____ there _____ _____?

6. A: Oh, the _____ is Gyeongju. _____?

1. A: 첫 번째 질문을 할게요. 어떻게 그곳에 가나요?
2. B: 기차로 그곳에 갈 수 있어요.
3. A: 그러면 그곳에 가는 데 얼마나 걸리나요?
4. B: 그곳에 가는 데 약 2시간 정도 걸려요.
5. A: 그곳에 비행기로 갈 수 있나요?
6. A: 오, 정답은 경주예요. 맞죠?

After You Read

1. Today, I went to _____ _____ _____ _____ _____ _____ my friends.

2. The maze _____ _____ _____ _____.

3. There were _____ _____, and I had to _____ _____ _____ about _____ _____ _____ _____ _____.

4. My friends said _____ I should just _____ my hand on one wall _____ _____ _____ and _____ _____ the same wall.

5. That solution was _____ but not _____ _____.

6. I _____ _____ very much at the park.

7. Also, I found _____ _____ _____ _____ _____ and _____ there and thought that _____ _____ are really _____.

1. 오늘 나는 친구들과 함께 근처의 미로 공원에 갔다.
2. 미로는 해결하기가 어려워 보였다.
3. 선택지가 많았고 나는 어느 길로 갈지 계속해서 결정해야만 했다.
4. 내 친구들이 내가 처음부터 벽 한쪽에 손을 얹고 계속 같은 쪽 벽을 따라가면 된다고 말했다.
5. 그 해결 방법은 간단했지만 별로 효과적이지 않았다.
6. 나는 미로 공원에서 매우 즐거웠다.
7. 또한, 나는 질서와 규칙성의 아름다움을 발견했고 인간은 정말 창조적이라고 생각했다.

Let's Write

1. I _____ _____ _____ survey about our class's preference _____ mountains _____ oceans.

2. _____ _____ the results, _____ is clear _____ our class _____ mountains _____ oceans.

3. You may wonder _____ _____ _____ _____ _____ _____.

4. _____ the _____ _____ they like mountains _____, I found key words _____ "more beautiful", "_____ _____", and "_____."

1. 나는 산과 바다 간의 우리 반의 선호도에 관한 간단한 설문 조사를 했다.
2. 결과를 보면, 우리 반이 바다보다 산을 더 선호한다는 것이 명확하다.
3. 여러분은 왜 우리 반이 산을 선호하는지 궁금할지도 모른다.
4. 그들이 산을 더 좋아하는 이유를 보자면, 나는 "더 아름다운", "더 신나는", 그리고 "더 멋진"과 같은 핵심어를 찾았다.

구석구석 지문 Test

※ 다음 우리말을 영어로 쓰시오.

Real Life Communication – C Communication Task

1. A: 첫 번째 질문을 할게요. 어떻게 그곳에 가나요?
   ➡ _____

2. B: 기차로 갈 수 있어요.
   ➡ _____

3. A: 그러면 그곳에 가는 데 얼마나 걸리나요?
   ➡ _____

4. B: 그곳에 가는 데 약 2시간 정도 걸려요.
   ➡ _____

5. A: 그곳에 비행기로 갈 수 있나요?
   ➡ _____

6. A: 오, 정답은 경주예요. 맞죠?
   ➡ _____

After You Read

1. 오늘 나는 친구들과 함께 근처의 미로 공원에 갔다.
   ➡ _____

2. 미로는 해결하기가 어려워 보였다.
   ➡ _____

3. 선택지가 많았고 나는 어느 길로 갈지 계속해서 결정해야만 했다.
   ➡ _____

4. 내 친구들이 내가 처음부터 벽 한쪽에 손을 얹고 계속 같은 쪽 벽을 따라가면 된다고 말했다.
   ➡ _____
   ➡ _____

5. 그 해결 방법은 간단했지만 별로 효과적이지 않았다.
   ➡ _____

6. 나는 미로 공원에서 매우 즐거웠다.
   ➡ _____

7. 또한, 나는 질서와 규칙성의 아름다움을 발견했고 인간은 정말 창조적이라고 생각했다.
   ➡ _____

Let's Write

1. 나는 산과 바다 간의 우리 반의 선호도에 관한 간단한 설문 조사를 했다.
   ➡ _____

2. 결과를 보면, 우리 반이 바다보다 산을 더 선호한다는 것이 명확하다.
   ➡ _____

3. 여러분은 왜 우리 반이 산을 선호하는지 궁금할지도 모른다.
   ➡ _____

4. 그들이 산을 더 좋아하는 이유를 보자면, 나는 "더 아름다운", "더 신나는", 그리고 "더 멋진"과 같은 핵심어를 찾았다.
   ➡ _____
   ➡ _____

영어 기출 문제집

적중100

1학기

정답 및 해설

지학 | 민찬규

중 3

적중100

Learning from Nature's Genius

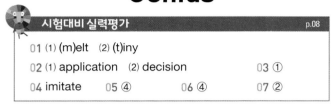

01 (1) (m)elt   (2) (t)iny
02 (1) application   (2) decision   03 ①
04 imitate   05 ④   06 ④   07 ②

01 주어진 보기의 단어는 반의어 관계이다. narrow 좁은, wide 넓은, melt 녹다, freeze 얼다, tiny 아주 작은, huge 거대한

02 보기에 주어진 단어는 동사-명사의 관계이다. absorb 흡수하다, absorption 흡수, apply 적용하다, application 적용, decide 결심하다, decision 결심

03 ①의 last는 "지속하다"의 뜻으로 동사로 쓰였다.

04 나는 기계를 발명하기 위하여 새의 날개를 모방하였기 때문에 "imitated"가 적절하다.

05 ① 다용도실 = an all-purpose room ② 놀라운 이야기 = an amazing story ③ 적용하다 = apply ④ 곤충 로봇에 관한 논문 = an article about a bug robot ⑤ 부리 = beak

06 "줄이다"는 뜻으로 "reduce"와 비슷한 말은 "diminish"이다. absorb 흡수하다, forgive 용서하다, decide 결심하다, explore 탐색하다

07 take a look at = 살펴보다, be good at = ~을 잘하다, 능숙하다

01 inventive
02 (i)nsect
03 make
04 why
05 (s)top
06 (1) bite   (2) bug   (3) burns   (4) burrs
07 (1) search   (2) stuck   (3) result   (4) only

01 "그녀는 매우 창의적인 생각을 가지고 있다." / invent 발명하다, inventive 창의적인

02 주어진 단어는 유의어 관계이다. beak (새의) 부리, bill 부리, bug 곤충, 벌레, insect 곤충

03 • 그들은 지도자와 연락을 해야 한다. • 나는 일기장에 다음 회의를 메모해 놓을 것이다. make contact with = 연락하다, make

a note of = ~을 메모하다, 기록하다

04 • 나는 몸이 좀 아팠다. 그것이 내가 일찍 떠난 이유이다. • 나는 네가 그토록 늦은 이유를 알고 싶다. That's why ~. = 그것이 ~한 이유이다, the reason why = ~한 이유

05 keep A from -ing (A가 ~하지 못하게 하다) = stop A from -ing

06 (1) 모기에 물린 자리 = a mosquito bite (2) bug spray = 방충제 (3) 타다 = burn (4) burr = 가시 식물

07 (1) in search of = ~을 찾아서 (2) be stuck to = ~에 달라붙다 (3) as a result of ~ = ~의 결과로 (4) not only ... but also ~ = ...뿐만 아니라 또한 ~인

1 Have you heard of a mosquito needle, Jian   2 ④

01 "~을 들어본 적이 있니?"는 "Have you heard of ~?"라고 한다.

1 T   2 T   3 F   4 T   5 F   6 F

Listen & Speak 1 A

know, painted, don't / think, great / also, inventor / What, invent / dreamed of, drew, flying, looked like / Did, also make, machine / creative idea inspired, inventors

Listen & Speak 1 B

Have you, needle / Can, explain it / made this, imitating, mouth / how will / know, bites, very painful, needle, cause less pain / How come / less contact / think, useless holder, candles last / possible / burns, melts, tube, form / fascinated, use, longer

what, fascinated, special / What, special / played / How, door / be changed, table / cool

have, guest / Great, be / fascinated, fact, lived, goat, three, Why, do / saw, playing, looked, peaceful, live / have, problems / Walking, was, difficult / any, like / planning, visit / wait, adventure

What, doing / article / interesting / really / Can, more / know, bugs, slip, narrow / why, hard / help, survivors / fascinating

시험대비 기본평가 p.16

01 ①   02 ④   03 ③

01 로봇 소녀 Sophia가 60가지가 넘는 얼굴 표정을 보여 줄 수 있다는 것에 대하여 관심을 나타내는 말로 "be fascinated by"가 되어야 한다.

02 주원이의 방문이 특별하다는 말을 듣고 왜 그 방문이 그렇게 특별하다고 생각하는지 이유를 묻는 의미로 "What makes ~?"가 들어가는 것이 적절하다.

03 (B) 양초 받침이 초를 오래 타도록 만들어 준다는 말에 대한 이유를 묻는다. (C) 양초가 녹을 때 받침대 아래 관에서 새로운 양초로 만들어진다는 설명을 하자 (A) 그 설명에 대한 관심을 표시한다.

시험대비 실력평가 p.17~18

01 ④   02 ①   03 ③   04 ①
05 ④   06 ⑤   07 ①   08 ⑤
09 ⑤   10 ④   11 ⑤

01 주어진 문장의 So는 결과를 유도하는 접속사이다. 다빈치가 새처럼 나는 기계를 꿈꾸었다는 문장 다음인 (D)가 적절한 위치이다.

02 많은 발명가들에게 영감을 주는 다빈치의 아이디어는 창의적이었다고 해야 자연스럽다. artistic 예술적인, usual 일상적인, common 평범한, ordinary 평범한

03 위 대화에서 모나리자를 그린 Leonardo da Vinci가 나는 것

을 꿈꾸어서 나는 기계를 발명하려고 했다는 것을 소개하지만 실제로 그 기계를 만들지는 못했기 때문에 ③은 이 대화를 통해 대답할 수 없다.

04 "Have you heard of a mosquito needle, Jian?"은 아는지를 묻는 말로 "You know ~, don't you?"에 해당한다.

05 새로운 "a mosquito needle"은 통증을 줄인다고 하였으므로 ④는 대화의 내용과 다르다.

06 주어진 빈칸에 들어가기에 적절한 말은 관심을 표현하는 말이지만, ⑤는 알고 있다는 의미로 빈칸에 적절하지 않다.

07 주어진 문장은 이유를 묻는 말로 3일 동안 염소처럼 산 것에 대한 이유를 묻는 의미로 (A)가 적절한 위치이다.

08 "I can't wait"는 매우 기대가 된다는 의미로 말하는 사람의 기대를 나타낸다.

09 a bug robot에 대한 관심을 표현하는 말로 "~에 매료되다"에 해당하는 "be fascinated by"가 적절하다.

10 빈칸에 들어가기에 적절한 말은 why이다. 이유를 말할 때는 why를 쓴다. ① which/that ② which/that ③ who ④ why ⑤ where

11 빈칸에 들어가는 것은 상대의 관심에 대하여 놀라움이나 흥미를 표현하는 말이 적절하다.

서술형 시험대비 p.19

01 I'm fascinated by
02 What
03 no → many
04 You know (that) Leonardo da Vinci painted the *Mona Lisa*, don't you?
05 dreamed, make
06 Are you aware of a mosquito needle, Jian?
07 How come

01 "~에 매료[매혹]되다"는 "be fascinated by"이다.

02 (B) 특별한 것이 무엇인지 물어보는 말로 문장의 주어 역할을 하는 의문대명사 what이 적절하다.

03 "She looks, talks, and even thinks like a human."을 보면 그 외에도 다른 능력이 많다고 하여야 한다.

04 "~에 대해서 알지?"라는 의미로 아는지 묻는 말은 "You know (that) ~, don't you?"이다.

06 아는지를 묻는 말로 aware를 포함하여 "Are you aware of ~?"가 적절하다.

07 빈칸에는 "어째서, 왜"의 뜻으로 이유를 묻는 "How come"이 적절하다.

3

핵심 Check   p.20~21

1 (1) remembered (2) economically (3) but
2 (1) who he is (2) I may ask you a question
   (3) how old I was

시험대비 기본평가   p.22

01 ②   02 ③

03 (1) I'm wondering how many books you have read
      until now.
   (2) Do you know why an elephant has a trunk?
   (3) Somi enjoys not only listening to music but
      also painting pictures.
   (4) He has not only a dog but also a cat.

01 간접의문문은 '의문사+주어+동사'의 순서로 쓰고, 의문사를 제
   외한 문장의 주어와 동사는 평서문의 형태가 되어야 한다.

02 'not only A but also B'는 'A뿐만 아니라 B도'라는 뜻으로 두
   개의 단어, 구, 절을 연결한다.

03 (1), (2) 간접의문문은 '의문사+주어+동사'의 순서로 쓴다. (3),
   (4) 'A뿐 아니라 B도 역시'의 문장은 'not only A but also B'
   의 형태로 쓴다.

시험대비 실력평가   p.23~25

01 ②   02 ①   03 ③   04 ④
05 ⑤
06 He enjoys not only playing the guitar but also
      dancing to the music.
07 how the bird entered the water so gracefully
08 ④   09 ③
10 Tell me why you met her last night.
11 (1) merely (2) as well (3) heathy (4) getting
   (5) knows 12 ②
13 He plays not only soccer but also tennis.
14 ①   15 ⑤   16 ④   17 ③
18 ②
19 (1) I don't know. When does this restaurant open?
   (2) I wonder. Is this address correct?
   (3) They are a couple in the movie. They are a
      couple in the real world, too.

01 간접의문문은 '의문사+주어+동사'의 순서로 쓰므로 'Tell me
   where you are going to have dinner.'로 쓰는 것이 적절하
   다.

02 not only A but also B: A뿐 아니라 B도

03 'They didn't know' 다음에 의문사절 'how they could
   reduce the noise'를 평서문의 형태로 바꿔 써야 한다.

04 not only A but also B = not only A but B = not only A
   but B ~ as well. = B as well as A ④ not A but B: A가
   아니라 B

05 첫 번째 문장에서는 빈칸 뒤에 완전한 절이 나오므로 what은
   적절하지 않고 when 또한 어색하다. 두 번째 문장에서는 동사
   bought의 목적어가 필요하므로 what이 적절하다.

06 'not only A but also B'에서 A와 B는 문법적으로 같은 형태
   여야 하며, enjoy는 동명사를 목적어로 취하므로 sing을 동명사
   dancing으로 써야 한다.

07 간접의문문이므로 '의문사+주어+동사'의 어순으로 쓴다.

08 'not only A but also B'는 'B as well as A'로 바꾸어 쓸 수
   있으며 이때 동사의 수는 B에 맞춘다. ① Either A or B: A 또
   는 B ② Neither A nor B: A도 B도 아니다

09 know의 목적어로 간접의문문이 나오는 경우이다. 의문사가 있
   는 경우에는 '의문사+주어+동사'로 쓰고, 의문사가 없는 경우에
   는 'if[whether]+주어+동사'의 어순으로 쓴다.

10 간접의문문에서 의문사가 주어인 경우에는 의문사 뒤에 바로 동
   사가 이어진다.

11 (1), (2) not only A but also B = not merely A but also B
   = not just A but also B = not simply A but also B = not
   only A but B as well = B as well as A (3), (4) 'not only A
   but also B'에서 A와 B는 문법적으로 같은 형태여야 한다. (4)에
   서 is 다음에 not only가 나왔으므로 is에 대응하는 gets가 아니
   라 getting에 대응하는 getting을 써야 함에 주의한다. (5) 'B as
   well as A'에서 동사의 수는 B에 맞춘다.

12 ① jog → jogging ③ also → but also ④ are → is ⑤
   our nation → for our nation

13 not only A but also B: A뿐만 아니라 B도

14 not only A but (also) B: A뿐만 아니라 B도

15 ⑤ 의문사구(how much)는 함께 붙여 써야 한다. ④번의 경우
   동사가 guess이지만 Yes나 No로 답할 수 있으므로 의문사를 문
   두에 쓰지 않았다.

16 'not only A but also B'에서 A와 B는 문법적으로 같은 형태여
   야 하므로, loves에 맞추어 wants로 써야 한다.

17 첫 번째 문장에서는 'not only A but (also) B' 구문의 but이
   적절하다. 두 번째 문장에서는 her job을 묻는 의문사 what이
   적절하다.

18 believe 동사가 있으므로 의문사를 문두에 써야 한다. When do you believe you'll become a manager?

19 (1) '의문사+주어+동사' 순서의 간접의문문을 직접의문문의 어순인 '의문사+동사+주어'로 바꾼다. (2) 'whether+주어+동사'의 어순을 의문문의 어순으로 바꾼다. (3) 'B as well as A'를 A(in the movie)와 B(in the real world)로 따로 쓴다.

서술형 시험대비
p.26~27

01 (1) I'm wondering what your goal is this year.
(2) Can you tell me if[whether] she called you last night?
(3) Do you know who directed the movie?
(4) What do you think I should wear?
(5) Can you tell me what they are talking about?

02 (1) She wants to know if[whether] you are sick.
(2) Can you tell me what children should wear in the swimming pool?
(3) This tunnel is not only narrow but also dark.

03 (1) Dolphins can not only hear sounds clearly but also communicate over long distances.
(2) He has experience as well as knowledge.

04 (1) It was not only strong but also easy to use.
(2) He as well as you is responsible for the problem.
(3) Not only do I study a lot, but I also play a lot.
(4) Where do you think he might be?
(5) I wonder if we will have good weather tomorrow.

05 why this computer won't turn on

06 (1) I want to learn tennis as well as taekwondo.
(2) He treated me to cake as well as to lunch.
(3) She composes good songs as well as likes playing the guitar.
(4) His brothers as well as Mark want to go to the concert.

07 c. He wondered how high the bird could fly.

08 (1) The director as well as actors is invited to the party.
(2) He looks not only smart but also friendly.
(3) Cathy not only is a smart girl but also has a warm heart.
(4) Do you know how old he is?
(5) What do you believe is causing this symptom?

09 (1) Where is the key?
(2) How did that happen?
(3) Could we go there?
(4) What is wrong with the computer?

01 (1), (5) 주절 뒤에 간접의문문을 '의문사+주어+동사'의 어순으로 쓴다. (2) 주절 뒤에 간접의문문을 'if[whether]+주어+동사'의 어순으로 쓴다. (3) 의문사가 주어인 경우에는 의문사 뒤에 바로 동사가 이어진다. (4) 주절에 think 동사가 있으므로 의문사를 문두로 보내야 한다.

02 (1), (2) 간접의문문은 '의문사 또는 if[whether]+주어+동사'의 순서로 쓴다. (3) not only A but (also) B: A뿐만 아니라 B도

03 not only A but also B = B as well as A: A뿐만 아니라 B도. B에 강조의 초점이 맞춰져 있다.

04 (1) 'not only A but also B'에서 A와 B는 문법적으로 같은 형태여야 하므로, strong에 맞추어 easy로 써야 한다. (2) 'B as well as A'에서 동사의 수는 B에 맞춘다. (3) 'Not only'가 문두에 나오면, 주어와 동사를 의문문 형식으로 도치시킨다. (4) 주절에 think 동사가 있으므로 의문사를 문두로 보내야 한다. (5) if가 이끄는 절이 wonder의 목적어로 쓰인 간접의문문(명사절)이므로 미래시제는 will을 써서 나타내야 한다.

05 직접의문문이 간접의문문이 될 때 '의문사+주어+동사'의 어순으로 쓴다.

06 (1)~(3) 'not only A but also B'는 'B as well as A'로 바꾸어 쓸 수 있다. (4) 'not only A but also B'와 'B as well as A'는 B에 동사의 수를 일치시킨다.

07 c. 하나의 의미 단위로 쓰이는 의문사구는 하나의 의문사로 취급하므로, '의문사구(how high)+주어(the bird)+동사(could fly)'의 어순으로 써야 한다.

08 (1) 'B as well as A'는 B에 동사의 수를 일치시킨다. (2) 'not only A but also B'에서 A와 B에는 대등한 형태의 말이 와야 한다. (3) 'not only A but also B'에서 A와 B에는 대등한 형태의 말이 와야 하므로 A와 B에 동사구가 오도록 고쳐야 한다. (4) 주절에 know 동사가 있는 간접의문문은 의문사를 문두로 보내지 않는다. (5) 주절에 believe 동사가 있는 간접의문문은 의문사를 문두로 보내야 한다.

09 간접의문문은 '의문사+주어+동사'의 어순으로 쓴다. 의문사가 없는 경우 의문사 대신 if나 whether를 쓰고, 의문사가 주어인 경우에는 의문사 뒤에 바로 동사가 이어진다. 이때 주절의 동사로 believe가 쓰인 경우 의문사를 맨 앞에 써야 한다.

교과서
Reading

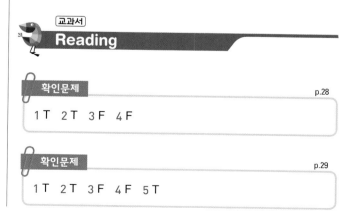

확인문제
p.28

1 T 2 T 3 F 4 F

확인문제
p.29

1 T 2 T 3 F 4 F 5 T

01 From, to, works fascinates us

02 not only, but also, it, solutions

03 one such person

04 how birds could fly

05 closely, made

06 Even though, successful, imitated, to try to make

07 Since, have, imitated, surprising abilities

08 Let's explore

09 high-speed train, had

10 entered, sudden increase, created

11 woke people up, caused

12 to solve, how they could reduce

13 the engineers was, in search of

14 saw, diving into

15 how the bird entered

16 studied more, discovered, narrow beak

17 redesigned, by imitating

18 not only, but also, with, less

19 One day, was hiking, with

20 On, home, burrs were stuck, hair

21 to know how that happened

22 took a closer look at, noticed that, were, straight

23 if he could apply, something useful

24 After, testing, invented

25 tiny needles, those of burrs, the other, hairy surface

26 were pressed, fastener

27 not only strong but also easy

28 Since, have used, different ways

29 is often used for

30 to play a number of

31 keeps, from floating

32 nothing useless, curious, ask

1 From flying birds to self-cleaning plants, the way nature works fascinates us.

2 Some people not only use nature but also imitate it to find solutions to their problems.

3 Leonardo da Vinci (1452–1519) was one such person.

4 He wondered how birds could fly.

5 He closely watched birds, made notes, and drew pictures of them.

6 Even though his invention was not successful, he imitated a bird's wings to try to make a flying

machine.

7 Since then, more and more people have successfully imitated the surprising abilities of nature's genius.

8 Let's explore some of them.

9 The high-speed train was first made in Japan. But it had one problem.

10 When the train entered a tunnel, the sudden increase in air pressure created a very loud sound.

11 It often woke people up and caused headaches.

12 A team of engineers tried to solve the problem, but they didn't know how they could reduce the noise.

13 One day, one of the engineers was watching a bird in search of a meal.

14 He saw the bird quickly and quietly diving into the water.

15 He wondered how the bird entered the water so gracefully.

16 So, he studied more about the bird and discovered its long, narrow beak.

17 He redesigned the front of the train by imitating the bird's beak.

18 It was successful. Now the new train travels not only more quietly but also 10% faster with 15% less electricity.

19 One day, a Swiss engineer, George de Mestral, was hiking in the woods with his dog.

20 On his way home, he saw that burrs were stuck to his clothes and his dog's hair.

21 He wanted to know how that happened.

22 He took a closer look at the burrs and noticed that the ends of the burr needles were not straight.

23 He wondered if he could apply that to make something useful.

24 After a lot of testing, he finally invented two new materials.

25 One had many tiny needles like those of burrs and the other had a hairy surface.

26 When they were pressed together, they became a very good fastener.

27 It was not only strong but also easy to use.

28 Since then, many people have used his invention in many different ways.

29 It is often used for clothing, shoes, and bags.

30 Some people use it to play a number of different games.

31 In space, it keeps things from floating away.

32 There is nothing useless in nature. We just have to become curious and ask questions.

01 ②   02 ④

03 They not only use nature but also imitate it.

04 ④   05 He imitated the bird's beak.

06 searching   07 ⑤   08 ③

09 (C)—(B)—(D)—(A)   10 curious

11 It is often used for clothing, shoes, and bags.

12 ④   13 ②   14 ②   15 ③

16 ④   17 fascinated 18 ⑤

19 The sudden increase in air pressure created a very loud sound.

20 ④

21 how the bird entered the water so gracefully

22 ⑤   23 needles   24 ③

25 It is used to keep things from floating away.

26 ③

---

01 발명이 성공하진 못했지만 나는 기계를 만들기 위하여 새의 날개를 모방했다는 의미가 자연스럽다. 따라서 양보절 접속사 Even though가 적절하다.

02 레오나르도 다빈치의 발명은 성공적이지 않았다고 하였다.

03 어떤 사람들은 문제 해결을 위하여 자연을 이용할 뿐만 아니라 모방하기도 한다.

04 기존 기차의 문제점을 해결하였으므로 '성공적'이었다고 말하는 것이 적절하다.

05 공학자는 새의 부리를 모방하여 기차의 전면부를 다시 디자인하였다.

06 지각동사의 목적격 보어로 현재분사를 사용하여 (A)와 같은 의미의 문장을 완성할 수 있다.

07 최초의 초고속 열차는 터널에 들어갔을 때 기압의 상승으로 인해 매우 시끄러운 소리를 내는 것이 문제였다.

08 기차가 터널에 들어갈 때 갑작스런 기압의 상승으로 인해 시끄러운 소음을 만들어내고, 이 소리에 사람들이 두통을 느낀다고 하였다.

09 (C) 개와 함께 하이킹을 하고 집으로 돌아오던 George de Mestral은 그의 옷과 개의 털에 가시식물이 붙어 있는 것을 봄 (B) 그 가시식물을 유심히 살펴봄 (D) 가시의 모양을 적용하여 유용한 것을 만들려고 하였고 두 개의 새로운 재료를 발명함 (A) 두 개의 재료 소개

10 무언가에 흥미를 가지고 더 알기를 원하는 것은 '호기심 많은 (curious)'이다.

11 George가 발명한 것은 옷, 신발, 가방을 위해 사용된다고 하였다.

12 ⓐ는 완전한 절을 이끄는 명사절 접속사이다. ① 지시대명사

②, ③ 관계대명사 ④ 명사절 접속사 ⑤ 지시 부사

13 George de Mestral은 스위스 공학자라고 하였다.

14 주어진 문장의 one such person은 문제를 해결하기 위하여 자연을 모방하는 사람을 가리키며, ②번에 이어지는 문장의 대명사 He가 가리키는 것은 주어진 문장의 레오나르도 다빈치이다.

15 (A)는 동명사이다. 따라서 명사를 수식하는 현재분사 ③번이 답이다.

16 자연의 놀라운 능력을 성공적으로 모방한 사례를 살펴보자고 하였으므로 ④번이 가장 적절하다.

17 자연이 작동하는 방식은 우리를 매료시킨다는 문장의 수동태이므로 fascinate의 과거분사 형태를 쓰는 것이 적절하다.

18 이어지는 내용은 새에게서 빠르고 조용하게 이동하는 방법을 배웠다는 것이므로 ⑤번이 가장 적절하다.

19 기차가 터널로 들어갈 때 갑작스런 기압의 상승으로 인해 시끄러운 소리를 낸다고 하였다.

20 다시 디자인한 기차는 예전 기차보다 10 퍼센트만큼 더 빠르게 달리고, 전기는 15 퍼센트만큼 덜 사용한다고 하였다.

21 새를 관찰한 후에, 공학자는 어떻게 새가 물에 그렇게 우아하게 들어가는지를 알아내기 위해 새에 관하여 더 연구했다고 하였다.

22 빈칸 (A)에는 '~인지 아닌지'라는 의미의 명사절 접속사 if[whether]가 쓰인다. 의문사가 없는 문장의 간접의문문을 만들 때 사용된다. ① how ② who ③ where ④ when ⑤ if[whether]

23 those는 복수명사 needles를 가리키는 말이다.

24 George de Mestral이 발명한 것은 튼튼하고 사용하기 편리하다.

25 George de Mestral이 발명한 고정 장치는 우주에서 물건이 떠다니지 않도록 하는 데 쓰이고 있다.

26 가시 식물의 가시는 끝이 곧지 않다고 하였다.

---

01 He wondered how birds could fly.

02 He closely watched birds, made notes, and drew pictures of them.

03 레오나르도 다빈치가 나는 기계를 만들기 위해서 새의 날개를 모방했을 때

04 He tried to make a flying machine.

05 가시가 자신의 옷과 개의 털에 들러붙은 것

06 He wondered if[whether] he could apply that to make something useful.

07 it keeps things from floating away

08 He noticed that the ends of the burr needles were not straight.

7

09 We have to become curious and ask questions.

10 (A) solve   (B) reduce   (C) imitating

11 He wondered how the bird entered the water so gracefully.

12 It had a long, narrow beak.

13 First, it travels more quietly. Second, it travels 10% faster with 15% less electricity.

14 Japan, air pressure, increased

01 wonder라는 동사의 목적어로 '의문사+주어+동사' 어순의 간접의문문이 쓰이는 것에 유의하자.

02 레오나르도 다빈치는 새가 어떻게 날 수 있는지 궁금해서 새를 관찰하고 기록하고 새의 그림을 그렸다.

03 비록 성공적이지는 못했지만, 레오나르도 다빈치는 새의 날개를 모방하여 나는 기계를 만들었다고 하였다.

04 레오나르도 다빈치는 나는 기계를 만들려고 노력했다.

05 that은 앞 문장의 'burrs were stuck to his clothes and his dog's hair를 가리키는 말이다.

06 '~인지 아닌지'라는 의미로 쓰이는 명사절 접속사 if 혹은 whether를 추가하여 문장을 완성할 수 있다.

07 fastener의 쓰임으로 보아 우주에서도 물건이 떠다니지 않게 하는 데 쓰인다고 말하는 것이 적절하다. keep Ving: 계속해서 V하다, keep A from Ving: A가 V하지 못하게 막다

08 George가 가시를 자세히 살펴보았을 때, 가시의 끝이 곧지 않은 것을 알아차렸다.

09 자연으로부터 배우기 위해서 우리는 호기심을 가지고 질문해야만 한다.

10 (A) 기차가 가진 소음 문제를 해결하려고 노력했다, (B) 하지만 소음을 줄이는 방법을 알 수 없었다, (C) 새의 부리를 모방함으로써 기차를 다시 디자인했다고 말하는 것이 가장 자연스럽다. by+Ving: V함으로써

11 공학자는 어떻게 새가 그렇게 우아하게 물속으로 들어가는지 궁금했다고 하였다.

12 공학자 중 한 명이 관찰한 새의 부리 모양은 길고 좁았다고 하였다.

13 다시 디자인한 기차는 예전 기차보다 더 조용히 달린다. 또한 15% 더 적은 전기를 사용하여 10%를 더 빠르게 달린다고 하였다.

14 일본에서 처음 만들어진 고속 열차가 가진 문제는 터널 안으로 들어갈 때 갑작스러운 기압 상승의 상승으로 인해 시끄러운 소리를 내는 것이었다.

01 ③　　02 ⑤　　03 ①　　04 ③

05 I'm fascinated by what plants can do.

06 You know that polar bears are good at swimming, don't you?　　07 ③

08 ⑤　　09 ③

10 How come it's less painful?

11 ⑤　　12 ⑤　　13 ⑤　　14 ①

15 ④　　16 ③　　17 ②

18 (1) She has not only a pretty face but also a warm heart.

(2) Success depends not only on talent, but also on effort.

(3) A goat eats fruit as well as leaves.

(4) Do you know what Chris had for lunch?

(5) I'm wondering if[whether] he will come back soon.

(6) When do you think he left home?

19 ④　　20 (B)–(A)–(C)　　21 ⑤

22 ⑤　　23 ②

24 climbing a tall building with just one's hands and feet

25 ⑤　　26 ③　　27 ⑤

28 기차가 터널 안으로 들어가면 시끄러운 소리를 내는 것

29 ④

01 make contact with ~와 연락하다, be covered with ~로 덮여 있다

02 동사 decide의 명사형인 decision이 적절하다.

03 "지하로 지나가는 통로"는 "tunnel 터널, 굴"을 가리킨다. path 길, subway 지하철, transport 운송하다, vehicle 탈것

04 inspire는 "영감을 불어넣다"의 의미이다.

05 "~에 매혹되다"는 "be fascinated by"로 나타낸다.

06 "~을 잘 알지, 그렇지 않니?"는 "You know ~, don't you?"이다.

07 이어지는 설명을 보면, 주어진 빈칸에는 어떻게 그것이 가능한지를 묻는 "How's that possible?"이 적절하다.

08 상대가 아는지를 물어보는 말로 "~을 들어본 적이 있니?"에 해당하는 것은 "Have you heard of/about ~?"이다.

09 내용상 모기의 입을 모방하여 새로운 주사 바늘을 만들었다는 의미로 "모방하다"에 해당하는 "imitate"의 동명사 "imitating"이 적절하다.

10 모기의 입을 모방해서 새로 만든 주사 바늘은 이전보다 더 나은 것으로 "You know mosquito bites are not very painful, don't you?"를 보면 통증이 더 적다는 것을 알 수 있다.

11 상대에게 알고 있는지를 묻는 말은 "You know ~, don't you?", "Have you heard ~?", "Are you aware that ~?"

등이다.

12 "He dreamed of flying like a bird."를 보면 다빈치가 만들려고 한 것은 날 수 있는 기계였을 것이라고 생각할 수 있다.

13 다빈치는 나는 기계를 그림으로 남겼지만 직접 그 기계를 만들지는 못했다.

14 ① 주절의 동사로 think가 쓰인 경우 의문사를 맨 앞에 써야 한다. ③ 주절의 동사로 guess가 쓰일 때는 의문사가 문두에 올 수도 있고 동사 뒤에 올 수도 있다.

15 not only A but also B = B as well as A

16 간접의문문은 의문사가 있는 경우 '의문사+주어+동사'의 순서로 써야 한다.

17 'not only A but also B'나 'B as well as A'가 주어로 쓰일 경우 동사의 수는 B에 일치시켜야 하므로 ②의 동사 'like'를 'likes'로 쓰는 것이 적절하다.

18 (1) not only A but (also) B: A뿐만 아니라 B도 (2) 'not only A but also B'에서 A와 B에는 대등한 형태의 말이 와야 한다. (3) not only A but also B = B as well as A (4) 간접의문문의 어순은 '의문사+주어+동사'이다. (5) if[whether]이 목적어로 쓰인 명사절이므로 미래는 미래시제로 나타낸다. (6) 주절의 동사로 think가 쓰인 경우 의문사를 맨 앞에 써야 한다.

19 ⓑ 의문사가 주어인 간접의문문이므로 주어인 의문사 다음에 바로 동사를 평서문의 어순으로 쓴다. Do you know who made this cake? ⓒ 주절의 동사로 think가 있으므로 간접의문문의 의문사를 맨 앞으로 보내야 한다. Who do you think is suitable for the new project? ⓓ 'not only A but also B'가 주어로 쓰일 경우 동사의 수는 B에 일치시킨다. Not only my friends but also my teacher likes my idea. ⓕ 'not only A but also B'에서 A와 B에는 같은 성격의 말이 와야 한다. So he got a good score not only in the English test but also in the math test.

20 (B) 레오나르도 다빈치는 새가 어떻게 날 수 있는지 궁금해서 새를 연구함 (A) 비록 그의 발명은 실패했지만 날 수 있는 기계를 만들기 위해 새의 날개를 모방했고 (C) 그때 이후로 점점 더 많은 사람들이 새의 날아다니는 능력을 성공적으로 모방해 왔음

21 자신의 문제에 대한 해결책을 발견하기 위해 자연을 모방하는 사람을 가리키는 말이다.

22 사람들이 성공적으로 자연을 모방한 사례를 의미하는 말이다.

23 ②번에 이어지는 문장의 the new material은 주어진 문장에서 과학자들이 발명한 a new material이다..

24 단지 손과 발만을 이용해서 높은 건물을 올라가는 것을 의미한다.

25 과학자들이 만든 새로운 물질은 강할 뿐만 아니라 사용하기 쉽다고 하였다.

26 언제 무리가 떠나고 사냥할지를 결정하고 어디로 갈지 결정하고 위험이 있을 때 무엇을 할지 아는 것은 모두 지도력

(leadership)과 관련이 있다.

27 decides에 병렬 연결되므로 knows라고 쓰는 것이 적절하다.

28 기차가 터널 안으로 들어가면 갑작스러운 기압의 상승으로 인해 시끄러운 소리를 내고, 이것이 승객들의 잠을 깨우고 두통을 야기한다고 하였다.

29 기차의 앞면을 다시 디자인하였다.

단원별 예상문제 p.46~49

01 (g)racefully　02 ①　　03 ④　　04 ④
05 ③　　06 ④　　07 ⑤　　08 ④
09 ④
10 Can you explain to me how much this machine costs?
11 (1) lovely　(2) efficiently
12 (1) Do you know when your school festival started?
(2) She enjoys not merely running but also swimming.
13 ③
14 (1) I'm wondering if[whether] you have read the notice about the contest.
(2) What do you suppose you will do?
15 ⑤　　16 ②　　17 ④　　18 ④
19 (B) if　(C) those　(D) the other
20 They should be pressed together.
21 how they survive the heat
22 ④　　23 ③　　24 ④

---

01 주어진 단어는 유의어 관계이다. creative 창의적인, inventive 창의적인, gracefully 우아하게, graciously 우아하게

02 "사람들은 다른 문화권의 전통에 끌리는 경우가 많다."는 의미로 "fascinate"가 적절하다.

03 "어째서 ~인가?"는 "How come ~?"이다. "~는 어때?"에 해당하는 제안은 "How about ~?"이다.

04 ① redesign ② pressure ③ reflect ④ solutions ⑤ reduce

05 이미 알고 있는지를 묻는 말은 know, hear, be aware 등으로 나타낼 수 있다.

06 (A) 그것이 어떻게 도움이 되니? = how will that help? (B) 어째서 ~이니? = How come ~?

07 새로운 주사 바늘이 통증을 덜 초래하는 이유는 이미 밝혀진 상태이므로 어울리지 않는 것은 ⑤이다.

08 (가)의 that은 동격의 명사절을 유도하는 접속사 that이다. ① 지시형용사 ② 관계대명사 ③ 지시대명사 ④ 접속사 ⑤ 관계대명사

09 염소가 산에서 뛰어노는 것을 본 것은 Thomas이다.

10 의문사구 'how much'를 함께 써야 한다.

11 'not only A but also B'에서 A와 B에는 대등한 형태의 말이 와야 한다. (1) healthy와 같은 형용사인 lovely가 적절하고, (2) 부사 hard에 맞춰 부사인 efficiently로 쓰는 것이 적절하다.

12 (1) Do you know의 목적어로 간접의문문을 '의문사+주어+동사'의 어순으로 쓴다. (2) not merely A but (also) B: A뿐만 아니라 B도

13 'not only A but also B'에서 A와 B에는 대등한 형태의 말이 와야 한다. study Latin의 study가 빠져야 한다.

14 (1) 의문사가 없으므로 주절 다음에 'if[whether]+주어+동사'의 어순으로 쓴다. (2) 주절의 동사로 suppose가 있으므로 간접의문문의 의문사를 맨 앞으로 보내야 한다.

15 첫 번째 문장에는 관계대명사 what, 두 번째 문장에는 간접의문문의 의문사로 eat의 목적어 what이 들어가야 한다.

16 'not only A but also B'에서 A와 B는 어법상 같은 성질의 것이어야 한다. at의 목적어로 동명사를 쓰는 것이 적절하다.

17 글의 내용으로 보아 ④번이 가장 적절하다.

18 George의 옷에 달라붙어 있던 것은 가시였다.

19 (B) '~인지 아닌지'라는 의미로 쓰이고 있으므로 if, (C) many tiny needles를 지칭하는 것이므로 those, (D) 둘 중 남은 하나를 가리키는 말은 the other이다.

20 아주 좋은 고정 장치로 쓰이기 위해서는 두 소재가 함께 붙어야 한다.

21 간접의문문의 어순은 '의문사+주어+동사'임에 유의한다.

22 사하라 사막의 개미들이 정오에 사냥하러 가는 것을 좋아한다는 말은 나와 있지 않다.

23 ③번 다음 문장의 them이 지칭하는 것은 주어진 문장의 birds이다.

24 위 글은 자연이 인간에게 영감을 주는 존재라는 것에 대하여 주로 말하고 있다.

서술형 실전문제
p.50~51

01 What's so special about her?

02 What

03 fascinating

04 can glide over water as well as swim well

05 (1) How do certain animals climb walls so easily?
   (2) What is the most important thing in life?
   (3) Was he sleepy or drunk?

06 (1) Do you know why she is crying?
   (2) What do you think she expected to happen as a result of her visit?
   (3) They not only made the cake but also ate it a lot.
   (4) You as well as your sister have to clean the room.

07 Is Spider-Man Possible in Real Life?

08 as well as

09 He saw that burrs were stuck to his clothes and his dog's hair.

10 가시의 끝 부분이 곧지 않은 것

11 One had many tiny needles like those of burrs and the other had a hairy surface.

01 무엇이 그리 특별한데? = What's so special?

02 그 외에 무엇인지를 묻는 말은 "What else ~?"이다.

03 사람을 매혹하는 의미로 사물이 사람의 감정을 생기게 할 때는 현재분사를 쓴다.

04 수영을 잘할 수 있을 뿐만 아니라 물 위로 활공할 수 있으므로 'as well as' 구문을 이용한다.

05 (1) 간접의문문으로 쓰인 문장을 '의문사+조동사+주어'의 의문문의 어순으로 바꾼다. (2) 주절의 동사 believe로 인해 의문사가 맨 앞으로 나간 것이므로 간접의문문을 '의문사+be동사+주어'의 의문문의 어순으로 바꾼다. (3) 의문사 없이 'if+주어+동사'의 간접의문문이므로 'be동사+주어'의 의문문의 어순으로 바꾼다.

06 (1) '의문사+주어+동사'의 어순으로 쓴다. (2) 주절의 동사로 think가 있으므로 간접의문문의 의문사를 맨 앞으로 보내야 한다. (3) 'not only A but also B'에서 A와 B에는 대등한 형태의 말이 와야 한다. (4) 'B as well as A'가 주어로 쓰일 경우 동사의 수는 B에 일치시킨다.

07 현실에서 스파이더맨이 가능한지에 관한 글이다.

08 not only A but also B = B as well as A: A뿐만 아니라 B도

09 집으로 오는 길에 George는 가시가 자신의 옷과 개의 털에 붙어 있는 것을 보았다.

10 가시가 자신의 옷과 개의 털에 붙은 이유가 가시의 끝 부분이 곧지 않은 것 때문이라고 생각하여, 이것을 유용한 무언가를 만들기 위해 사용할 수 있는지 궁금해 했다는 의미이다.

11 두 개의 새로운 재료 중 하나는 가시 식물과 같은 조그만 가시들이 많이 있는 것이었고, 다른 하나는 털로 덮인 표면이 있다고 하였다.

p.52

|모범답안|

01 fascinates / invention / Genius / imitate

02 not only as a door but also as a table for table tennis

03 how certain animals climb walls so easily / what their feet look like / how they stick to walls / sticks to any surface / strong / easy to use

01 imitate 모방하다, fascinate 매혹하다, redesign 다시 디자인하다, genius 천재, invention 발명

02 이 문은 문으로도 쓰일 수 있고 탁구대로도 쓰일 수 있으므로 'not only A but also B' 구문을 이용한다.

단원별 모의고사

p.53~56

01 fascination 02 ②
03 (1) genius (2) fasteners (3) dive (4) front
04 ①   05 ②   06 slip into
07 ③   08 ①   09 ④   10 ③
11 ②   12 ⑤   13 ①
14 listening to music as well as running   15 ③
16 (1) as well as (2) as well as
   (3) What does she do?
   (4) I don't know where I should go.
17 (D)—(B)—(A)—(C)
18 woke up, have headaches
19 ③   20 ⑤   21 ③
22 ⓐ, ⓒ, ⓓ - ⓑ, ⓔ   23 ②   24 ⑤

01 두 단어의 관계는 동사-명사의 관계이다. explore 탐험하다, exploration 탐험, fascinate 매혹하다, fascination 매혹

02 "새 입 위에 있는 딱딱하고 보통 뾰족한 부분"은 "새의 부리", 즉 beak이다.

03 (1) genius 천재 (2) fastener 잠금장치, 접착포 (3) dive 잠수하다 (4) front 앞쪽

04 keep A from -ing = A가 ~하지 못하게 하다 / 그 요란한 소음은 아기가 잠을 자지 못하게 했다.

05 "That's why"는 결과를 유도하는 표현이다. 좁은 틈으로 도망가는 것의 결과는 잡기가 어렵다는 것이다.

06 "A bug robot can do the same"은 "some bugs can slip into narrow spaces"의 내용을 가리킨다.

07 "Yeah. That's why it's hard to catch them."이라는 대답을 보면 Henry는 벌레가 좁은 틈으로 도망가는 것을 알고 있었다.

08 주어진 문장은 처음 듣는 a mosquito needle에 대한 설명을 요청하는 문장으로 구체적인 설명이 시작되기 전인 (A)가 적절한 위치이다.

09 ① a mosquito needle에 대해서 들은 적이 없는 것은 소녀이다. ② 설명을 하는 사람은 소년이다. ③ 과학자들이 모방한 것은 모기의 입이다. ⑤ 세상에 쓸모없는 것은 없다고 했다.

10 ① Do you know what this means? ② I wonder if[whether] you could point me in the right direction for the bus station. ④ I'm not sure if she will be our new leader in the near future. ⑤ Do you know why Jonathan left so early?

11 'not only A but also B'에서 A와 B에는 대등한 형태의 말이 와야 한다. I like not only studying but also going hiking.

12 not A but B: A가 아니라 B

13 '~인지 아닌지'의 의미를 가진 의문사가 없는 간접의문문이므로 'if나 whether'가 적절하다.

14 B as well as A: A뿐만 아니라 B도. running이 나와 있으므로 listen도 listening으로 써야 한다.

15 know의 목적어로 간접의문문을 이끄는 것이 자연스럽다.

16 (1), (2) not only A but also B = B as well as A (3), (4) 간접의문문의 어순은 '의문사+주어+동사'이다.

17 (D) 초고속 열차의 문제점 제시 (B) 이 문제점을 해결하려고 노력하던 어느 날 먹이를 찾는 새를 관찰함 (A) 새가 빠르고 조용히 물속으로 뛰어드는 것을 보고 새를 연구함 (C) 새의 부리를 모방함으로써 기차를 다시 디자인하여 기존 기차의 문제를 해결함

18 기차가 터널에 들어가면 시끄러운 소리가 사람들의 잠을 깨우고 두통을 일으켰다고 하였다.

19 know의 목적어로 쓰이는 간접의문문이므로 how they could reduce라고 쓰는 것이 적절하다.

20 다시 디자인한 기차는 예전 기차보다 15 퍼센트 더 적은 전기로 10 퍼센트 더 빨리 이동한다고 하였으므로 ⑤번이 글의 내용과 일치한다.

21 이어지는 문장이 앞 문장의 결과를 이끌고 있으므로 ③번이 가장 적절하다.

22 ⓐ, ⓒ, ⓓ는 벽을 쉽게 오르는 동물들을, ⓑ, ⓔ는 과학자들을 가리키는 말이다.

23 자연을 창조하는 것이 아니라 모방하는 것이므로 imitate라고 쓰는 것이 적절하다.

24 점점 더 많은 사람들이 자연 속 천재의 능력을 성공적으로 모방해 왔다고 하였으므로 ⑤번은 글의 내용과 일치하지 않는다.는 것이 적절하다.

I Don't See It That Way

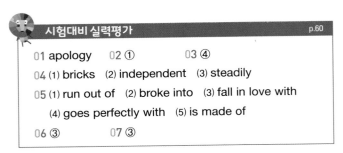

시험대비 실력평가   p.60

01 apology   02 ①   03 ④

04 (1) bricks   (2) independent   (3) steadily

05 (1) run out of   (2) broke into   (3) fall in love with

     (4) goes perfectly with   (5) is made of

06 ③   07 ③

01 주어진 단어는 동사와 명사의 관계를 나타낸다. apologize: 사과하다, apology: 사과

02 '통제할 수 없는 방식으로 입과 코를 통해 갑작스럽고 요란하게 공기를 내보내다'를 의미하는 말은 sneeze(재채기하다)이다.

03 against: ~에 맞서, 반대하여

04 brick: 벽돌, independent: 독립적인, steadily: 꾸준히

05 fall in love with: ~와 사랑에 빠지다, go perfectly with: ~와 잘 어울리다, be made of: ~로 만들어지다, break into: 침입하다, run out of: ~이 다 떨어지다

06 주어진 문장에서 frame은 '누명을 씌우다'를 의미하며 이와 같은 의미로 쓰인 것은 ③번이다. 나머지는 모두 '틀'을 의미한다.

07 be afraid of: ~을 두려워하다, instead of: ~ 대신에, be made of: ~로 만들어지다

서술형 시험대비   p.61

01 irresponsible

02 (1) impolite   (2) apology   (3) framed   (4) bricks

     (5) completely

03 (1) on your own   (2) his point of view

     (3) at least   (4) instead of

04 (1) The blooming flowers are very pretty, but they make me sneeze.

     (2) You deserve a rest after all that hard work.

     (3) A stork holds a fish in its beak.

05 (1) I never thought about his point of view.

     (2) I ran out of sugar.

     (3) Everything happens for a reason.

     (4) How does the company make money?

01 주어진 단어는 반의어 관계를 나타낸다. responsible: 책임감이 있는, irresponsible: 책임감이 없는

02 completely: 완전하게, frame: 누명을 씌우다, apology: 사과, brick: 벽돌, impolite: 무례한

03 on one's own: 혼자서, point of view: 관점, 견해, at least: 적어도, instead of: ~ 대신에

04 sneeze: 재채기하다, deserve: ~을 받을 만하다, beak: 부리, stork: 황새

05 point of view: 관점, 견해, run out of: ~이 다 떨어지다, make money: 돈을 벌다

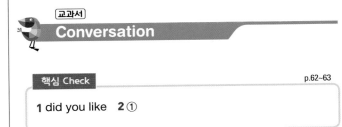

Conversation   교과서

핵심 Check   p.62~63

1 did you like   2 ①

교과서 대화문 익히기

Check(√) True or False   p.64

1 T   2 F   3 F   4 F

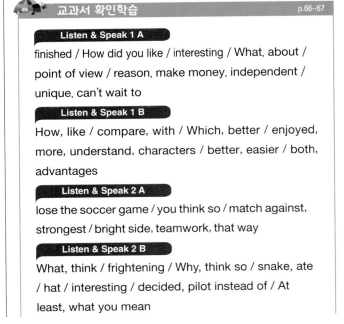

교과서 확인학습   p.66~67

Listen & Speak 1 A

finished / How did you like / interesting / What, about / point of view / reason, make money, independent / unique, can't wait to

Listen & Speak 1 B

How, like / compare, with / Which, better / enjoyed, more, understand, characters / better, easier / both, advantages

Listen & Speak 2 A

lose the soccer game / you think so / match against, strongest / bright side, teamwork, that way

Listen & Speak 2 B

What, think / frightening / Why, think so / snake, ate / hat / interesting / decided, pilot instead of / At least, what you mean

How do, like / To me, toilet / greatest / Why, think so / different point of view, real-life objects / something new / right, objects, different

turtle, mean / think so / sleeping, wake him up, fair / that way, be responsible for

시험대비 기본평가   p.68

01 I'm looking forward to reading the book.

02 ⑤   03 (C) → (B) → (A) → (E) → (D)

01 I can't wait to ~ = I'm looking forward to ~ing: ~이 몹시 기대되다

03 (C) 이야기를 알고 있음을 대답 → (B) 거북이에 대한 의견 표현 → (A) 이유 질문 → (E) 거북이에 대한 이유 설명 → (D) 반대하는 의견 표현

시험대비 실력평가   p.69~70

01 ②   02 ④   03 ④   04 ①

05 (A) lose the soccer game   (B) Class 3
    (C) the strongest players
    (D) look on the bright side

06 ⑤   07 ⑤

08 What do you think about my drawing

09 (1) frightening   (2) snake   (3) ate an elephant
    (4) picture of a hat

01 주어진 문장은 책이 더 좋은 이유를 설명해 주고 있으므로 (B) 에 들어가는 것이 적절하다.

02 ④ Brian은 이야기를 이해하기가 더 쉬워서 영화가 더 좋았다.

03 주어진 문장이 앞 문장의 the bright side를 설명해 주고 있으 므로 (D)에 들어가는 것이 적절하다.

04 주원이는 축구 경기를 질까봐 걱정했다가 김 선생님과의 대화를 통해 용기를 얻었음을 알 수 있다.

05 나는 내일 우리 팀이 축구 경기에서 질까봐 걱정이 되었다. 나의 팀은 3반과 경기를 가질 것이다. 그들은 학교에서 가장 강한 선 수들을 지녔다. 하지만 김 선생님은 내가 밝은 면을 보도록 하셨 다. 그녀는 내게 우리의 강한 팀워크를 상기시키셨다. 나는 우리 가 그들을 이길 수 있을 것이라고 생각한다. 나는 우리 팀원들과 다시 연습을 했다. 나는 경기를 기대하고 있다.

06 ⑤번을 제외한 나머지는 모두 이유를 묻는 표현이다.

07 'So, he didn't create something new?'라는 물음에 Ms. Parker는 'That's right.'라고 답하고 있다.

09 내가 Mike의 그림을 보았을 때, 매우 무서웠다. 왜냐하면 그것은 내게 코끼리를 먹은 뱀을 보여 주었기 때문이다. 반면에 Mike는 내게 많은 사람들이 그것을 모자 그림이라고 생각한다고 말했다. 그것은 매우 흥미로웠다. 나는 모든 사람들이 다른 관점들을 갖고 있다고 생각했다.

서술형 시험대비   p.71

01 point of view

02 Heungbu, Nolbu's

03 He wanted Heungbu to make money on his own and be independent.

04 (A) mean   (B) he didn't wake up the rabbit
    (C) sleeping   (D) responsible

05 (C) → (E) → (D) → (B) → (A)

02 태호가 읽은 책은 놀부의 관점에서 쓰인 흥부의 이야기이다.

03 그 책에서 놀부는 흥부가 스스로 돈을 벌고 자립할 수 있기를 바 랐다.

04 Jack과 Sora는 '토끼와 거북이' 이야기에 대해 다른 의견을 갖고 있었다. Jack은 이야기에서 거북이가 못됐다고 주장했다. 왜냐하 면 거북이는 토끼가 자고 있는 것을 보았지만 토끼를 깨우지 않았 기 때문이다. 반면에 소라는 거북이가 그를 깨워야 할 책임이 없 다고 주장했다.

05 (C) 영화와 책 중 선호하는 것 질문 → (E) 선호하는 것 대답 및 이유 설명 → (D) 반응 및 의견 표현 → (B) 반응 및 추측 표 현 → (A) 동의 표현

교과서
Grammar

핵심 Check   p.72~73

1 (1) hadn't had   (2) had happened

2 (1) to meet   (2) that

01 (1) see → to see   (2) accept → to accept

    (3) meeting → to meet   (4) leave → left 또는 had left

    (5) plays → played 또는 had played

02 I had played a computer game until my mom

    told me to stop playing it.

03 ②

04 (1) The bus had left when she reached the

    terminal.

    (2) I knew her well, for I had often seen her.

    (3) I found that I had lost my watch.

01 (1), (2), (3) 감정형용사 뒤에 to부정사가 쓰여 이유나 원인을 나타내는 문장. '주어+동사+감정형용사+to부정사' 어순이다. (4) 고객이 떠난 것이 내가 사무실에 도착했던 것보다 먼저 일어난 일이므로 leaves를 had left나 과거형 left로 고치는 것이 적절하다. (5) 엄마가 어렸을 때 연주했던 바이올린이므로 plays를 played나 had played로 쓰는 것이 적절하다.

02 엄마가 컴퓨터 게임을 그만하라고 하실 때까지 계속 컴퓨터 게임을 한 것이므로 계속 용법의 과거완료가 적절하다.

03 (1) 그녀가 터미널에 도착한 것보다 버스가 떠난 것이 앞선 사건이므로 had left가 적절하다. (2) 내가 그녀를 아는 이유는 이전에 종종 그녀를 보았다는 앞선 사건이 있기 때문이므로 had seen으로 쓰는 것이 적절하다. (3) 시계를 잃어버린 것이 알아차린 것보다 앞선 사건이므로 had lost로 쓰는 것이 적절하다.

01 뒤의 bought → had bought   **02** ③

03 (1) (완)   (2) (경)   (3) (대)

04 (1) (to부정사를 이용) She was surprised to hear of his

    failure.

    (부사절 that을 이용) She was surprised that she

    heard of his failure.

    (2) (must be 이용) He must be mad to do such a

    thing.

    (3) (과거완료 이용) She had left the door wide open.

    (4) (전후 관계를 따져 과거완료 이용) All of my friends

    thought carefully what she had said.

05 (1) had read   (2) had played   (3) had gone

06 ②   **07** ⑤   **08** ①, ②   **09** ③

10 (1) When I arrived home, I found someone had

    broken into my house.

    (2) Rachel said that she had not seen her before.

    (3) He had injured his leg so he couldn't play

soccer.

    (4) He had studied French for three years before

    he went to France.

11 (1) to   (2) be   (3) see

12 (1) picked → had picked   (2) that → to

13 ③   **14** ③, ⑤

15 (1) She was disappointed that she got a bad

    grade.

    (2) I was glad that I heard you're alive and well.

    (3) She felt unhappy that she saw the accident.

    (4) I feel very proud that I am a part of the team.

    (5) I was somewhat surprised that I saw him.

16 ①

17 (1) ②   (2) didn't cleaned → hadn't cleaned

01 '네가 전에 사줬던 가방과 꼭 같은 가방을 산 것'으로 you가 산 것이 앞선 시제이므로 bought를 had bought로 고쳐야 한다.

02 나는 그 이야기를 읽고 정말로 충격 받았다. '감정 형용사+to부정사'로 to부정사 뒤에 오는 내용은 원인이나 이유를 나타낸다.

03 (1) 수지가 파티에 도착했을 때, Eric은 이미 집에 가고 없었다. (2) 그녀는 네가 그녀에게 말하기 전에 그 소문에 대해 들었던 적이 있니? (3) 나는 그가 그 전날 내게 거짓말을 한 것을 깨달았다.

04 (1) '감정 형용사+to부정사'로 to부정사 뒤에 오는 내용은 원인이나 이유를 나타낸다. to부정사 뒤에 오는 내용은 부사절 that을 이용하여 쓸 수도 있다. (2) 'must be 감정형용사 to부정사'이며 to부정사 뒤에 나오는 내용은 원인이나 이유를 나타낸다. (3) 과거완료는 'had+p.p.'로 'had left'를 쓴 5형식 문장이다. (4) 그녀가 말했던 것이 곰곰이 생각하는 것보다 앞선 사건이므로 had said로 쓴다.

05 (1) 경위를 설명하는 것보다 신문에서 읽은 것이 더 이전 상황이므로 had+p.p.로 쓴다. (2) 대과거로 표현하라는 지시에 따라 had played로 쓴다. (3) 이미 사라져 없어진 것이므로 had p.p.로 쓴다.

06 나는 어려운 상황에 대처하는 그녀의 능력에 놀랐다. 빈칸 뒤에 명사가 왔으므로 to부정사 자리가 아니다. be amazed at: ~에 놀라다

07 ⑤ Jenny was bored to study math for 3 hours. Jenny는 3시간 동안 수학 공부를 해서 지겨웠다.

08 ① '감정형용사+to부정사'로 to부정사 뒤에 오는 말은 원인이나 이유를 나타낸다. ② '감정형용사+to부정사'를 '감정형용사 that S+V'로 바꿔 쓸 수 있다. ③ solve →solved ④ solved → solve ⑤ solved → to solve

09 과거완료는 'had+p.p.'이므로 been이 들어가야 한다.

10 과거보다 앞선 시제를 과거완료로 나타내고 과거완료는 'had+p.p.'로 쓰고 부정은 'had+not+p.p.'로 쓴다.

11 어법에 맞게 배열하면, (1) They were surprised to find that he had already left. (2) I'll be glad to get home. (3) I was sad to see them go.이다.

12 (1) Alice는 Ted가 전에 Jane과 딸기를 땄다는 것을 알고 있었다. 딸기를 같이 딴 것이 알고 있는 것보다 이전 상황이므로 had picked가 적절하다. (2) 나쁜 소식을 전해서 유감이에요. '감정형용사+to부정사'이다. to부정사 뒤의 내용은 이유나 원인을 나타낸다.

13 ③ be anxious to부정사: ~하기를 열망하다. knowing을 to know로 바꾸어야 적절하다. ① 그들이 결혼했다는 소식을 들으면 슬플 거예요. ② 그녀는 의사가 되길 간절히 열망했다. ③ 그녀는 혈액검사 결과를 알고 싶어 했다. ④ 당신을 손님으로 맞게 되어 영광입니다. ⑤ 나는 그렇게 하면 기쁠 것이다.

14 아빠는 내가 비밀을 이야기하기 전에 그것을 알고 있었다. 과거완료는 had+p.p.로 쓰며 전후 관계를 명확하게 하는 부사절이 올 경우에는 주절에 과거 동사를 쓸 수 있다.

15 (1) 그녀는 나쁜 성적을 받아 실망했다. (2) 나는 네가 무사히 살아 있다는 소식을 듣고 기뻤어. (3) 그녀는 사고를 목격하고 매우 마음 아프게 생각했다. (4) 나는 이 팀의 일원이 된 것이 정말 자랑스럽습니다. (5) 나는 그를 보게 되어 약간 놀랐다.

16 Rachel이 지갑에서 돈을 꺼내러 갔을 때, 그는 누군가가 지갑을 가져간 것을 알았다. Rachel이 간 것보다 누군가가 지갑을 가져간 것이 앞서므로 앞선 것을 과거완료로 나타내는 것이 적절하다.

17 몇 주 동안 집을 치우지 않아서 집이 더러운 것이므로 치우지 않은 것이 이전 상황에 속한다. 그러므로 hadn't cleaned로 쓰는 것이 적절하다.

서술형 시험대비
p.78~79

01 (1) She had not told me it before she wore my clothes. 또는 She did not tell me it before she wore my clothes.
  (2) I had never met such a beautiful girl before I met Jane. 또는 I didn't meet such a beautiful girl before I met Jane.
  (3) All the tickets had been sold out when I entered the website.
  (4) They had gone to work when he called.

02 (1) You must be proud of yourself.
  (2) They are very proud to be Korean.

03 (1) glad to be (2) proud to support
  (3) anxious to finish (4) am interested in
  (5) very sad to hear (6) had left

04 (1) is proud to (2) be tired of
  (3) be full of / be filled with

05 (1) I was very proud of myself as I had won the prize at the contest.
  (2) I had no money as I had lost my wallet.
  (3) My mother scolded my sister as my sister had bothered me.

06 around 2010, he had played soccer every day after school

07 (1) is diligent enough to clean
  (2) is creative enough to make

08 happy to be with my friend

01 (1), (2)의 경우 before로 시간의 전후 관계가 명백하므로 과거 시제로도 쓸 수 있다. (3) 표를 사러 웹 사이트에 들어간 것보다 표가 매진된 것이 이전 상황이므로 과거완료 시제를 사용한다. (4) 그가 전화한 것보다 출근하고 없는 것이 이전 상황이므로 과거완료 시제를 사용한다.

02 be proud of+명사[대명사], be proud to부정사: ~을 자랑스러워하다

03 (1) 여행이 너무 힘들어서 난 집에 가면 기쁠 거야. (2) 나는 그들의 일을 지원해 줄 수 있어 자랑스럽다. (3) 그녀는 학교를 마치고 취직하기를 열망했다. (4) 나는 수학에 관심이 있다. (5) 우리는 네가 떠난다는 소식을 들어서 매우 슬퍼. (6) 그 원숭이들은 여행객들이 그들을 위해 남겨 둔 바나나를 먹었다.

04 (1) be proud to be+명사 (2) be tired of: ~에 지치다 (3) be full of = be filled with: ~로 가득 차 있다

05 (1) 나는 대회에서 상을 타서 내 자신이 매우 자랑스러웠다. (2) 나는 지갑을 잃어버려서 돈이 없었다. (3) 언니가 나를 괴롭혀서 엄마는 언니를 혼냈다.

06 '2010년쯤까지 방과 후 축구를 매일 했었다'를 경험을 나타내는 had p.p.를 사용한다.

07 (1) 그는 혼자서 축구장 청소를 할 만큼 부지런하다. (2) 두 컵으로 엔진을 만들 만큼 이 사진은 창의적이다.

08 나는 내 친구와 함께여서 행복하다. '감정형용사+to부정사'이며 to부정사 뒤에 나오는 내용은 감정에 대한 원인이나 이유가 된다.

15

확인문제   p.80

1 T 2 F 3 F 4 T 5 F

확인문제   p.81

1 T 2 T 3 F 4 T 5 F

01 Welcome to, was taken to, for blowing down

02 the third little pig

03 what happened to

04 time to build our, with straw, sticks, bricks

05 completely blew down

06 blew down, made of, couldn't

07 How, doing now

08 shocked to lose, resting in

09 let's meet, tell us what happened

10 is wrong

11 about a sneeze, a terrible cold

12 What, mean

13 was making, for

14 ran out of, to ask, for

15 knocked on, fell down

16 called

17 had just grabbed, coming on

18 sneezed, sneeze, fell down

19 by what had happened

20 happened to

21 why did you go to

22 that cup of sugar

23 had built, of

24 called out, to trouble you, in

25 what he answered, bother me

26 How impolite, deserved, knocking

27 When, came, breaking into

28 were framed

29 going to borrow, exciting

30 Could, lend me

31 which do you think is

1 Reporter: Welcome to Animal World News. Last Sunday, a wolf was taken to the police station for blowing down pigs' houses.

2 Today, we have the third little pig and the wolf with us.

3 Mr. Pig, could you explain what happened to you and your brothers?

4 Pig: Yes. My brothers and I thought it was time to build our own houses, so we built houses with straw, sticks, and bricks.

5 One day, the wolf came and completely blew down my brothers' houses.

6 He almost blew down my house, but it was made of bricks, so he couldn't.

7 Reporter: How are your brothers doing now?

8 Pig: They are shocked to lose their houses. They are resting in my house.

9 Reporter: Thank you, Mr. Pig. Now, let's meet our second guest, the wolf. Mr. Wolf, could you tell us what happened?

10 Wolf: This whole "Big Bad Wolf" thing is wrong.

11 The real story is about a sneeze from a terrible cold and a cup of sugar.

12 Reporter: What do you mean?

13 Wolf: Back then, I was making a birthday cake for my dear old grandmother.

14 I ran out of sugar. I walked down the street to ask my neighbor for a cup of sugar.

15 When I knocked on the door, it fell down.

16 Then I called, "Little pig, are you in?"

17 I had just grabbed the broken door when I felt a sneeze coming on.

18 I sneezed a great sneeze and you know what? The whole straw house fell down.

19 I was very surprised by what had happened.

20 Unfortunately, the same thing happened to the second little pig's house.

21 Reporter: Then why did you go to the third little pig's house?

22 Wolf: I still needed that cup of sugar, so I went to the next house.

23 The third little pig had built his house of bricks.

24 I called out, "I'm sorry to trouble you, but are you in?"

25 And do you know what he answered? "Go away. Don't bother me again!"

26 How impolite! I thought I deserved an apology, so I kept knocking.

27 When the police came, of course they thought I was breaking into this pig's house.

28 Reporter: Do you think you were framed?

29 Wolf: Yes. The news reporters of the town thought a sick wolf going to borrow a cup of sugar didn't sound very exciting.

30 So, they made me the "Big Bad Wolf." Could you maybe lend me a cup of sugar?

31 Reporter: Thank you for your time. Everyone, which do you think is the true story, the pig's or the wolf's?

시험대비 실력평가
p.86~89

01 ③　　　　　02 ④

03 It's because they thought it was time to build their own houses.

04 ②　　　05 sneeze　　06 ④　　　07 ④

08 It was made of straw.　　09 ⑤

10 exciting　11 ④　　　12 ③　　　13 ④

14 ③　　　　15 explain

16 build their own houses, straw sticks, bricks

17 what happened　　　　18 (B)—(A)—(C)

19 ④　　　　20 ⑤　　　21 ②　　　22 ④

23 ④

24 The wolf thinks that the news reporters of the town made him the "Big Bad Wolf" because they thought a sick wolf going to borrow a cup of sugar didn't sound very exciting.

01 대답으로 미루어 보아 형제들의 현재 상태를 묻는 말이 들어가는 것이 가장 자연스럽다.

02 돼지 삼형제는 지푸라기, 막대, 벽돌로 집을 지었다고 하였다.

03 돼지 삼형제가 집을 지은 이유는 자신들의 집을 지을 때라고 생각했기 때문이다.

04 인터뷰 손님으로 셋째 돼지와 늑대가 왔다고 하였다.

05 늑대의 답변으로 보아 모든 사건은 늑대의 재채기와 설탕 한 컵으로 인한 것이었음을 알 수 있다.

06 늑대의 입장에서는 '불행히도' 두 번째 집에서도 똑같은 일이 발생했다고 말하는 것이 가장 자연스럽다.

07 지각동사 feel의 목적격보어로 동사원형, 현재분사, 과거분사가 쓰일 수 있으며, 재채기를 할 것 같았다는 의미이므로 coming이나 come을 쓰는 것이 적절하다.

08 늑대의 말에 따르면 첫 번째 이웃의 집은 지푸라기로 만들어졌다.

09 사과를 받을 만하다고 생각했다고 하였으므로 무례하다고 말하

10 감정을 유발하는 것은 현재분사형 형용사를 쓴다.

11 여전히 설탕이 필요했기 때문에 세 번째 돼지의 집으로 갔다고 하였으므로, 늑대가 세 번째 돼지의 집으로 간 이유는 ④번이 가장 적절하다.

12 늑대는 돼지의 집을 침입할 의도가 아니었다.

13 빈칸 (A)에는 '이유'를 나타내는 전치사 for가 들어간다. ① take care of: ~을 돌보다 ② rely on: ~에 의존하다 ③ die of: ~으로 죽다 ④ except for: ~을 제외하고 ⑤ break down: 고장나다

14 위 글은 뉴스 진행자가 돼지와 늑대를 인터뷰하는 글이다.

15 무언가를 분명하고 이해하기 쉽게 만드는 것은 '설명하다(explain)'이다.

16 그들의 집을 짓기 위해서 세 마리의 돼지는 짚, 나무 막대기, 벽돌을 사용했다.

17 의문대명사 what을 이용하여 간접의문문 문장을 만들 수 있다.

18 (B) 할머니 생일 케이크를 만들던 중 설탕이 다 떨어져 이웃집 문을 두드림 → (A) 문이 떨어졌고, 부서진 문을 움켜잡았을 때 재채기가 나오는 걸 느낌 → (C) 재채기를 아주 크게 함

19 '같은 일'이라는 것은 '그의 재채기로 인하여 집이 무너진 것'을 의미한다.

20 글의 내용으로 보아 늑대는 돼지들의 집을 무너지게 할 의도가 없었음을 알 수 있다.

21 간접의문문은 '의문사+주어+동사+'의 어순으로 쓰지만, 생각 동사 think, believe, guess, suppose 등은 의문사를 문두로 보낸다. 따라서 ②번은 적절하지 않다.

22 돼지의 응답이 무례하다고 생각했기 때문에 사과를 받아 마땅하다고 말하는 것이 적절하다.

23 셋째 아기 돼지는 늑대에게 다시는 귀찮게 하지 말라며 무례하게 대했다.

24 마을의 신문 기자들은 설탕 한 컵을 빌리려는 아픈 늑대가 별로 흥미롭지 않다고 생각했기 때문에 늑대를 '덩치 크고 못된 늑대'로 만든 것이라고 늑대는 생각한다.

서술형 시험대비
p.90~91

01 Because he blew down pigs' houses.

02 It is made of bricks.

03 They are so shocked to lose their houses and they are resting at the third little pig's house.

04 There are the third little pig and the wolf as guests

of Animal World News.

05 What do you mean?

06 He was making a birthday cake for his grandmother.

07 He walked down the street in order to ask his neighbor for a cup of sugar.

08 It fell down.

09 It's because the wolf sneezed a great sneeze.

10 had visited

11 it was impolite

12 apology

13 ④번 → borrow

14 breaking into, knocking, was framed

01 늑대가 경찰에 잡혀간 이유는 돼지들의 집을 불어 넘어뜨렸기 때문이다.

02 셋째 돼지의 말에 따르면 그의 집은 벽돌로 만들어졌다.

03 첫째 아기 돼지와 둘째 아기 돼지는 집을 잃고 충격을 받아서 셋째 아기 돼지의 집에서 쉬고 있다고 하였다.

04 Animal World News에 셋째 아기 돼지와 늑대가 손님으로 왔다.

05 mean: 의미하다

06 늑대는 할머니를 위한 생일 케이크를 만들던 중이었다.

07 늑대는 이웃에게 설탕 한 컵을 달라고 하기 위해 길을 걸어갔다고 하였다.

08 늑대가 이웃의 문을 두드렸을 때 문이 떨어졌다고 하였다.

09 늑대가 재채기를 아주 크게 했기 때문에 짚으로 만든 집 전체가 무너졌다.

10 설탕을 얻기 위해 셋째 아기 돼지의 집으로 가기 전 다른 집들을 방문했다는 사실을 유추할 수 있다.

11 늑대는 돼지의 말이 무례하다고 생각했다.

12 당신이 무언가에 관해 미안하다고 말하는 것은 '사과(apology)'이다.

13 글의 내용상 늑대는 설탕을 빌려주려던 것이 아니라 빌리려던 것이다. 따라서 lend가 아닌 borrow를 쓰는 것이 적절하다.

14 해석: 경찰은 늑대가 돼지의 집을 침입하고 있다고 생각했지만 사실 늑대는 문을 두드리고 있던 중이었다고 말한다. 늑대는 또한 자신이 누명을 썼다고 주장한다.

영역별 핵심문제
p.93~97

01 compare

02 (1) apology, kept (2) bother (3) framed, crime
   (4) lend   03 ③   04 ③   05 ①

06 ⓐ the rabbit, ⓑ the turtle   07 ⑤

08 ④   09 ⑤

10 He was worried because Class 3 has the strongest players in the school.

11 It is the best teamwork. 12 ①

13 (1) They will be excited to teach you again.

   (2) I was scared to be left home alone.

   (3) She answered that she would be happy to come.

14 ①, ②, ③

15 He had already left when I got to the airport.

16 I would be glad to pick you up at the airport.

17 (1) I fought with my sister when I saw that she had made my clothes dirty.

   (2) We were embarrassed when we knew that our car had gone.

   (3) I cried when I brought to mind that my boyfriend had forgotten our anniversary.

18 ①

19 She was sad to let him leave.

20 (1) lost in the race because he had taken a nap during the race

   (2) was happy to win the race

21 ②   22 ③   23 ⑤   24 ④

25 ②   26 ⑤

01 주어진 단어는 명사와 동사의 관계를 나타낸다. comparison: 비교, compare: 비교하다

02 apology: 사과, keep ~ing: 계속 ~하다, bother: 괴롭히다, frame: 누명을 씌우다, crime: 범죄, lend: 빌려주다

03 '사람이 법에 의해 처벌받을 수 있는 불법적인 행동이나 행위'를 가리키는 말은 crime(범죄)이다.

04 I can't wait to ~: 너무 ~하고 싶다, be taken to: ~에 끌려가다, run out of: ~이 다 떨어지다, point of view: 관점, 견해

05 밑줄 친 (A)는 '못된, 나쁜'을 의미하며 이와 같은 의미로 쓰인 것은 ①번이다. 나머지는 모두 '의미하다'를 뜻한다.

07 ⑤ Jack이 거북과 토끼의 경주가 공정하지 않다고 생각하는지는 알 수 없다.

08 (A) 선행사 a snake에 대한 주격 관계대명사로 that, (B) 뒤에 명사가 이어지므로 instead of, (C) 선행사를 포함하는 관계대명사 what이 적절하다.

09 위 대화를 통해 Mike가 무슨 모자를 그렸는지 알 수 없다.

10 그는 학교에서 가장 강한 선수들이 3반에 있기 때문에 걱정했다.

11 주원이네 반의 강점은 팀워크가 가장 좋다는 것이다.

12 이어지는 설명에서 너무 작고 신기가 어렵다는 불편함을 나타내고 있으므로 좋아한다는 대답과 어울리지 않는다.

13 (1) 그들은 너희를 다시 가르치게 되어 신이 날 것이다. (2) 나는 집에 홀로 남겨져서 무서웠다. (3) 그녀가 기꺼이 오겠다고 대답했다.

14 나는 우리가 코로나 19에 대한 실험이 성공했기 때문에 기뻤다. ② 나는 그때까지는 아픈 적이 없었다. ③ 그녀는 그녀의 오빠가 거기에 가고 싶어 한다는 것을 몰랐다. ④ '감정형용사+to부정사' 구문으로 to부정사 뒤에는 동사원형이 와야 한다. 명사가 올 경우에 proud는 to를 of로 고치는 것이 적절하다. ⑤ 그는 그의 남동생에게 화났다. be angry with를 써야 하므로 to를 with로 고치는 것이 적절하다.

15 과거완료는 had+p.p.로 쓰기 때문에 내가 공항에 도착한 것보다 그가 떠난 것이 이전 상황이므로 떠나고 없었다는 내용에 과거완료시제를 사용한다.

16 '감정형용사+to부정사'로 to부정사 뒤에 나오는 내용은 감정의 원인이나 이유를 나타낸다.

17 3개 문장 모두 과거에 있었던 일을 쓴 것이다. 과거 상황에서도 사건의 전후 관계가 있는 것으로 앞서 일어난 상황에는 had p.p.를 써서 영작하는 것이 적절하다.

18 ① 나는 그를 다시 보게 되어 기뻤다. '감정형용사+to부정사' 문장으로 that을 to로 고치는 것이 적절하다.

19 감정형용사+to부정사'로 to부정사 뒤에 나오는 내용은 감정의 원인이나 이유를 나타낸다.

20 (1) 토끼는 경기 도중 낮잠을 잤기 때문에 경기에서 졌다. (2) 거북이는 경기에서 이겨 기뻤다.

21 뉴스에서 셋째 아기 돼지와 늑대를 모셨다고 하였으므로 돼지와 늑대의 인터뷰가 이어진다고 보는 것이 가장 적절하다.

22 Reporter는 뉴스에서 이야기를 하고 있는 중이다.

23 밑줄 친 (A)는 감정의 원인을 나타내는 to부정사이다. ⑤번은 판단의 근거를 나타내고 있다.

24 돼지는 늑대가 자신의 형제들의 집을 날려버린 사건에 대해 주로 이야기하고 있다.

25 늑대는 자신의 이야기가 진짜 이야기라며 이에 관하여 서술하고 있으므로 "덩치 크고 못된 늑대" 사건은 옳지 않다고 말하는 것이 적절하다. right→wrong

26 늑대가 케이크를 언제 만들고 있었는지는 위 글을 읽고 답할 수 없다.

단원별 예상문제
p.98~101

01 (1) (o)bjects (2) responsible (3) steadily (4) stepmother
02 (1) grabbed (2) straw (3) framed (4) sneeze
    (5) trouble
03 (1) My house was too weak for the wolf to blow down.
    (2) Let's take a look at this picture together.

(3) I think it goes perfectly with your skirt.
04 ⓒ → wake him up   05 ⑤
06 ⓐ → frightening   07 ⑤
08 ⓒ → (to) understand
09 (A) the book (B) the movie (C) the book helped her understand the characters better
    (D) the movie (E) to understand the story
10 ⑤
11 (1) enjoyed helping (2) had told (3) was happy to
12 (1) I told my mother that I had finished my homework.
    (2) It was written that my aunt had wanted to give a doll to her daughter.
    (3) He told me that he had wanted to play in Manchester.
13 ③
14 We were unfortunate to lose the game.
15 ⑤
16 재채기를 하자 짚으로 만든 집이 무너진 것   17 ④
18 ⑤   19 He kept knocking.   20 ④

01 object: 물체, 물건, responsible: 책임이 있는, steadily: 꾸준히, stepmother: 계모

02 frame: 누명을 씌우다, straw: 짚, 지푸라기, grab: 붙잡다, trouble: 귀찮게 하다, sneeze: 재채기하다

03 blow down: 바람을 불어 넘어뜨리다, take a look at: ~을 살펴보다, go perfectly with: ~와 매우 잘 어울리다

04 이어동사의 목적어가 인칭대명사일 때 대명사는 동사와 부사 사이에 위치한다.

05 '토끼와 거북이' 이야기에서 누가 공정한지 알 수 없다.

06 frightening: 무서운

08 help는 목적격보어로 동명사를 취하지 않는다.

09 Brian과 Yura는 영화 'Good Friends'에 대해 이야기했다. 그들은 그것에 대해 다른 의견을 갖고 있었다. Yura는 영화보다 책을 선호했다. 왜냐하면 책은 그녀가 인물들을 이해하는 데 도움이 되었기 때문이다. 반면에 Brian은 영화를 더 좋아했다. 왜냐하면 그가 이야기를 이해하는 것이 더 쉬웠기 때문이다. 그들은 그것들 둘 다 각각의 장점이 있다는데 동의했다.

10 위 대화를 통해 유라가 생각하는 영화의 단점은 알 수 없다.

11 (1) 나는 아빠를 도와서 즐거웠다. (2) 나는 그녀가 회의 중 말했던 아이디어에 대해 계획을 만들었다. (3) 나는 할머니에게 핸드폰 사용에 대해 알려드려 기뻤다.

12 대과거는 had+p.p.로 쓴다.

13 ③ 나는 불에 타고 있는 빌딩을 보고 충격 받았다. that → to ①

19

왕자는 신데렐라를 찾아서 행복했다. ② 너를 여기서 만나 반가워. ④ 내 친구들은 그 소식을 듣고 유감스러웠다. ⑤ 나는 파티에 초대되어 흥분했다.

14 '감정형용사+to부정사' 구문으로 to부정사는 부사적 용법으로 사용되었다.

15 늑대의 말로 보아 지독한 감기로 인한 재채기와 설탕 한 컵에 관한 것임을 알 수 있다.

16 재채기를 하자 짚으로 만든 집이 무너져 늑대가 놀란 것이다.

17 늑대가 부서진 문을 막 움켜잡았을 때 재채기가 나오는 것을 느꼈다고 하였다.

18 돼지와 늑대의 이야기라는 의미이므로 the pig's or the wolf's가 적절하다.

19 사과 받기를 원했던 늑대는 셋째 아기 돼지의 집 문을 계속 두드렸다고 하였다.

20 늑대를 인터뷰하고 있는 Reporter가 늑대의 말을 믿는다는 말은 위 글에 나와 있지 않다.

서술형 실전문제
p.102~103

01 She thinks it is the greatest piece of art of the 20th century.

02 He used real-life objects to create art.

03 He simply wanted people to look at the objects in a different way.

04 (1) Suji was bored to read a boring book.
(2) Suji was happy to see her brother enjoy the party.
(3) Suji was excited to join a popular club in her school.
(4) Suji was surprised to receive a present that she hadn't think ever.

05 went, was glad to, told, knew, had seen

06 Because they lost their houses due to the wolf.

07 could you explain what happened to you and your brothers?

08 (A) deserved (B) knocking (C) breaking

09 He visited pigs' houses in order to borrow a cup of sugar.

01 그녀는 그것이 20세기의 가장 위대한 예술 작품이라고 생각한다.

02 미술가는 작품을 만들기 위해 실생활 물건을 사용했다.

03 미술가는 그저 사람들이 다른 방식으로 사물을 바라보기를 원했

04 (1) 수지는 지루한 책을 읽어 지루해 했다. (2) 수지는 남동생이 파티를 즐기는 것을 보고 기뻤다. (3) 수지는 학교에서 인기 있는 동아리에 가입하여 즐거웠다. (4) 수지는 그녀가 생각지 못한 선물을 받아 놀랐다.

05 지난 주 나는 기념품 가게에 갔다. 나는 거기에서 새 학급 친구를 만나 반가웠다. 그는 나를 전에 봤기 때문에 나에 대해 알고 있다고 말했다.

06 돼지들이 충격을 받은 이유는 늑대 때문에 집을 잃어서였다.

07 요청하는 말에 could를 쓸 수 있으며, '무슨 일이 일어났는지'는 간접의문문을 활용하여 답할 수 있다.

08 (A) 사과를 받아 마땅하다고 생각했다는 의미이므로 deserve이며, 주절의 시제가 과거이므로 deserved라고 쓰는 것이 적절하다. (B) keep+Ving: 계속해서 V하다 (C) break into: ~에 침입하다

09 글의 내용으로 미루어 보아, 늑대는 설탕 한 컵을 빌리기 위해 돼지들의 집을 방문했음을 알 수 있다.

창의사고력 서술형 문제
p.104

|모범답안|

01 (1) the real-life objects (2) in a different way

02 (A) blew down (B) a sneeze from a terrible cold
(C) true (D) friend
(E) the wolf going to a hospital that day

01 미술 작품의 특별한 점은 미술가가 작품을 만들기 위해 실생활 물건을 사용했다는 것과 미술가가 사람들이 다른 방식으로 사물을 바라보기를 원했다는 것이다.

단원별 모의고사
p.105~109

01 ④   **02** ⑤

03 (1) was taken to (2) blew down (3) breaking into
(4) make sense

04 ④   **05** ⑤

06 (A) yesterday (B) point of view (C) for a reason
(D) make money (E) reading the book

07 He liked the movie better because it was easier to understand the story.

08 She preferred the book because it helped her understand the characters better.

09 Why do you think so?   **10** ⑤

11 ③   **12** ⑤

13 (1) They were shocked to lose their houses.

01 '불운에 의해'를 가리키는 말은 unfortunately(불행하게도)이다.

02 grab: 잡다

03 be taken to: ~에 끌려가다, blow down: 바람을 불어 넘어뜨리다, break into: ~에 침입하다, make sense: 이해가 되다

04 (A) How did you like it?: 그것은 어땠니?, (B) dependent: 의존적인, independent: 독립적인, (C) common: 흔한, unique: 독특한

05 위 대화를 통해 흥부가 스스로 돈을 벌기를 원했는지는 알 수 없다.

06 오늘 태호는 나에게 재미있는 책을 소개해 줬다. 그는 책을 어제 다 읽고 내용을 설명했다. 책은 놀부의 관점에서 쓰인 흥부에 대한 이야기였다. 태호는 내게 놀부는 이유가 있어서 흥부를 도와주지 않았다고 이야기했다. 놀부는 흥부가 스스로 돈을 벌고 자립하기를 바랐다. 매우 독특하고 재미있게 들렸다. 나는 이 책을 읽기가 기대된다.

07 Brian은 영화를 더 좋아했다. 왜냐하면 영화가 이야기를 이해하는 데 더 쉬웠기 때문이다.

08 유라는 책이 등장인물을 더 잘 이해하도록 도와줬기 때문에 책을 더 선호했다.

10 주원이는 자기네 반의 팀워크가 가장 좋다는 김선생님의 말에 동의한다.

11 주어진 문장은 20세기의 가장 위대한 작품이라는 설명에 대한 이유로 적절하므로 (C)가 적절하다.

12 위 대화를 통해 미술가가 작품을 만들기 위해 실생활 물건을 어떻게 사용했는지는 알 수 없다.

13 (1) '감정형용사+to부정사' 구문으로 to부정사에 이어지는 내용은 감정의 원인이나 이유가 된다. (2) 과거에 완료된 상황을 설명한 문장으로 재채기가 나오려 할 때 막 부서진 문을 잡았다는 상황을 묘사한 것이다.

14 It is surprising that he should do such a thing. 그가 그러한 것을 해야 한다는 사실이 참으로 놀랍다. It is lucky that I live in Korea. 내가 한국에 살아서 다행이다. I was happy that you will go to study abroad. 네가 해외에 가 공부하게 되어 기쁘다.

15 ④ that을 to로 바꾸는 것이 적절하다. ① 네가 1등을 해서 기쁘구나. ② 너의 친구가 여기에 오다니 이상하다. ③ 너는 뉴스를 듣고 놀랐니? ④ We are afraid to go to the hospital tomorrow. 우리는 내일 병원에 가야 해서 두렵다. ⑤ 그녀는 너를 자랑스러워한다.

16 그는 이번 여름 방학에 사파리 여행을 갈 생각을 해서 기뻤다.

17 (1) 나는 기억했다 • 소파 옆 의자에 앉아 기타를 연주했었던 것을 • 나의 엄마와 내 남동생이 바둑을 두었던 것을
(2) 나는 나의 사랑스러운 고양이가 할머니 무릎 위에 앉아 있었던 것을 기억했다.

18 늑대가 문을 고의로 부순 것은 아니었다. on purpose: 고의로, 일부러

19 늑대가 셋째 아기 돼지의 집을 날려버릴 수 없었던 이유는 그의 집이 벽돌로 만들어져서이다.

20 돼지는 늑대가 와서 형들의 집을 완전히 날려버렸다고 말한다. 반면에, 늑대는 지독한 감기로 인한 재채기 때문에 집이 무너졌다고 말한다.

21 늑대는 할머니를 위한 생일 케이크를 만들던 중 설탕이 다 떨어졌다고 하였다.

22 아픈 늑대의 이야기가 흥미를 유발하지 않는다는 의미이므로 현재분사형 형용사 exciting을 쓰는 것이 적절하다.

23 (B) 셋째 아기 돼지의 집으로 가서 그를 부름 → (A) 돼지가 무례하게 행동함 → (C) 늑대는 돼지의 행동에 대한 사과를 원함

24 이어지는 늑대의 말로 보아 늑대는 자신이 누명을 썼다고 생각함을 알 수 있다.

25 늑대가 돼지의 문을 계속해서 두드린 이유는 그가 돼지의 무례한 응답에 대해 사과를 받아 마땅하다고 생각했기 때문이다.

Which Way to Go?

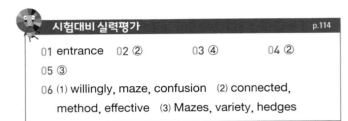

시험대비 실력평가   p.114

01 entrance   02 ②   03 ④   04 ②

05 ③

06 (1) willingly, maze, confusion (2) connected, method, effective (3) Mazes, variety, hedges

01 주어진 관계는 반의어 관계를 나타낸다. entrance: 입구, exit: 출구

02 주어진 문장에서 place는 '두다, 놓다'를 의미하며 이와 같은 의미로 쓰인 것은 ②번이다. 나머지는 모두 '장소'를 뜻한다.

03 make a choice: 선택하다, make a decision: 결정하다, make a plan: 계획을 세우다

04 '보통 들판, 정원, 마당, 도로 등의 가장자리를 따라 조밀하게 줄지어 심겨진 덤불 또는 작은 나무'를 나타내는 말은 'hedge(산울타리)'이다.

05 willingly: 기꺼이

06 willingly: 기꺼이, confusion: 혼란, connect: 연결하다, method: 방법, effective: 효과적인, a variety of: 다양한, hedge: 산울타리

서술형 시험대비   p.115

01 (1) regularity (2) worth (3) compare (4) exchange
    (5) decide

02 (1) This simple method may not be effective in certain types of mazes.
    (2) You can find the origin of the labyrinth in Greek mythology.
    (3) Please line up in the order of arrival.

03 (1) turn around (2) you (s)et for (3) a (v)ariety of

04 (1) We're really looking forward to seeing you again.
    (2) The first street we tried turned out to be a dead end.
    (3) Now is the time when we have to make a decision.
    (4) They go horseback riding once a month.
    (5) I must come up with an excuse.

01 compare: 비교하다, decide: 결정하다, regularity: 규칙성, worth: ~의 가치가 있는, ~할 가치가 있는, exchange: 교환하다

02 method: 방법, effective: 효과적인, maze: 미로, origin: 기원, labyrinth: 미궁, in the order of: ~의 순서로

03 turn around: 돌다, 돌아서다, be set for: ~할 준비가 되다., a variety of: 다양한

04 (1) look forward to: ~하기를 기대하다, (2) dead end: 막다른 길, (3) make a decision: 결정하다, (4) horseback riding: 승마 (5) come up with: ~을 생각해 내다

교과서
Conversation

핵심 Check   p.116~117

1 Is it possible to exchange them for the red shoes?
2 ②

교과서 대화문 익히기

Check(√) True or False   p.118

1 T   2 F   3 T   4 F

교과서 확인학습   p.120~121

Listen & Speak 1 A
possible, exchange / these days, why, making the decision, look better

Listen & Speak 1 B
decide, during / is it possible / exciting, horseback riding / a lot / schedule / excited / looking forward to

Listen & Speak 2 A
suggest, decide / about, reasonable / get to / fourth / next to / pleasure

Listen & Speak 2 B
coming, coming / worried / post office / How do I get to / Go straight for / turn right, go straight / Turn right, go straight

Real Life Communication
Are you all set for / in front of / got it, get to, decided

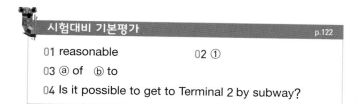

/ choices / reliable / possible to, by subway / take

Let's Check 1

origin, labyrinth / Labyrinth, mythological prison / angry, put, labyrinth

시험대비 기본평가
p.122

01 reasonable   02 ①

03 ⓐ of   ⓑ to

04 Is it possible to get to Terminal 2 by subway?

02 ①번을 제외한 나머지는 모두 길을 물어보는 말이다.

03 in front of: ~앞에, get to: ~에 가다

시험대비 실력평가
p.123~124

01 prison   02 ④   03 ⓐ → worried

04

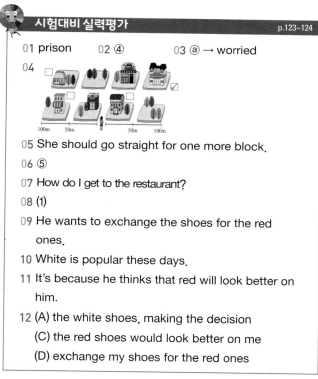

05 She should go straight for one more block.

06 ⑤

07 How do I get to the restaurant?

08 (1)

09 He wants to exchange the shoes for the red ones.

10 White is popular these days.

11 It's because he thinks that red will look better on him.

12 (A) the white shoes, making the decision

   (C) the red shoes would look better on me

   (D) exchange my shoes for the red ones

01 '처벌로서 범죄자를 가두거나 재판 받기 전 범죄로 고소된 사람들이 갇히는 건물'을 가리키는 말은 'prison(감옥)'이다.

02 크레타의 왕이 괴물에게 화가 나서 괴물을 감옥에 가두었다.

03 걱정스러움을 나타내는 과거분사형 형용사 worried가 적절하다.

05 민주는 우체국에서 킴스 베이커리에 가기 위해 한 블록 더 직진해야 한다.

06 ⑤번을 제외한 나머지는 모두 추천을 하는 표현이다.

09 소년은 신발을 빨간색으로 교환하기를 원한다.

10 흰색이 요즘 인기가 많다.

11 소년은 빨간색이 그에게 더 잘 어울릴 것이라고 생각하기 때문에 신발을 교환하기를 원한다.

12 나는 어제 흰색 신발을 샀다. 그것들은 너무 인기가 많았고 나는 결정하는 데 많은 시간이 걸렸다. 집에 돌아온 후, 나는 빨간색 신발이 내게 더 잘 어울릴 거라고 생각했다. 내가 신발가게에 방문해서 내 신발을 빨간색으로 교환할 수 있는지 물어보았을 때, 나는 교환할 수 있었다. 나는 내 빨간색 신발이 매우 좋다.

서술형 시험대비
p.125

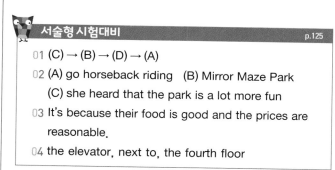

01 (C) → (B) → (D) → (A)

02 (A) go horseback riding   (B) Mirror Maze Park

   (C) she heard that the park is a lot more fun

03 It's because their food is good and the prices are reasonable.

04 the elevator, next to, the fourth floor

01 (C) 가능성 질문 → (B) 인기 있는 색상 설명 → (D) 교환하고자 하는 이유 설명 → (A) 대답

02 지나의 가족은 곧 제주도를 방문할 계획을 세웠다. 지나와 엄마는 이에 대해 이야기했다. 모든 것이 좋아보였지만 지나는 말을 타러 가는 계획을 바꾸고 싶어했다. 대신에, 그녀는 거울 미로 공원을 방문하고 싶었다. 왜냐하면 그녀는 공원이 훨씬 더 재미있다고 들었기 때문이다. 엄마는 두 번째 날 일정을 바꾸기로 결정해서 지나는 여행에 매우 신이 났다.

04 소라는 파파첸스에 건물 안에 엘리베이터를 이용해서 갈 수 있다. 파파첸스는 4층 엘리베이터 옆에 있다.

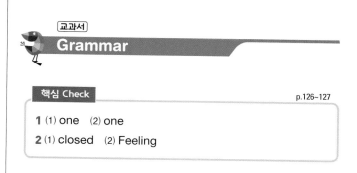

교과서

Grammar

핵심 Check
p.126~127

1 (1) one   (2) one

2 (1) closed   (2) Feeling

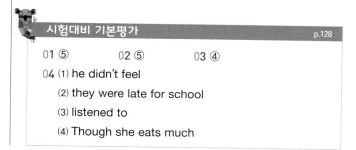

시험대비 기본평가
p.128

01 ⑤   02 ⑤   03 ④

04 (1) he didn't feel

   (2) they were late for school

   (3) listened to

   (4) Though she eats much

01 둘 중 첫 번째는 one, 나머지 하나는 the other로 쓴다.

02 분사구문을 만들 때, 주절과 주어가 같으면 주어를 생략하고 분사를 쓴다. 접속사와 주어를 모두 쓸 때는 분사구문으로 쓸 수 없으며, 완료분사구문은 주절보다 시제가 앞설 때 쓴다.

03 둘 중 나머지 하나를 가리킬 때는 the other를 써야 한다.

04 분사구문은 분사를 활용하여 부사절을 부사구로 줄인 표현이다. 대개 양보, 동시동작, 이유, 시간, 조건 등의 부사절이며, 절로 전환할 때에는 동사의 시제 등에 유의해야 한다. (4)는 내용상 양보이므로 Though 외에도 Although, Even though 등의 접속사가 가능하다.

01 ①   02 ③   03 ④   04 ④
05 ⑤   06 Tiring → Tired, or → nor
07 (1) Reading from left to right, it reads "evil"
     (2) Seeing the duck from under the water
08 ②   09 ⑤   10 ⑤   11 ④
12 ②   13 ⑤   14 ③
15 Not wanting to regret it again,
16 The girl having played with her friends without
     wearing a mask,   17 ④   18 ②

01 '마술에 흥미를 느낀 것이 그녀가 마술사가 되도록 했다.'이므로 문장에서 주어로 쓰인 '동명사'이다. 나머지는 모두 분사구문을 이끄는 분사이다.

02 ① one → it ② each는 단수 취급 are → is ④ neither는 nor와 함께 '둘 중 어느 것도 아니다'라는 뜻으로 쓴다. or → nor ⑤ 정해지지 않은 명사를 앞에서 수식하는 단어와 함께 쓸 때 one을 쓰는 것이 적절하다. it → one

03 ① Don't → Not ② Being → It being 독립분사구문 ③ Opened → Opening ⑤ Caught → Catching

04 두 학생 모두를 나타낼 때는 both, 둘 중 누구도 안 되는 경우는 no one 또는 neither one으로 쓰는 것이 적절하다.

05 'with+목적어+분사' 구문은 '목적어의 능동/수동' 여부가 중요하다. '눈을 감은 채 산책'한 것은 눈이 '감겨진 것'이므로 closed가 적절하다.

06 '하루 종일 전염병 환자들을 돌보느라 지쳐서, 그녀와 그녀의 동료의사 둘 다 시민들이 보내준 격려의 선물을 풀어볼 힘조차 없었다.'라는 내용이다. 지친 것은 수동이므로 Tired가 적절하며, neither와 nor를 함께 써서 '두 사람 모두 힘이 없었다'라는 부정의 표현을 쓰는 것이 적절하다. *infectious disease: 전염병

07 (1) '왼쪽에서 오른 쪽으로 읽으면, 그것은 "evil"이라고 읽혀지지

만, 반대 방향으로는 "live"가 된다.' (2) '오리를 물 아래에서 보면, 당신은 오리의 발이 결코 첨벙거리는 것을 멈추지 않는다는 것을 알게 될 것이다.' *paddle: 노를 것다, 첨벙거리다

08 ②는 분수 5분의 1에서 1을 뜻하는 '수사'로 쓰였다. 나머지는 모두, 같은 종류의 불특정한 사람 또는 사물을 가리키는 부정대명사이다.

09 <보기>와 ①~④는 모두 '이유'를 의미하는 분사구문으로, 부사절로 전환할 때, Because 또는 Since, As 등의 접속사를 써야 한다. ⑤는 내용상 '양보'의 의미이다.

10 특정한 대상을 가리키는 경우 it 또는 that 등의 대명사를 사용한다.

11 같은 종류의 불특정한 사람 또는 사물을 가리키고 앞에 수식어가 오는 경우, 부정대명사 one 또는 ones를 사용하는데, new 앞에 a가 없으므로 ones가 적절하다. one 앞에 형용사가 있는 경우 보통 부정관사 a를 써 준다.

12 그녀의 자녀는 세 명인데, 동사는 goes로서, 단수 형태이므로, Each가 적절하다. Both 또는 Either는 세 명 이상에는 쓰지 않는 부정대명사이며, All 또는 Some은 동사가 go가 되어야 한다.

13 '비슷한 하나'이므로 it을 부정대명사 one으로 바꾼다.

14 both는 둘 모두를 가리키며 복수 취급하는 대명사이다. has → have

15 분사구문의 부정은 분사 앞에 not이나 never를 쓴다. 내용상 부사절이라면 접속사 Though 또는 Although가 적절하다.

16 종속절과 주절의 주어가 다르므로, 일단 주어를 생략하지 않는다.(독립분사구문) 그리고 종속절의 시제가 주절(현재)보다 앞서기 때문에 완료분사구문을 활용하여 문맥에 맞게 주어진 단어를 배열한다.

17 내용상 '이유'를 나타내는 분사구문이므로, 접속사는 As가 적절하다. ③의 As soon as는 보기의 Feeling 앞에 전치사 On이 있을 경우에 가능하다.

18 불특정 대상의 복수 형태로서 '다른 많은 것들'을 의미할 때는 many other ones가 적절하다.

01 (1) Sarah chose the first one, then another, but neither
   (2) Could you show me a slightly bigger one?
   (3) she doesn't have enough money for one
   (4) while others are afraid of cats

02 (1) While he fixed his computer,

(2) Because he has nothing to worry about,

(3) If you look at the mazes closely,

(4) Though he was sick all day long,

03 (1) Should Mina buy the red grapes or the green ones?

(2) Frank didn't catch any fish in the lake last weekend.

(3) Each of the students has been to Bulguksa in Gyoungju.

(4) She has two pets and one is bigger than the other.

04 (1) Stuck in the maze, she calmly reviewed the map.

(2) It is really dangerous to cross the street listening to music.

05 (1) is → are (2) are → is (3) another → others

(4) one → ones (5) have → has (6) another → other

06 one is a honeybee, another is a ladybug, and the other is a spider

07 (1) Some like red roses and others love white ones.

(2) Harry sold his computer and purchased a new one.

(3) Either one of them has to do something helpful.

01 부정대명사 one, another, neither, others 등을 적절히 활용하여, 우리말에 맞게 주어진 단어들을 알맞게 배열한다.

02 문제에 쓰인 분사구문은 각각 동시동작, 이유, 조건, 양보 등의 의미로 쓰였다. (1) 컴퓨터를 고치면서, Jerry는 라디오 쇼를 들었다. (2) 걱정할 것이 아무것도 없기 때문에, 그 어린 소년은 장난감을 갖고 잘 논다. (3) 미로를 자세히 들여다보면, 당신은 질서와 규칙성의 아름다움을 발견할 것이다. (4) 하루 종일 아팠음에도 불구하고, Benny는 그 어려운 과제를 마침내 해결했다.

03 (1) 같은 종류의 불특정한 대명사로, 앞에 수식어를 받는 복수 형태는 ones (2) 부정문이나 의문문은 any (3) each of 뒤에는 복수명사가 오며 동사는 단수이나 취급 (4) 둘 중에 먼저 지칭하는 불특정한 하나는 one, 나머지 하나는 the other로 쓴다.

04 (1) 미로에 갇힌 채, 그녀는 차분하게 지도를 검토했다. (2) 음악을 들으며, 길을 건너는 것은 정말 위험하다.

05 (1) Both는 항상 복수 동사를 쓴다. (2) Neither는 '둘 중 어느 것도 아니다'라는 의미로서 대명사가 되면 단수 취급한다. (3) Some ~ others (4) dolls와 병렬 구조가 되어야 하고, 앞에

부정관사 a도 없으므로(buy 뒤에 a를 쓰는 것도 좋지만, 문제의 조건은 어색한 한 단어를 찾는 것임), ones가 적절하다. (5) 대명사 either는 단수 취급한다. (6) furniture는 불가산 명사이므로 another를 쓸 수 없다. 불가산 명사와 복수명사 앞에는 other가 적절하다.

06 거미줄에 곤충 세 마리가 있다, 하나는 꿀벌, 또 다른 하나는 무당벌레, 그리고 나머지 하나는 거미이다.

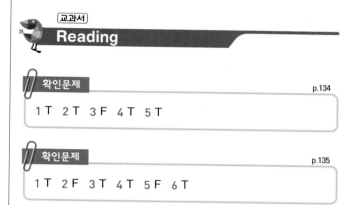

교과서 Reading

확인문제   p.134

1 T 2 T 3 F 4 T 5 T

확인문제   p.135

1 T 2 F 3 T 4 T 5 F 6 T

교과서 확인학습 A   p.136~137

01 Comparing, below, notice, differences

02 For example, on the left, called, has

03 on the right, called, has both, and

04 the origin of, mythology

05 is said to be, that

06 notice that, a single path

07 no dead ends

08 don't have to worry about, enter it

09 all the way to the end

10 To get out, have to turn around, came in

11 in, different

12 to make, dead ends

13 making, which way to go

14 If, are not careful, lose

15 are, considered left-brain

16 willingly visit, enjoy, planned confusion

17 them came up with

18 most reliable one, to, on, the very beginning

19 following that wall

20 like walking

21 Unfortunately, effective, certain types, are not connected

22 are made with, different materials, hedges, and

23 In fact, be printed, drawn

24 Here is, called
25 from, in the order
26 give it a try, to escape
27 are, fun, the end
28 Looking at them, order, regularity
29 how creative human beings are
30 there is, stop, take some time
31 be worth visiting

p.138~139

교과서 확인학습 B

1 Comparing the two pictures below, you can easily notice some differences.

2 For example, the picture on the left is called a labyrinth and only has an entrance.

3 The picture on the right is called a maze and has both an entrance and an exit.

4 You can find the origin of the labyrinth in Greek mythology.

5 It is said to be a prison that you cannot escape.

6 But you may notice that the labyrinth has only a single path.

7 There are no dead ends.

8 This means you don't have to worry about getting out of it when you enter it.

9 If you follow the path all the way to the end, you will reach the center.

10 To get out, you simply have to turn around and walk back out the way you came in.

11 When you are in a maze, it's a different story.

12 There are many choices to make and dead ends to frustrate you.

13 You have to keep making decisions about which way to go.

14 If you are not careful, you can easily lose your way.

15 These days, mazes are often considered left-brain puzzles.

16 Many people willingly visit maze parks and enjoy the "planned confusion."

17 And some of them came up with their own solutions.

18 The easiest and most reliable one is to place a hand on one wall from the very beginning.

19 Then you just keep following that wall.

20 It's like walking in a dark room.

21 Unfortunately, this simple method may not be effective in certain types of mazes, especially when all of the walls are not connected.

22 Mazes are made with a variety of different materials, like walls and rooms, hedges, bricks, mirrors, and even snow.

23 In fact, they can also be printed or drawn on paper.

24 Here is one as an example. This is called a number maze.

25 You start from point A and have to go in the order of 1 → 9 → 8 → 5 → 1 → 9 → … .

26 Why don't you give it a try? You have 30 seconds to escape!

27 Labyrinths and mazes are truly fun, but that's not the end of the story.

28 Looking at them closely, you may find the beauty of order and regularity.

29 They may also show you how creative human beings are.

30 If there is a maze park on your next trip, why don't you stop and take some time to enjoy it?

31 It will surely be worth visiting!

p.140~143

시험대비 실력평가

01 Comparing   02 ④   03 notice
04 ③   05 ④   06 ③   07 ⑤
08 The dead ends make us frustrated.
09 Be careful   10 ④   11 ②
12 A number maze is presented
13 30 seconds is given to solve the number puzzle.
14 ②   15 a labyrinth, an entrance, an exit
16 ⑤   17 ①   18 ③   19 ②
20 ④   21 all of the walls are connected
22 ③   23 labyrinths and mazes   24 ⑤

01 접속사가 없으므로 분사구문을 이끌기 위하여 Comparing이라고 쓰는 것이 적절하다.

02 글의 내용으로 보아, 미궁은 통로가 하나이기 때문에 빠져나오기 위해서는 미궁의 중앙에서 돌아서서 들어간 길대로 걸어 나오면 된다.

03 누군가나 무언가를 인지하게 되는 것은 '알아차리다(notice)'이다.

04 미궁은 그리스 신화에서 감옥으로 표현된다고 하였다.

05 주어진 문장은 '단지 그 벽을 계속 따라가면 된다'는 의미이므로 시작 지점부터 한쪽 벽에 손을 댄 문장 뒤에 들어가는 것이 가장 적절하다.

06 These days는 Nowadays와 함께 '오늘날'이라는 의미로 쓰인다.

07 미로가 좌뇌형 퍼즐로 간주되며 사람들은 미로 공원에 일부러 방문하여 미로를 즐긴다고 하였다. 따라서 (B)와 같이 표현한 이유는 미로가 사람들을 혼란스럽게 하기 위하여 신중하게 계획된 것임을 알 수 있다.

08 막다른 길은 우리를 좌절하게 만든다고 하였다. 좌절을 느끼는 것이므로 과거분사로 표현하는 것이 적절하다.

09 조심하지 않으면 길을 잃기 쉽다고 하였다. 따라서 Be careful이라고 쓰는 것이 적절하다.

10 밑줄 친 (A)는 숫자 퍼즐을 시도해 보라는 의미이므로 ④번이 가장 적절하다.

11 미로를 만들기 위해서 사용될 수 있는 것은 벽과 방, 울타리, 벽돌, 거울, 눈 등이다.

12 종이에 인쇄된 미로의 예시로 제시된 것은 숫자 미로이다.

13 숫자 퍼즐을 해결하기 위해 주어진 시간은 30초이다.

14 차이점이 어떤 것인지를 구체적으로 예를 들어 나타내고 있다. 따라서 ②번이 가장 적절하다.

15 미궁과 달리 미로는 입구뿐만 아니라 출구도 가지고 있다.

16 (B)는 '막다른 길'이라는 의미로 ⑤번이 가장 적절하다.

17 ⓐ 주절의 주어가 같으므로 분사구문의 주어가 생략되었다. 주어 You가 비교하는 주체이므로 현재분사를 쓴다. ⓑ and는 동사 is와 병렬 관계이므로 has를 쓴다. ⓒ enter는 타동사이므로 전치사 없이 목적어를 취할 수 있다.

18 미궁은 통로가 하나라고 하였다.

19 (B) 많은 사람들이 미로 공원을 기꺼이 방문함 (A) 그들 중 몇몇은 자기들만의 해결 방법을 찾아냄. 가장 쉽고 믿을 만한 방법 소개 (C) 그 방법은 마치 어두운 방을 걷는 것과 같음

20 미로에는 결정할 많은 선택지가 있고 우리를 좌절하게 만들 막다른 길들이 있다고 하였다. 어느 길로 갈지 계속 선택을 해야 하므로 조심하지 않으면 길을 잃기 쉽다고 하였다. 따라서 ④번이 가장 적절하다.

21 벽에 손을 대고 그 벽을 따라가는 것은 모든 벽이 이어져 있는 경우 효과가 있다.

22 빈칸 (A)에는 '~에서부터'라는 의미로 쓰이는 전치사 'from'이 들어간다. ① be filled with: ~로 가득 차다 ② pay attention to: ~에 관심을 기울이다 ③ graduate from: ~를 졸업하다 ④ turn down: ~을 거절하다 ⑤ be crowded with: ~으로 붐비다

23 미궁과 미로를 가리키는 인칭대명사이다.

24 글쓴이는 미로 공원이 들를 가치가 있을 것이라고 하였다.

01 Comparing the two pictures below

02 People call it a labyrinth.

03 We can find the origin of the labyrinth in Greek mythology.

04 It means that you don't have to worry about getting out of it when you enter it.

05 a prison, to escape, a single path

06 We can find the center.

07 many choices to make, dead ends to frustrate us

08 mazes are often considered left-brain puzzles

09 solution

10 The easiest and most reliable way to get out of a maze is to place a hand on one wall from the very beginning and keep following that wall.

11 reliable

12 It will surely be worth visiting!

13 A variety of different materials, like walls and rooms, hedges, bricks, mirrors, and even snow are used to make mazes.

14 The writer suggests taking some time to enjoy the maze park.

01 분사구문을 이용하여 빈칸을 완성할 수 있다. 주절의 주어와 부사절의 주어가 같으므로 부사절의 주어를 생략하고, 접속사 역시 생략한 후 동사를 현재분사로 만들면 된다.

02 사람들은 하나의 입구만 가진 것을 '미궁'이라고 부른다.

03 미궁의 기원은 그리스 신화에서 찾을 수 있다고 하였다.

04 미궁에 막다른 길이 없이 통로가 하나라는 의미는 거기에 들어갈 때 빠져나올 것을 걱정하지 않아도 된다는 것을 의미한다.

05 해석: 미궁은 그리스 신화에서 감옥인데, 그것은 탈출하는 것이 불가능하다. 그러나 사실 통로가 하나밖에 없기 때문에 그곳을 나오는 것은 쉽다.

06 통로를 따라 끝까지 가면 우리는 미궁의 중앙을 발견할 수 있다.

07 미로는 미궁과 달리 많은 선택지가 있고 우리를 좌절하게 만드는 막다른 길들이 있다고 하였다.

08 consider A B: A를 B라고 간주하다[여기다]

09 사람들이 미로를 빠져나가기 위해 찾아낸 해결 방법 중 하나를 의미하는 말이다.

10 미로를 빠져나오기 위하여 가장 쉽고 믿을 만한 해결 방법은 시작 지점부터 한쪽 벽에 손을 대고 계속 그 벽을 따라가는 것이다.

11 '믿을 가치가 있는; 의지할 가치가 있는'것은 '믿을 만한 (reliable)'이다.

12 be worth Ving: V할 가치가 있다

13 미로는 벽과 방, 울타리, 벽돌, 거울, 심지어는 눈 등 많은 다양한 재료로 제작된다고 하였다.

14 글쓴이는 다음 여행에 미로 공원이 있으면 들러서 즐겨 볼 것을 제안하고 있다.

01 unreasonable　　　02 ⑤　　　03 ⑤
04 ④
05 (1) exit　(2) frustrate　(3) prison　(4) reliable
　　(5) worth
06 (1) When I passed through the maze, I met a
　　　wolf.
　　(2) Their food is good and the prices are
　　　reasonable.
07 ③　　　　08 ④　　　　09 ⓓ → excited
10 maze　　　11 ⑤　　　12 ③　　　13 ④
14 ①　　　15 ②, ⑤　　　16 ⑤
17 (1) is　(2) are　(3) Each　(4) likes　(5) another
　　(6) is　(7) neither　　　18 ③　　　19 ③
20 ④　　　21 dead end　22 ②　　　23 ⑤
24 ④　　　25 It(=The maze) looked hard to solve.
26 ③　　　27 It covers about 5 kilometers.

01 주어진 관계는 반의어 관계를 나타낸다. reasonable: 적당한, unreasonable: 부적절한, 부당한

02 '일반적인 고대의 신화들; 특정 문화나 사회 등의 고대 신화들'을 나타내는 말은 'mythology(신화)'이다.

03 주어진 문장과 나머지는 모두 '의미하다, 뜻하다'를 의미하지만 ⑤번은 '인색한'을 뜻한다.

04 entrance: 입구

05 frustrate: 좌절시키다, prison: 감옥, worth: 가치; 가치가 있는 exit: 출구, reliable: 믿을 만한

06 maze: 미로, wolf: 늑대, resonable: 적당한

07 (A) exchange A for B: A와 B를 교환하다 (B) look better on ~: ~에게 더 좋아 보이다

08 소년이 신발에 얼마를 지불했는지는 대화를 통해 알 수 없다.

09 감정을 나타내는 과거분사 excited가 적절하다.

10 '통과할 길을 찾기가 어렵도록 설계된 공원이나 정원에 만들어진 벽이나 울타리에 의해 분리된 통로 시스템'을 가리키는 말은 'maze(미로)'이다.

12 길을 묻는 질문에 방향이나 가는 법을 설명하는 대답이 와야 한다.

13 유도부사 There가 있는 부사절을 분사구문으로 바꾸는 경우, '독립분사구문'이 된다. 독립분사구문에서 주절과 다른 주어를

앞에 쓰는 것처럼 유도부사 There를 문두에 놓고, 분사와 주어를 배치하는 것이 적절하다.

14 '비록 김여사께서 최근에 많은 사람들을 만나지만, 그녀는 전보다 더 외로움을 느낀다.'라는 양보의 부사절이다. 접속사와 주어를 생략하고, 동사 meets를 Meeting으로 바꾸면 된다.

15 ② athletes → athlete, Every는 단수 명사를 수식하고, 단수 동사를 쓴다. ⑤ one → ones, 불특정한 복수는 부정대명사 ones를 쓰는 것이 적절하다. 이 예문에서 형용사 small이 없다면, two ones로 쓰는 것보다 two만 쓰는 것이 좋다.

16 분사구문의 부정은 분사 앞에 not을 쓴다. 접속사를 쓸 경우, 접속사 뒤에 주어가 오면 분사구문은 쓸 수 없다.

17 (1) 부정대명사 either는 단수 (2) both는 복수 (3) Every와 Each 중에서 대명사로 쓸 수 있는 것은 Each이다. (4) 부정대명사 neither는 단수 (5) 접시(a plate)가 더러워서, 다른 하나를 더 달라고 하는 것이므로 another (6) 'some of+전체'는 전체에 맞춰 수를 일치시킨다. (7) 관계대명사 뒤의 동사가 is, 즉 단수이므로 neither가 적절하다. 'Julie는 두 개의 악기를 연주할 수 있는데, 그 중 어느 것도 현악기가 아니다.'라는 문장이다.
*stringed: 현악기인

18 분사구문에서의 비인칭 주어 It과 주절의 주어가 다르므로, 'It raining all day' 형태의 독립분사구문이 적절하다.

19 미궁은 통로가 하나이며 막다른 길이 없으므로 들어갈 때 빠져나올 것을 걱정하지 않아도 된다고 하였다. 따라서 빠져나오기 위해서는(To get out) 단지 돌아서 들어간 길대로 걸어 나오면 된다는 말이 가장 적절하다.

20 미로는 많은 선택지가 있고 막다른 길들이 있기 때문에 우리가 좌절할 수 있다.

21 한쪽 끝이 폐쇄된 길이나 통로는 '막다른 길(dead end)'이다.

22 밑줄 친 (B)는 choices를 수식하는 형용사로 쓰인 to부정사이다. ①, ④ 부사적 용법 중 목적(~하기 위해서) ② 형용사적 용법 ③ 명사적 용법 진주어 ⑤ 부사적 용법 중 감정의 원인

23 글쓴이는 미로 공원에서 매우 즐거웠다고 하였다. 따라서 ⑤번이 글의 내용과 일치한다.

24 주어진 문장의 That solution은 글쓴이의 친구가 말해준 '처음부터 벽 한쪽에 손을 얹고 계속 같은 쪽 벽을 따라가는' 방법을 가리키므로 ④번이 적절하다.

25 글쓴이에게 미로는 해결하기가 어려워 보였다.

26 세계의 유명한 미로에 관해 소개하는 글이다. 따라서 ③번이 가장 적절하다.

27 파인애플 정원 미로는 약 5킬로미터에 이를 정도로 크다.

01 (1) exchange   (2) frustrate

02 (1) He escaped from the prison this morning.

   (2) They tried to come up with effective ways to solve the problem.

   (3) Is it possible to survive on Mars?

   (4) The three-story building has about 10,000 books for kids.

03 ⓓ → making   04 ①   05 ⑤

06 How do I get to your place from here?   07 ⑤

08 Are you all set for the trip this weekend?

09 They are going to meet at 11 a.m. in front of the clock tower.

10 They will get there by subway.   11 ①

12 ①, ④

13 (1) Going to the nearby maze park with my parents,

   (2) Looking at the labyrinths closely,

   (3) Not having been invited to the wedding,

14 ⑤   15 ②   16 ③   17 ④

18 A number maze is an example of the printed maze.

19 ④   20 ④

21 They are so high that people can't see over them

01 (1) '동시에 서로에게 특별한 종류의 어떤 것을 주다'를 가리키는 말은 'exchange(교환하다)'이다. (2) '원하는 것을 하거나 이룰 수 없어서 짜증나거나 초조하게 느끼도록 만들다'를 가리키는 말은 'frustrate(방해하다, 좌절시키다)'이다.

02 prison: 감옥, escape: 탈출하다, come up with: ~을 생각해내다, Mars: 화성, survive: 생존하다, story: 층

03 spend+시간+~ing: ~하는 데 시간을 보내다

04 대화의 내용으로 보아 상점의 판매원과 고객의 관계이다.

05 여자가 빨간색 신발이 소년에게 더 잘 어울려서 그것을 추천했다는 것은 대화의 내용과 일치하지 않는다.

09 Mina, Jiho, Claire와 Henry는 시계탑 앞에서 11시에 만날 것이다.

10 Mina, Jiho, Claire와 Henry는 터미널 2에 지하철로 갈 것이다.

11 권유하는 의문문에서는 any 대신 some을 쓸 수 있으며, cookies가 복수이므로 another, one, that 등은 부적절하다.

12 ② Writing → Written 또는 Being written ③ Worked → Working ⑤ Being looked → Looking

13 부사절을 분사구문으로 만들 때, 일반적으로 접속사를 생략한 후 주어가 같으면 주어도 생략하고, 동사를 V-ing 형태로 바꾸는

데 Being은 보통 생략한다. 주절보다 시제가 앞서면 Having been 형태가 되고, 부정문의 경우 not은 분사 앞에 쓴다.

14 each는 단수 취급이므로, were → was가 적절하다.

15 해결 방법을 찾아냈다는 의미이므로 came up with라고 쓰는 것이 자연스럽다. come down with: (병으로) 앓아눕다

16 미로 공원에 일부러 방문하는 많은 사람들을 가리키는 말이다.

17 미로는 벽과 방, 울타리, 벽돌, 거울, 심지어는 눈 등 많은 다양한 재료로 제작된다고 하였다.

18 미로는 종이에 인쇄되거나 그려질 수도 있다고 말하며 예로 든 것은 숫자 미로이다.

19 햄프턴 궁정 미로가 윌리엄 통치 시기에 만들어졌다는 것만 나와 있을 뿐 누가 만들었는지는 위 글에 나와 있지 않다.

20 미로는 만들어지는 것이므로 수동태를 쓰는 것이 적절하다.

21 so ~ that S can't V: 너무 ~해서 V할 수 없는

01 She wants to visit Mirror Maze Park on the second day.

02 It was to go horseback riding.

03 It's because she heard the Mirror Maze Park is a lot more fun.

04 (1) Comparing the two pictures below,

   (2) Not understanding Tom's method of getting out of the maze,

   (3) Following through the path to the end,

05 ⑤ Having been infected with the virus before, Anne is well aware of the fear of the disease.

06 ①

07 It's because it has only a single path without dead ends.

08 미궁: ⓑ, ⓒ, 미로: ⓐ, ⓓ

09 We may lose our way.

10 walk back out the way you came in

01 지나는 두 번째 날에 거울 미로 공원에 방문하기를 원한다.

02 원래는 두 번째 날에 말을 타러 가려고 했다.

03 지나는 거울 미로 공원이 훨씬 더 재미있다고 들었기 때문에 일정을 바꾸길 원한다.

04 주어진 어휘에 접속사들이 없으므로, 분사구문을 배열하는 문제이다. 각각 (1) 시간, (2) 이유, (3) 조건의 부사절을 분사구문으로 만든 것으로, 접속사를 생략하고 주절과 동일한 주어를 생략한 후, 동사를 분사로 만든다.

05 부사절과 주절의 주어가 같을 때, 분사구문에 주어를 쓰지 않는다. 내용상 '전에 그 바이러스에 감염된 적이 있기 때문에, Anne은 그 병의 무서움을 잘 알고 있다.'는 것이므로, Anne과 she는 동일 인물, 따라서 독립분사구문으로 쓸 필요가 없으며, Anne을 주절의 주어 자리에 쓰는 것이 적절하다.

06 ① 사자의 표정은 채소를 좋아하지 않으므로 그림과 일치한다. ② 사자 옆의 작은 토끼는 손을 올려놓지 않았다. ③ 사슴과 토끼가 당근을 집어들었다. ④ 사자는 채소를 좋아하지 않는다. ⑤ 왼쪽 끝의 토끼는 수염이 없다.

07 미궁에 들어갈 때 빠져나올 것을 걱정하지 않아도 되는 이유는 미궁은 통로가 하나이고 막다른 길이 없기 때문이다.

09 조심하지 않으면 길을 잃기 쉽다고 하였다.

10 '걸어 나오다'는 'walk back out'이며 '들어간 길대로'는 'the way you came in'이다.

창의사고력 서술형 문제
p.158

|모범답안|

01 (A) Andrew's house
   (B) she was lost
   (C) the post office
   (D) Kim's Bakery
   (E) turn right and go straight for about 100 meters

02 (1) I'd like to buy a pink one. I would also like the one with a rose on it.
   (2) I want to get a blue one. I also love the one with a parrot on it.
   (3) I'll choose a sky-blue one. I also like the one with a rainbow colored star on it.

01 민주는 Mason과 지안과 Andrew의 집에서 모이기로 했다. 민주가 늦을 때 Andrew는 그녀가 길을 잃었는지 걱정했다. 그가 그녀에게 전화했을 때, 그녀는 우체국 근처에 있었다. Andrew는 민주에게 그의 집에 어떻게 올 수 있는지 설명했다. 민주는 한 블록 정도 직진하면 킴스 빵집을 볼 수 있었다. 이후, 그녀는 오른쪽으로 돌아 약 100미터 정도 직진해야 했다.

02 그림을 잘 관찰하고, 색과 무늬의 특징을 적절히 조합하여 어법에 맞게 영작한 답이면 된다.

단원별 모의고사
p.159~163

01 suggestion   02 ①
03 (1) We got lost in the maze.
   (2) Don't be frustrated by today's failure.

---

   (3) We're looking for someone who is reliable and hard-working.
04 (1) (c)onsidered   (2) entrance   (3) (c)losely, regularity   (4) exchange
05 (1) a variety of   (2) dead ends   (3) in the order of   (4) lose your way   (5) making decisions
06 (A) old mythological prison   (B) Minotaur   (C) the king of Crete   (D) labyrinth
07 He can borrow it this Friday.
08 ④   09 ⑤
10 He was worried that she was lost.
11 She is supposed to get together with Mason and Jian.
12 She should turn right and go straight for about 100 meters.
13 ④   14 ④   15 ⑤   16 ②
17 (1) Some eat pizza, and others take it home.
   (2) Both are interested in catching fish.
18 ③   19 ④   20 ③
21 follow the path all the way to the end
22 ④   23 ②
24 Looking at them closely
25 We may find the beauty of order and regularity of them.
26 ⑤

01 주어진 관계는 동사와 명사의 관계를 나타낸다. suggest: 제안하다, suggestion: 제안

02 '방, 건물 또는 어떤 장소에 들어가기 위해 사용되는 문, 통로 등'을 가리키는 말은 'entrance(입구)'이다.

03 maze: 미로, frustrate: 좌절시키다, reliable: 믿을 만한

04 consider: 여기다, entrance: 입구, closely: 자세히, regularity: 규칙성, exchange: 교환하다

05 make decisions: 결정하다, a variety of: 다양한, lose one's way: 길을 잃다, dead end: 막다른 길, in the order of: ~의 순서로

06 미궁은 반인반수 괴물, 미노타우루스를 가두기 위한 옛 신화의 감옥이었다. 이것은 크레타 왕에 의해서 지어졌다. 왜냐하면 그가 그 괴물에 화가 났고 왕은 그것을 미궁에 가두기를 원했기 때문이다.

07 주원은 Alice에게 이번 주 금요일에 책을 빌릴 수 있다.

08 주어진 문장은 장소를 묻는 질문에 대한 대답으로 적절하므로 ④번이 적절하다.

09 위 대화에서 소라가 누구와 중국 음식점을 가는지는 알 수 없다.

10 Andrew는 민주가 길을 잃었을까봐 걱정했다.

11 민주는 Andrew의 집에서 Mason과 지안과 함께 모이기로 되어 있다.

12 민주는 오른쪽으로 돌아 약 100미터 정도 직진하면 Andrew의 집에 도착한다.

13 '컴퓨터 언어를 배운 것'과, '그 프로그램을 이해할 수 없었다'는 내용은 '시간'을 나타내는 when으로 표현하면 어색하다. '양보'의 접속사 though로 표현하는 것이 적절하다.

14 두 개 중 하나를 제외한 나머지 하나는 the other가 적절하다.

15 '한식당을 찾고 있는 것이라면, 한 군데를 알려 줄게.'라는 문장이므로, 불특정한 대상을 가리키는 부정대명사 one을 쓰는 것이 적절하다.

16 '급히 쓰여졌기 때문에 그 책은 오류가 많다'는 내용이므로 완료형 수동태 분사구문 'Having been written'이 적절하다.

17 (1) 부정대명사 some과 others를 활용하되, 사람들을 뜻하므로 some도 복수 취급하는 것에 유의한다. (2) 두 사람을 모두 가리키는 단어 Both와 are를 활용하도록 한다.

18 ①, ④, ⑤ '주절과 종속절의 주어'가 다르므로, 분사구문 앞에 주어를 써서 독립분사구문으로 표현하는 것이 적절하다. ① Having cut → The hero having cut ② 주절과 종속절의 주어가 같으면, 분사구문의 주어는 생략한다. Sharon going → Going, ④ Reading → Mom reading, ⑤ Being → There being

19 This가 가리키는 것은 미궁에는 막다른 길이 없이 통로가 하나라는 것이다. 이것이 의미하는 것은 미궁에 들어갈 때 빠져나올 것을 걱정하지 않아도 된다는 의미이다.

20 미로에서 조심해야 하는 이유는 길을 잃기 쉽기 때문이다.

21 통로를 따라 끝까지 가면 미궁의 중앙에 도착할 것이라고 하였다.

22 ④번은 간접의문문으로 의문사 how가 creative를 수식하고 있으므로 옳은 문장이다. 따라서 ④번의 설명은 바르지 않다.

23 미궁과 미로는 재미에 더해서 질서와 규칙성이라는 아름다움도 있다는 의미이므로 ②번이 가장 적절하다.

24 주절의 주어와 부사절의 주어가 같으므로 부사절의 주어를 생략하고 동사를 현재분사로 만들어 분사구문을 완성할 수 있다.

25 미궁과 미로를 자세히 들여다보면 질서와 규칙성이라는 아름다움을 발견할 수 있을지도 모른다고 하였다.

26 산울타리가 너무 높아서 사람들이 그 너머를 볼 수 없다고 하였다.

교과서 파헤치기

Lesson 3

단어 TEST Step 1   p.02

01 고속의	02 가시 식물	03 설명하다
04 모방하다	05 흡수하다	06 만능의, 다용도의
07 매혹하다	08 받침, 걸이	
09 잠금장치, 고정 장치		10 기사, 논문
11 (새의) 부리	12 접촉	13 물린 상처
14 압력	15 다시 디자인하다	16 적용하다
17 탐색하다	18 천재	19 털이 많은
20 증가; 증가하다	21 주목하다	22 해결책
23 고통스러운	24 영감을 불러일으키다	
25 성공적인	26 초래하다	27 우아하게
28 갑작스러운	29 표면	30 줄이다
31 반사하다	32 생존자	33 길이
34 필요성	35 활주하다	
36 ~와 연락하다, 접촉하다		37 떠다니다
38 A가 ~하지 못하게 하다		39 ~로 가는 길에
40 ~에 붙다	41 A뿐만 아니라 B도 역시	
42 결과적으로	43 그것이 ~하는 이유이다.	

단어 TEST Step 2   p.03

01 absorb	02 bug	03 creative
04 apply	05 length	06 beak
07 bite	08 all-purpose	09 explore
10 gracefully	11 observe	12 painful
13 successful	14 imitate	15 increase
16 burr	17 article	18 cause
19 weight	20 inspire	21 high-speed
22 survivor	23 invention	24 closely
25 contact	26 necessity	27 fascinate
28 genius	29 notice	30 pressure
31 redesign	32 surface	33 reduce
34 sudden	35 in search of	
36 make contact with		37 be stuck to
38 be covered with		
39 keep A from -ing		40 float away
41 as a result	42 on one's way to	
43 not only A but also B		

단어 TEST Step 3   p.04

1 headache, 두통   2 narrow, 좁은

3 all-purpose, 만능의, 다용도의   4 invention, 발명

5 talent, 타고난 재능   6 hairy, 털이 많은
7 observe, 관찰하다   8 tunnel, 터널, 굴
9 genius, 천재   10 beak, (새의) 부리
11 dive, 뛰어들다, 잠수하다   12 imitate, 모방하다
13 redesign, 다시 디자인하다   14 wing, 날개
15 fastener, 잠금장치, 고정 장치   16 survivor, 생존자

대화문 TEST Step 1   p.05~06

Listen & Speak 1 A

know, painted, don't / think, great artist / also, great inventor / What, invent / dreamed of flying like, drew, flying, looked like / Did, also make, machine / creative idea inspired, other inventors

Listen & Speak 1 B

Have you heard, needle / Can, explain it / made this, imitating, mosquito's mouth / how will / know, bites, very painful, don't you, needle, cause less pain / How come, less painful / Like, less contact with / think, nothing useless

Listen & Speak 2 A2

holder, candles last twice / possible / When, burns, melts into, tube below, form / fascinated, use, longer

Listen & Speak 2 A3

what, fascinated by, special / What makes, special / played table tennis / How, door / be changed into, table / cool

Listen & Speak 2 B

have, guest / Great, be / fascinated, fact, lived like, goat, for three days, Why, do / saw goats playing, looked, peaceful, live like / Didn't, have, problems / Walking on, was, difficult / any, to live like / planning, visit / can't wait to, adventure

Real Life Communication

What, doing / reading an article / interesting / really fascinated by / Can, more / know, bugs, slip into narrow spaces / why, hard / help, survivors, earthquakes, big fires / fascinating

대화문 TEST Step 2   p.07~08

Listen & Speak 1 A

G: You know that Leonardo da Vinci painted the *Mona Lisa*, don't you?

B: Sure. I think he was a really great artist.

G: He was also a great inventor.

B: What did he invent?

G: He dreamed of flying like a bird. So, he drew a flying machine that looked like a bird.

B: Did he also make that machine?

G: No, but his creative idea inspired many other inventors.

Listen & Speak 1B

B: Have you heard of a mosquito needle, Jian?

G: A mosquito needle? Can you explain it to me?

B: Some scientists made this new needle by imitating a mosquito's mouth.

G: That's interesting. So how will that help?

B: You know mosquito bites are not very painful, don't you? The new needle will also cause less pain.

G: That's great. How come it's less painful?

B: Like a mosquito's mouth, it makes less contact with our skin.

G: Wow, I think that there's nothing useless in the world!

Listen & Talk 2 A-2

G: This candle holder can make candles last twice as long.

B: Really? How's that possible?

G: When a candle burns, it melts into the tube below the holder to form a new candle.

B: Wow, I am so fascinated by the idea! Now we can use candles longer.

Listen & Speak 2 A3

B: You know what? I'm really fascinated by the special door in Juwon's room.

G: What makes the door so special?

B: Juwon and I played table tennis on it.

G: How could you play table tennis on a door?

B: The door can be changed into a table.

G: That's cool!

Listen & Speak 2 B

W: Today, we have a special guest, Thomas Thwaites, the Goat Man. Hello, Thomas.

M: Hello, Anna. Great to be here.

W: Thomas, I'm so fascinated by the fact that you lived like a goat in the Alps for three days. Why did you do that?

M: One day, I saw goats playing on the mountain. They looked so peaceful that I wanted to live like them.

W: Didn't you have any problems being a goat?

M: Walking on all four legs was very difficult for me.

W: Do you have any plans to live like a goat again?

M: Sure. I'm planning my second visit to the Alps.

W: I can't wait to hear about your next adventure. Thank you, Thomas, for your time.

Real Life Communication

Henry: What are you doing, Mina?

Mina: I'm reading an article about a bug robot.

Henry: A bug robot? Is it interesting?

Mina: Yes. I'm really fascinated by this thing.

Henry: Can you tell me more about it?

Mina: You know that some bugs can slip into narrow spaces, don't you?

Henry: Yeah. That's why it's hard to catch them.

Mina: A bug robot can do the same. It can help to find survivors after earthquakes or big fires.

Henry: That's really fascinating!

본문 TEST Step 1   p.09~11

01 flying, self-cleaning, way, fascinates

02 only, also, it, solutions

03 one such person

04 how birds could fly

05 closely, made, drew, of

06 though, successful, imitated, try

07 Since, have, imitated, abilities

08 Let's explore, of

09 high-speed train, made, had

10 entered, sudden increase, loud

11 woke people up, caused

12 solve, how, could reduce

13 engineers, in search of

14 saw, quietly diving into

15 how, bird entered, gracefully

16 more, discovered, narrow beak

17 redesigned, front, by imitating

18 not, but, with, less

19 One, was hiking, with

20 On, home, burrs, stuck

21 know how that happened

22 took, closer, noticed, straight

23 if, apply, something useful

24 After, testing, invented, materials

25 tiny, burrs, other, surface

26 were pressed, became, fastener

27 only strong but, easy

28 Since, used, different ways

33

29 is often used for

30 use, play, number, different

31 keeps, from floating away

32 nothing useless, curious, ask

01 From, to self-cleaning, works fascinates us

02 not only, but also, imitate it, solutions

03 one such person

04 how birds could fly

05 closely, made notes

06 Even though, successful, imitated, to try to make, flying machine

07 Since, have, imitated, surprising abilities, nature's genius

08 Let's explore

09 high-speed train, had

10 entered, sudden increase, created, loud sound

11 woke people up, caused

12 tried to solve, how they could reduce

13 the engineers was, in search of

14 saw, quickly, quietly diving into

15 how the bird entered, gracefully

16 studied more, discovered, narrow beak

17 redesigned, front, by imitating, break

18 not only, but also, with, less electricity

19 One day, was hiking, with

20 On, way home, burrs were stuck to, hair

21 to know how that happened

22 took a closer look at, noticed that, were, straight

23 if he could apply, something useful

24 After, lot, testing, invented

25 tiny needles, those of burrs, the other, hairy surface

26 were pressed together, fastener

27 not only strong but also easy

28 Since, have used, many different ways

29 is often used for

30 to play a number of different

31 keeps, from floating away

32 nothing useless, curious, ask

1 나는 새에서 자정 작용을 하는 식물까지, 자연이 기능하는 방식은 우리를 매료시킵니다.

2 몇몇 사람들은 그들의 문제에 대한 해결책을 찾기 위해 자연을 이용할 뿐만 아니라 자연을 모방하기까지 합니다.

3 레오나르도 다빈치(1452-1519)가 이러한 사람들 중 한 사람이었습니다.

4 그는 새들이 어떻게 날 수 있는지 궁금했습니다.

5 그는 새를 자세히 관찰했고, 기록했으며, 그림으로 그렸습니다.

6 그의 발명은 비록 성공하지 못했지만, 그는 나는 기계를 만들어 보려고 새의 날개를 모방했습니다.

7 그 후로, 점점 더 많은 사람들이 자연 속 천재의 놀라운 능력을 성공적으로 모방해 오고 있습니다.

8 그들 중 몇 가지를 알아봅시다.

9 고속 열차는 일본에서 처음 만들어졌습니다. 하지만 그것은 한 가지 문제점이 있었습니다.

10 열차가 터널에 들어갔을 때, 갑작스러운 기압의 상승은 매우 시끄러운 소리를 발생시켰습니다.

11 그것은 종종 사람들의 잠을 깨웠고 두통을 일으켰습니다.

12 한 공학자 팀이 그 문제를 해결하려 했지만, 그들은 어떻게 소음을 줄일 수 있을지 몰랐습니다.

13 어느 날, 공학자들 중 한 사람이 먹이를 찾고 있는 새를 관찰하고 있었습니다.

14 그는 새가 빠르고 조용하게 물속으로 뛰어드는 것을 보았습니다.

15 그는 새가 어떻게 그렇게 우아하게 물속으로 들어가는지 궁금했습니다.

16 그래서 그는 그 새에 대해 더 연구했고, 새의 길고 좁은 부리를 발견했습니다.

17 그는 새의 부리를 모방하여 열차의 앞면을 다시 디자인했습니다.

18 그것은 성공적이었습니다. 이제 새로운 열차는 더 조용할 뿐만 아니라 전기는 15% 덜 사용하면서 10% 더 빠르게 이동합니다.

19 어느 날, 스위스 공학자 George de Mestral은 그의 개와 숲에서 하이킹하고 있었습니다.

20 집으로 돌아오는 길에, 그는 가시 식물이 자신의 옷과 개의 털에 붙어 있는 것을 보았습니다.

21 그는 어떻게 그런 일이 일어났는지 알고 싶었습니다.

22 그는 가시 식물들을 자세히 들여다보았고, 가시의 끝이 곧지 않다는 것을 알아챘습니다.

23 그는 유용한 뭔가를 만드는 데 그것을 적용할 수 있을지 궁금했습니다.

24 수많은 실험 후에, 그는 마침내 두 가지 새로운 소재를 발명했습니다.

25 하나는 가시 식물과 같은 조그만 가시들이 많이 있는 것이었고, 다른 하나는 털로 덮인 표면이 있는 것이었습니다.

26 두 소재를 함께 붙이면, 매우 훌륭한 고정 장치가 되었습니다.

27 그것은 튼튼할 뿐만 아니라 사용하기도 쉬웠습니다.

28 그 후로, 많은 사람들이 그의 발명품을 다양한 방법으로 사용해 오고 있습니다.

29 그것은 옷, 신발, 가방에 흔히 사용됩니다.

30 몇몇 사람들은 여러 가지 게임을 하기 위해 그것을 사용합니다.

31 우주에서, 그것은 물건들이 떠다니는 것을 막아줍니다.

32 자연에 쓸모없는 것은 하나도 없습니다. 우리는 그저 호기심을 갖고 질문을 던지면 됩니다.

본문 TEST Step 4~Step 5
p.16~20

1 From flying birds to self-cleaning plants, the way nature works fascinates us.

2 Some people not only use nature but also imitate it to find solutions to their problems.

3 Leonardo da Vinci (1452–1519) was one such person.

4 He wondered how birds could fly.

5 He closely watched birds, made notes, and drew pictures of them.

6 Even though his invention was not successful, he imitated a bird's wings to try to make a flying machine.

7 Since then, more and more people have successfully imitated the surprising abilities of nature's genius.

8 Let's explore some of them.

9 The high-speed train was first made in Japan. But it had one problem.

10 When the train entered a tunnel, the sudden increase in air pressure created a very loud sound.

11 It often woke people up and caused headaches.

12 A team of engineers tried to solve the problem, but they didn't know how they could reduce the noise.

13 One day, one of the engineers was watching a bird in search of a meal.

14 He saw the bird quickly and quietly diving into the water.

15 He wondered how the bird entered the water so gracefully.

16 So, he studied more about the bird and discovered its long, narrow beak.

17 He redesigned the front of the train by imitating the bird's beak.

18 It was successful. Now the new train travels not only more quietly but also 10% faster with 15% less electricity.

19 One day, a Swiss engineer, George de Mestral, was hiking in the woods with his dog.

20 On his way home, he saw that burrs were stuck to his clothes and his dog's hair.

21 He wanted to know how that happened.

22 He took a closer look at the burrs and noticed that the ends of the burr needles were not straight.

23 He wondered if he could apply that to make something useful.

24 After a lot of testing, he finally invented two new materials.

25 One had many tiny needles like those of burrs and the other had a hairy surface.

26 When they were pressed together, they became a very good fastener.

27 It was not only strong but also easy to use.

28 Since then, many people have used his invention in many different ways.

29 It is often used for clothing, shoes, and bags.

30 Some people use it to play a number of different games.

31 In space, it keeps things from floating away.

32 There is nothing useless in nature. We just have to become curious and ask questions.

구석구석지문 TEST Step 1
p.21

Culture & Life

1. North Pole
2. survive the cold, black skin to easily absorb
3. Each of, has, air space
4. helps, stay warm

Culture & Life

1. Ants, North Africa
2. not only, hottest place on earth
3. the hottest time, go hunting
4. how they survive the heat
5. are covered with, that reflect the heat from

Culture & Life Project

1. run very fast, don't you
2. One of the reasons, strong feet
3. by imitating, horse's foot
4. When, wear, not only, but also look taller

구석구석지문 TEST Step 2
p.22

Culture & Life

1. Polar Bears, North Pole
2. Polar bears survive the cold because they have black skin to easily absorb the heat from the sun.
3. Each of their hairs has an air space.
4. This also helps them stay warm.

Lesson 4

단어 TEST Step 1 · p.23

01 사과하다	02 귀찮게 하다	03 독특한
04 반응, 응답	05 창조적인	06 책임이 있는
07 부리	08 재채기하다	09 비교하다
10 실제로	11 범죄	12 다시 만든 이야기
13 불행하게도, 안타깝게도		14 꾸준히
15 장점	16 짚, 지푸라기	17 ~을 받을 만하다
18 계모	19 빌리다	20 황새
21 불평하다	22 누명을 씌우다, 테를 두르다	
23 괴롭히다	24 부양하다, 지지하다	
25 붙잡다	26 털이 많은	27 무례한
28 자립심이 강한, 독립적인		29 마른
30 평화롭게	31 충격을 받은	32 완전하게
33 예술 작품	34 무례한	35 침입하다
36 ~로 만들어지다	37 ~ 대신에	38 관점, 견해
39 끌려가다	40 ~이 다 떨어지다	
41 ~와 사랑에 빠지다		42 스스로
43 의미가 통하다, 이해가 되다		

단어 TEST Step 2 · p.24

01 beak	02 character	03 crime
04 steadily	05 stepmother	06 brick
07 grab	08 unfortunately	09 hairy
10 impolite	11 completely	12 rude
13 straw	14 artwork	15 frame
16 independent	17 apology	18 support
19 sweat	20 compare	21 similar
22 actually	23 complain	24 response
25 deserve	26 palace	27 advantage
28 apologize	29 responsible	30 skinny
31 prefer	32 bother	33 sneeze
34 trouble	35 break into	36 on one's own
37 point of view	38 instead of	39 be made of
40 run out of	41 be taken to	42 at least
43 fall in love with		

단어 TEST Step 3 · p.25

1 rude, 무례한   2 hairy, 털이 많은
3 unfortunately, 불행하게도, 안타깝게도
4 skinny, 바싹 마른, 너무 마른   5 deserve, ~을 받을 만하다
6 trouble, 귀찮게 하다   7 beak, 부리   8 stork, 황새

9 similar, 비슷한, 유사한　10 apology, 사과

11 straw, 짚, 지푸라기　12 crime, 범죄

13 sweat, 땀을 흘리다　14 sneeze, 재채기하다

15 independent, 자립심이 강한, 독립적인

16 complain, 불평하다

Listen & Speak 1 A

Have, finished / How did you like / interesting / What, about / right / point of view / say / reason, make money, independent / unique, can't wait to read

Listen & Speak 1 B

How, like / compare, with / Which, better / enjoyed, more, helped me understand, characters / better, easier to understand / both, advantages / right

Listen & Speak 2 A

worried / lose the soccer game / you think so / match against, the strongest players / bright side, the best teamwork / that way

Listen & Speak 2 B

What, think / frightening / Why, think so / snake, ate / hat / interesting / why, decided, pilot instead of / At least, what you mean

Real Life Communication

take a look at, How do, like / To me, more than, toilet / greatest piece of art / Why, think so / different point of view, real-life objects / something new / right, objects in a different way / learned a lot

Let's Check

course / turtle, mean / Why, think so / sleeping, wake him up, fair / that way, be responsible for, should / interesting

Listen & Speak 1 A

G: Have you finished the book, Taeho?

B: Yes. I finished it yesterday, Anna.

G: How did you like it?

B: It was interesting.

G: What is the book about?

B: You know the story of Heungbu, right? In the book, Nolbu tells the story from his point of view.

G: What does he say?

B: Well, he says he didn't help Heungbu for a reason. He wanted Heungbu to make money on his own and be independent.

G: Wow, it's a unique story! I can't wait to read the book. Thanks, Taeho.

Listen & Speak 1 B

B: How did you like the movie *Good Friends*, Yura?

G: I liked it. It was fun to compare the movie with the original book.

B: Which did you like better, the movie or the book?

G: Well, I liked the movie, but I think I enjoyed the book more. The book helped me understand the characters better.

B: That's interesting. To me, the movie was better because it was easier to understand the story.

G: That's true. I guess they both have their own advantages.

B: You're right.

Listen & Speak 2 A

W: You look worried, Juwon.

B: I think we will lose the soccer game tomorrow, Ms. Kim.

W: Why do you think so?

B: We will have a match against Class 3. They have the strongest players in the school.

W: Look on the bright side. They might have strong players, but your class has the best teamwork.

B: You're right. I didn't think about it that way. I'll go and practice!

Listen & Speak 2 B

M: What do you think about my drawing, Prince?

B: Wow, this picture is very frightening!

M: Why do you think so?

B: I mean the picture shows a snake that ate an elephant.

M: You're right. Actually, many people thought it was a picture of a hat.

B: Really? That's interesting.

M: I know. That's why I decided to become a pilot instead of a painter.

B: Haha. At least I can understand what you mean.

M: Thank you, Prince.

Real Life Communication

Ms. Parker: Now, take a look at this work of art. How do you like it?

Jinho: Well, is it even art?

Henry: To me, it isn't more than a toilet.

Ms. Parker: It is not just art. I think it is the greatest

37

piece of art of the 20th century.

Mina: Why do you think so?

Ms. Parker: It is a perfect example of a different point of view. The artist used real-life objects to create art.

Claire: So, he didn't create something new?

Ms. Parker: That's right. He simply wanted people to look at the objects in a different way.

Mina: Thank you so much, Ms. Parker. I learned a lot today!

Let's Check

B: Do you know the story *The Rabbit and the Turtle*?

G: Of course, I do.

B: I think the turtle in the story is mean.

G: Why do you think so?

B: The turtle sees the rabbit sleeping but doesn't wake him up. It is not fair.

G: I don't see it that way. Why should the turtle be responsible for the rabbit? I don't think he should be.

B: That's interesting.

본문 TEST Step 1   p.30~31

01 Welcome, taken, blowing down
02 third little pig, with
03 explain what happened to
04 build, built, straw, bricks
05 One, completely blew down
06 blew down, made of
07 How, doing now
08 shocked to lose, resting
09 let's, guest, what happened
10 whole, thing, wrong
11 real, sneeze, terrible cold
12 What do, mean
13 Back, was making, for
14 ran out, walked down
15 knocked on, fell down
16 called, Little, in
17 had, grabbed, coming on
18 sneezed, sneeze, fell down
19 by what had happened
20 Unfortunately, same, happened to
21 why did you go
22 needed, cup, sugar, next
23 third, had built, of

24 called out, trouble, in
25 what, answered, away, bother
26 impolite, deserved, apology, knocking
27 came, course, breaking into
28 think, were framed
29 going to borrow, exciting
30 made, Could, lend, cup
31 which do you think

본문 TEST Step 2   p.32~33

01 Welcome to, was taken to, for blowing down pigs' houses
02 the third little pig, with
03 explain what happened to
04 time to build our, so, with straw, sticks, bricks
05 completely blew down, brothers' houses
06 almost blew down, made of, so, couldn't
07 How, doing now
08 shocked to lose, resting in
09 let's meet, tell us what happened
10 whole, is wrong
11 real story, about a sneeze, a terrible cold
12 What, mean
13 was making, for
14 ran out of, walked down, to ask, for
15 knocked on, fell down
16 called, in
17 had just grabbed, sneeze coming on
18 sneezed, sneeze, straw, fell down
19 by what had happened
20 Unfortunately, happened to
21 why did you go to
22 that cup of sugar
23 had built, of
24 called out, to trouble you, in
25 what he answered, Go away, bother me
26 How impolite, deserved, apology, so, kept knocking
27 When, came, of course, breaking into
28 were framed
29 thought, going to borrow, exciting
30 Could, lend me
31 which do you think is

1 리포터: 'Animal World News'에 오신 것을 환영합니다. 지난 일요일, 돼지들의 집들을 바람을 불어 넘어뜨린 늑대가 경찰서로 연행되었습니다.

2 오늘, 우리는 셋째 아기 돼지와 늑대를 모셨습니다.

3 Pig씨, 당신과 당신 형제들에게 무슨 일이 일어났는지 설명해 주시겠어요?

4 돼지: 네. 제 형제들과 저는 각자의 집들을 지을 때라고 생각했어요. 그래서 우리는 짚, 나무 막대기, 그리고 벽돌로 집을 지었어요.

5 어느 날, 늑대가 와서 제 형들의 집들을 바람을 불어 완전히 날려 버렸어요.

6 그는 제 집도 거의 날려 버릴 뻔했는데, 벽돌로 만들어져서 그럴 수가 없었죠.

7 리포터: 당신의 형제들은 지금 어떻게 지내고 있나요?

8 돼지: 그들은 집을 잃어서 충격을 받았어요. 그들은 제 집에서 쉬고 있어요.

9 리포터: 감사합니다. Pig씨. 이제 두 번째 손님인 늑대를 만나 보시죠. Wolf씨, 무슨 일이 있었는지 말씀해 주시겠어요?

10 늑대: 이 모든 '덩치 크고 못된 늑대' 사건은 잘못된 거예요.

11 진짜 이야기는 지독한 감기로 인한 재채기와 설탕 한 컵에 관한 거예요.

12 리포터: 무슨 말씀인가요?

13 늑대: 그때, 저는 사랑하는 할머니를 위해 생일 케이크를 만들고 있었어요.

14 설탕이 다 떨어졌더라고요. 저는 이웃에게 설탕 한 컵을 달라고 부탁하기 위해 길을 걸어갔어요.

15 제가 이웃집 문을 두드렸을 때, 문이 떨어졌어요.

16 그다음에 저는 "아기 돼지 씨, 안에 계신가요?"라고 불렀어요.

17 제가 부서진 문을 막 움켜잡았을 때 재채기가 나오는 걸 느꼈어요.

18 저는 재채기를 아주 크게 했고, 그거 아세요? 짚으로 만든 집 전체가 무너졌어요.

19 저는 일어난 일에 매우 놀랐어요.

20 안타깝게도, 둘째 아기 돼지의 집에서도 같은 일이 일어나고 말았어요.

21 리포터: 그렇다면 셋째 아기 돼지의 집에 왜 갔죠?

22 늑대: 저는 여전히 설탕 한 컵이 필요했어요. 그래서 옆집으로 갔어요.

23 셋째 아기 돼지는 벽돌로 집을 지었더라고요.

24 제가 소리쳤어요, "귀찮게 해 드려 죄송하지만, 안에 계신가요?"

25 그리고 그가 뭐라고 대답했는지 아세요? "가버려, 다신 귀찮게 하지 마!"

26 얼마나 무례한가요! 저는 사과를 받아 마땅하다고 생각했기 때문에 계속 문을 두드렸어요.

27 경찰이 왔을 때, 물론 그들은 제가 이 돼지의 집에 침입하고 있다고 생각했죠.

28 리포터: 당신은 당신이 누명을 썼다고 생각하나요?

29 늑대: 네. 마을의 신문 기자들은 설탕 한 컵을 빌리러 간 아픈 늑대가 별로 흥미롭지 않다고 생각했겠죠.

30 그래서 그들은 저를 '덩치 크고 못된 늑대'로 만든 거예요. 당신은 아마 제게 설탕 한 컵쯤은 빌려 줄 수 있으시겠죠?

31 리포터: 시간 내 주셔서 감사합니다. 여러분, 어떤 이야기가 진짜 이야기라고 생각하시나요, 돼지의 이야기일까요, 아니면 늑대의 이야기일까요?

1 Reporter: Welcome to Animal World News. Last Sunday, a wolf was taken to the police station for blowing down pigs' houses.

2 Today, we have the third little pig and the wolf with us.

3 Mr. Pig, could you explain what happened to you and your brothers?

4 Pig: Yes. My brothers and I thought it was time to build our own houses, so we built houses with straw, sticks, and bricks.

5 One day, the wolf came and completely blew down my brothers' houses.

6 He almost blew down my house, but it was made of bricks, so he couldn't.

7 Reporter: How are your brothers doing now?

8 Pig: They are shocked to lose their houses. They are resting in my house.

9 Reporter: Thank you, Mr. Pig. Now, let's meet our second guest, the wolf. Mr. Wolf, could you tell us what happened?

10 Wolf: This whole "Big Bad Wolf" thing is wrong.

11 The real story is about a sneeze from a terrible cold and a cup of sugar.

12 Reporter: What do you mean?

13 Wolf: Back then, I was making a birthday cake for my dear old grandmother.

14 I ran out of sugar. I walked down the street to ask my neighbor for a cup of sugar.

15 When I knocked on the door, it fell down.

16 Then I called, "Little pig, are you in?"

17 I had just grabbed the broken door when I felt a sneeze coming on.

18 I sneezed a great sneeze and you know what? The whole straw house fell down.

19 I was very surprised by what had happened.

20 Unfortunately, the same thing happened to the second little pig's house.

21 Reporter: Then why did you go to the third little pig's house?

22 Wolf: I still needed that cup of sugar, so I went to the next house.

23 The third little pig had built his house of bricks.

24 I called out, "I'm sorry to trouble you, but are you in?"

25 And do you know what he answered? "Go away. Don't bother me again!"

26 How impolite! I thought I deserved an apology, so I kept knocking.

27 When the police came, of course they thought I was breaking into this pig's house.

28 Reporter: Do you think you were framed?

29 Wolf: Yes. The news reporters of the town thought a sick wolf going to borrow a cup of sugar didn't sound very exciting.

30 So, they made me the "Big Bad Wolf." Could you maybe lend me a cup of sugar?

31 Reporter: Thank you for your time. Everyone, which do you think is the true story, the pig's or the wolf's?

peacefully and Minsu is the prince who is looking for the princess.

5. A: Sorry, but that's not the answer.

Before You Read

1. Everyone deserves a fun story like this. - *Book Weekly*

2. I think I should make an apology to the wolf. I'd never thought about his point of view. - *The Book Times*

3. I still don't know whose story is true, but I learned that everyone can be framed for a crime. - *Library & Paper*

After You Read

1. The Pig's Story

2. The three little pigs decided to build their own houses.

3. So, they built houses with different things.

4. One day, the wolf came and blew down the first and the second little pigs' houses completely.

5. But the wolf couldn't blow down the third pig's house because it was made of bricks.

구석구석지문 TEST Step 1   p.40

Communication Task

1. guess, title of the story

2. I think

3. Why, think so

4. who is sleeping peacefully, prince who is looking for

5. not the answer

Before You Read

1. Everyone deserves, like

2. make an apology, never thought, his point of view

3. whose story is true, that, can be framed for

After You Read

1. Pig's Story

2. three little pigs, to build their own houses

3. built, with different things

4. One day, came and blew down, second little pigs' houses completely

5. couldn't blow down, because, was made of

구석구석지문 TEST Step 2   p.41

Communication Task

1. A: Can anyone guess the title of the story?

2. B: I think it is *Sleeping Beauty*.

3. A: Why do you think so?

4. B: I think Semi is the princess who is sleeping

단어 TEST Step 1 p.42

01 결정, 결심	02 차이	03 특히
04 편리한	05 막다른 길	
06 방해하다, 좌절시키다		07 산울타리
08 미, 아름다움	09 기원	10 해결책
11 혼란, 혼동	12 비교하다	13 불행하게도
14 미로	15 미궁	16 실제로
17 기꺼이	18 연결하다, 이어지다	
19 ~할 가치가 있는	20 괴물	21 자세히
22 여기다	23 제안하다	24 교환하다
25 감옥	26 (가격이) 적당한	27 효과적인
28 신화	29 탈출하다	30 규칙성
31 입구	32 믿을 만한	33 선택
34 출구	35 ~에서 나오다, 도망치다	
36 ~을 기대하다	37 시도하다, 한번 해보다	
38 결정하다	39 돌다, 돌아서다	40 길을 잃다
41 다양한	42 ~을 생각해 내다	43 선택하다

단어 TEST Step 2 p.43

01 confusion	02 beauty	03 reliable
04 decide	05 suggest	06 closely
07 monster	08 escape	09 floor
10 careful	11 frustrate	12 exit
13 mythology	14 choice	15 convenient
16 hedge	17 consider	18 labyrinth
19 maze	20 difference	21 entrance
22 notice	23 exit	24 prison
25 connect	26 order	27 reasonable
28 decision	29 regularity	30 unfortunately
31 solution	32 willingly	33 compare
34 effective	35 a variety of	36 get out of
37 make a choice	38 turn around	
39 look forward to		40 give it a try
41 come up with	42 make a decision	
43 lose one's way		

단어 TEST Step 3 p.44

1 exit, 출구 2 worth, ~할 가치가 있는
3 connect, 연결하다, 이어지다 4 origin, 기원
5 choice, 선택 6 entrance, 입구
7 difference, 차이 8 exchange, 교환하다
9 labyrinth, 미궁 10 mythology, 신화
11 escape, 탈출하다 12 prison, 감옥
13 confusion, 혼란 14 frustrate, 방해하다, 좌절하다
15 hedge, 산울타리 16 maze, 미로

대화문 TEST Step 1 p.45~46

Listen & Speak 1 A
bought, possible, exchange / popular these days /
why, making the decision, look better on / problem

Listen & Speak 1 B
decide, to visit during / plan I made / is it possible, on
/ exciting, horseback riding / a lot / Let's change,
schedule / excited / looking forward to

Listen & Speak 2 A
beed, help / suggest, decide between / about,
reasonable / get to / fourth floor, over there, next to /
for, help / pleasure

Listen & Speak 2 B
coming, coming / worried, lost / What about / post
office, How do I get to / Go straight for / turn right,
go straight / Turn right, go straight

Real Life Communication
Are you all set for / be late, in front of / got it, get to,
decided / choices, subway / reliable / possible to, by
subway / already checked / take the subway

Let's Check 1
reading / origin, labyrinth / Labyrinth, mythological
prison / monster / forgot / angry, put, labyrinth

대화문 TEST Step 2 p.47~48

Listen & Speak 1 A
W: How may I help you?
B: Hi! I bought these shoes yesterday. Is it possible
   to exchange them for the red shoes?
W: Oh, actually white is really popular these days.
B: I know, and that's why I spent a long time making
   the decision yesterday. But I think that red will
   look better on me.
W: Okay, no problem.

G: Mom, did you decide where to visit during our family trip to Jeju?

W: Almost. Come here and see the plan I made.

G: It looks good. Hmm… Mom, is it possible to visit Mirror Maze Park on our second day?

W: It sounds exciting, but I remember you said you wanted to go horseback riding.

G: I know, but I heard the park is a lot more fun. Please ….

W: All right. Let's change our schedule for the second day.

G: Thank you! I'm very excited about the trip.

W: It's great to hear that you're looking forward to the trip.

Listen & Speak 2 A

M: Hi, do you need any help?

G: Yes, please. Could you suggest a good Chinese restaurant in this building? I can't decide between the two.

M: Hmm…. What about Pappa Chen's? Their food is good and the prices are reasonable.

G: Sounds great! How do I get to the restaurant?

M: It's on the fourth floor. You can use the elevator over there. Pappa Chen's is next to the elevator.

G: Great! Thank you very much for your help.

M: My pleasure. Enjoy your dinner.

Listen & Speak 2 B

B: Hey, Minju, where are you?

G: Oh, Andrew, I'm coming. I'm coming.

B: Good. I was worried that you were lost.

G: I think I'm okay. What about Mason and Jian?

B: They are already here at my house.

G: Good! Oh, I see the post office. How do I get to your place from here?

B: You are almost here. Go straight for one more block. Then you will see Kim's Bakery.

G: Kim's Bakery? Okay ….

B: Then turn right and go straight for about 100 meters.

G: Turn right and go straight …. Okay, thanks! I'll see you soon.

Real Life Communication

Mina: Are you all set for the trip this weekend?

Jinho, Claire, & Henry: Yes!

Mina: Good! Don't be late! We're meeting at 11 a.m. in front of the clock tower.

Jinho: You got it! How do we get to the airport? I don't

think we've decided yet.

Henry: Jinho is right. We have two choices, bus or subway.

Claire: What about the subway? It's more reliable than the bus.

Henry: Is it possible to get to Terminal 2 by subway?

Claire: Yes, I already checked.

Mina: Good. Okay, then let's take the subway.

Let's Check 1

B: What are you reading, Alice?

G: It's about the origin of the labyrinth.

B: Labyrinth? Wasn't that an old mythological prison to keep the half-man, half-bull monster?

G: Oh, Juwon, you know about the story.

B: Not really. I forgot the name of the monster.

G: The Minotaur. The king of Crete was angry at it and put it in a labyrinth.

본문 TEST Step 1   p.49~50

01 Comparing, below, notice, differences

02 example, called, labyrinth, entrance

03 called, maze, both, and

04 find, origin, labyrinth, mythology

05 said, be, prison, escape

06 notice that, single path

07 no dead ends

08 have, worry, getting, enter

09 follow, way, end, reach

10 get, have, around, came

11 When, in, maze, different

12 choices, make, ends, frustrate

13 keep making, which way

14 If, careful, lose, way

15 These, mazes, considered left-brain

16 willingly visit, planned confusion

17 came up with, solutions

18 reliable, place, very beginning

19 keep following, wall

20 like walking, dark

21 Unfortunately, effective, certain, connected

22 made, different materials, hedges

23 In fact, printed, drawn

24 Here, as, called, maze

25 from point, in, order

26 give, try, seconds, escape

27 Labyrinths, are, fun, end

28 Looking, beauty, order, regularity
29 how creative human beings
30 there, why, stop, take
31 be worth visiting

01 Comparing, below, notice, differences
02 For example, on the left, called, labyrinth, has, entrance
03 on the right, called, has both, and, exit
04 the origin of, mythology
05 is said to be, that, cannot escape
06 notice that, a single path
07 no dead ends
08 don't have to worry about, enter it
09 all the way to the end, will reach
10 To get out, have to turn around, came in
11 in, maze, different
12 to make, dead ends to frustrate
13 keep making, which way to go
14 If, are not careful, lose
15 are, considered left-brain
16 willingly visit, enjoy, planned confusion
17 them came up with, solutions
18 most reliable one, to, on, the very beginning
19 following that wall
20 like walking
21 Unfortunately, effective, certain types, are not connected
22 are made with, different materials, like, hedges, bricks, and
23 In fact, be printed, drawn
24 Here is, called, maze
25 from, in the order
26 Why don't, give it a try, to escape
27 are, fun, the end
28 Looking at them closely, beauty, order, regularity
29 how creative human beings are
30 there is, stop, take some time
31 surely be worth visiting

1 아래 두 그림을 비교하면 몇 가지 차이를 쉽게 알아차릴 수 있습니다.
2 예를 들면, 왼쪽 그림은 미궁이라 불리고 입구만 있습니다.

3 오른쪽 그림은 미로라 불리며 입구와 출구가 둘 다 있습니다.
4 미궁의 기원은 그리스 신화에서 찾을 수 있습니다.
5 그것은 여러분이 빠져나올 수 없는 감옥으로 알려져 있습니다.
6 하지만 여러분이 알아차릴 수 있듯, 미궁은 통로가 하나입니다.
7 막다른 길이 없습니다.
8 이것은 여러분이 거기에 들어갈 때 빠져나올 것을 걱정하지 않아도 된다는 것을 의미합니다.
9 통로를 따라 끝까지 가면, 여러분은 미궁의 중앙에 도착할 것입니다.
10 빠져나오기 위해서는, 여러분은 단지 돌아서 들어간 길대로 걸어 나오면 됩니다.
11 미로 안에 있을 때에는 완전히 상황이 다릅니다.
12 결정할 많은 선택지가 있고 여러분을 좌절하게 만들 막다른 길들이 있습니다.
13 어느 길로 갈지 계속 선택을 해야만 합니다.
14 조심하지 않으면 길을 잃기 쉽습니다.
15 오늘날, 미로는 흔히 좌뇌형 퍼즐로 간주됩니다.
16 많은 사람들이 미로 공원에 기꺼이 방문하여 '계획된 혼란'을 즐깁니다.
17 그리고 그들 중 몇몇은 자기들만의 해결 방법을 찾아냈습니다.
18 가장 쉽고 믿을 만한 해결 방법은 시작 지점부터 한쪽 벽에 손을 대는 것입니다.
19 그러고는 여러분은 단지 그 벽을 계속 따라가면 됩니다.
20 이것은 마치 어두운 방을 걷는 것과 같습니다.
21 불행하게도, 이 간단한 방법은 어떤 종류의 미로에서는 특히 모든 벽이 이어져 있지는 않은 경우 효과가 없을지도 모릅니다.
22 미로는 벽과 방, 울타리, 벽돌, 거울, 심지어는 눈 등 많은 다양한 재료로 제작됩니다.
23 사실, 미로는 종이에 인쇄되거나 그려질 수도 있습니다.
24 여기 그 예가 하나 있습니다. 이것은 숫자 미로라고 불립니다.
25 여러분은 A 지점에서 출발하여 1, 9, 8, 5, 1, 9 …의 순서로 이동해야 합니다.
26 한번 시도해 보시죠? 빠져나가는 데 30초가 주어집니다!
27 미궁과 미로는 정말 재미있지만, 그것이 전부가 아닙니다.
28 자세히 들여다보면, 여러분은 질서와 규칙성이라는 아름다움을 발견할 수 있을지도 모릅니다.
29 그것들은 또한 인간이 얼마나 창조적인가를 보여줄지도 모릅니다.
30 다음 여행에 미로 공원이 있으면, 들러서 즐겨보는 것은 어떨까요?
31 분명히 들를 가치가 있을 것입니다!

1 Comparing the two pictures below, you can easily notice some differences.
2 For example, the picture on the left is called a labyrinth and only has an entrance.

3 The picture on the right is called a maze and has both an entrance and an exit.

4 You can find the origin of the labyrinth in Greek mythology.

5 It is said to be a prison that you cannot escape.

6 But you may notice that the labyrinth has only a single path.

7 There are no dead ends.

8 This means you don't have to worry about getting out of it when you enter it.

9 If you follow the path all the way to the end, you will reach the center.

10 To get out, you simply have to turn around and walk back out the way you came in.

11 When you are in a maze, it's a different story.

12 There are many choices to make and dead ends to frustrate you.

13 You have to keep making decisions about which way to go.

14 If you are not careful, you can easily lose your way.

15 These days, mazes are often considered left-brain puzzles.

16 Many people willingly visit maze parks and enjoy the "planned confusion."

17 And some of them came up with their own solutions.

18 The easiest and most reliable one is to place a hand on one wall from the very beginning.

19 Then you just keep following that wall.

20 It's like walking in a dark room.

21 Unfortunately, this simple method may not be effective in certain types of mazes, especially when all of the walls are not connected.

22 Mazes are made with a variety of different materials, like walls and rooms, hedges, bricks, mirrors, and even snow.

23 In fact, they can also be printed or drawn on paper.

24 Here is one as an example. This is called a number maze.

25 You start from point A and have to go in the order of 1 → 9 → 8 → 5 → 1 → 9 → … .

26 Why don't you give it a try? You have 30 seconds to escape!

27 Labyrinths and mazes are truly fun, but that's not the end of the story.

28 Looking at them closely, you may find the beauty

of order and regularity.

29 They may also show you how creative human beings are.

30 If there is a maze park on your next trip, why don't you stop and take some time to enjoy it?

31 It will surely be worth visiting!

구석구석지문 TEST Step 1   p.59

Real Life Communication – C Communication Task

1. Let me ask, How, get there
2. can go, by train
3. how long, take to get
4. takes about, to get
5. it possible to get, by airplane
6. answer, Right

After You Read

1. the nearby maze park with
2. looked hard to solve
3. many choices, keep making decisions, which way to go
4. that, place, from the beginning, keep following
5. simple, very effective
6. enjoyed myself
7. the beauty of order, regularity, human beings, creative

Let's Write

1. took a short, between, and
2. Looking at, it, that, prefers, to
3. why our class prefers mountains
4. Regarding, resons why, more, like, more exciting, lovelier

구석구석지문 TEST Step 2   p.60

Real Life Communication – C Communication Task

1. A: Let me ask you the first question. How do you get there?
2. B: I can go there by train.
3. A: Then how long does it take to get there?
4. B: It takes about 2 hours to get there.
5. A: Is it possible to get there by airplane?
6. A: Oh, the answer is Gyeongju. Right?

After You Read

1. Today, I went to the nearby maze park with my friends.

2. The maze looked hard to solve.

3. There were many choices, and I had to keep making decisions about which way to go.

4. My friends said that I should just place my hand on one wall from the beginning and keep following the same wall.

5. That solution was simple but not very effective.

6. I enjoyed myself very much at the park.

7. Also, I found the beauty of order and regularity there and thought that human beings are really creative.

Let's Write

1. I took a short survey about our class's preference between mountains and oceans.

2. Looking at the results, it is clear that our class prefers mountains to oceans.

3. You may wonder why our class prefers mountains.

4. Regarding the resons why they like mountains more, I found key words like "more beautiful", "more exciting", and "lovelier."

MEMO

MEMO